Instructor's Resource Guide

Ron Larson

ISBN 13: 978-1-938260-01-8

123456789-VLP-16 15 14 13 12

Table of Contents

College Semester Syllabus

Sections	Days	Content
1.1	1	1.1 Order of Operations & Formulas
1.2	1	1.2 Rounding & Calculators
Quiz, 1.3	1	1.1–1.2 Quiz, 1.3 Using Percent
1.4, Quiz, Review	1	1.4 Unit Conversions, 1.3–1.4 Quiz, Chapter Review
2.1	1	2.1 Unit Prices
2.2	1	2.2 Markup & Discount
Quiz, 2.3	1	2.1–2.2 Quiz, 2.3 Consumption Taxes
2.4 Quiz, Review	1	2.4 Budgeting, 2.3–2.4 Quiz, Chapter Review
Assess	1	Test Chapters 1 and 2
3.1	1	3.1 Sets & Set Diagrams
3.2	1	3.2 Statements & Negations
Quiz, 3.3	1	3.1–3.2 Quiz, 3.3 Deductive & Inductive Reasoning
3.4 Quiz, Review	1	3.4 Fallacies in Logic, 3.3–3.4 Quiz, Chapter Review
4.1	1	4.1 Exponential Growth
4.2	1	4.2 Inflation & the Consumer Price Index
Quiz, 4.3	1	4.1–4.2 Quiz, 4.3 Exponential Decay
4.4, Quiz, Review	1	4.4 Depreciation, 4.3–4.4 Quiz, Chapter Review
Assess	1	Test Chapters 3 and 4
5.1	1	5.1 Flat Tax & Political Philosophy
5.2	1	5.2 Graduated Income Tax
Quiz, 5.3	1	5.1–5.2 Quiz, 5.3 Property Tax
5.4, Quiz, Review	1	5.4 Social Security & Payroll Taxes, 5.4 Quiz, Chapter Review

Sections	Days	Content
6.1	1	6.1 Introduction to Lending
6.2	1	6.2 Buying Now, Paying Later
Quiz, 6.3	1	6.1–6.2 Quiz, 6.3 Home Mortgages
6.4 Quiz, Review	1	6.4 Savings & Retirement Plans, 6.3–6.4 Quiz, Chapter Review
Assess	1	Test Chapters 5 and 6
7.1	1	7.1 Linear Patterns
7.2	1	7.2 Exponential Patterns
Quiz, 7.3	1	7.1–7.2 Quiz, 7.3 Quadratic Patterns
7.4, Quiz, Review	1	7.4 Fibonacci & Other Patterns, 7.3–7.4 Quiz, Chapter Review
8.1	1	8.1 Assigning a Measure to Likelihood
8.2	1	8.2 Estimating Likelihood
Quiz, 8.3	1	8.1–8.2 Quiz, 8.3 Expected Value
8.4, Quiz, Review	1	8.4 Expecting the Unexpected, 8.3–8.4 Quiz, Chapter Review
Assess	1	Test Chapters 7 and 8
9.1	1	9.1 Information Design
9.2	1	9.2 Describing "Average"
Quiz, 9.3	1	9.1–9.2 Quiz, 9.3 Describing Dispersion
9.4, Quiz, Review	1	9.4 Describing by Sampling, 9.3–9.4 Quiz, Chapter Review
10.1	1	10.1 Health & Fitness
10.2	1	10.2 The Olympics
Quiz, 10.3	1	10.1–10.2 Quiz, 10.3 Professional Sports
10.4, Quiz, Review	1	10.4 Outdoor Sports, 10.3–10.4 Quiz, Chapter Review
Assess	1	10.4 Outdoor Sports, 10.3–10.4 Quiz, Chapter Review

Course Total: 45 Days

College Trimester Syllabus

Sections	Days	Topics
1.1 and 1.2	1	Order of Operations & Formulas, Rounding & Calculators
1.3 and 1.4	1	Using Percent, Units & Conversions
2.1 and 2.2	1	Unit Prices, Markup & Discount
2.3 and 2.4	1	Consumption Taxes, Budgeting
Review	1	Test Chapters 1 and 2
3.1 and 3.2	1	Sets & Set Diagrams, Statements & Negations
3.3 and 3.4	1	Deductive & Inductive Reasoning, Fallacies in Logic
4.1 and 4.2	1	Exponential Growth, Inflation & the Consumer Price Index
4.3 and 4.4	1	Exponential Decay, Depreciation
Review	1	Review Chapters 3 and 4
Assess	1	Test Chapters 3 and 4
5.1 and 5.2	1	Flat Tax & Political Philosophy, Graduated Income Tax
5.3 and 5.4	1	Property Tax, Social Security & Payroll Taxes
6.1 and 6.2	1	Introduction to Lending, Buying Now, Paying Later
6.3 and 6.4	1	Home Mortgages, Savings & Retirement Plans
Review	1	Review Chapters 5 and 6
Assess	1	Test Chapters 5 and 6
7.1 and 7.2	1	Linear Patterns, Exponential Patterns
7.3 and 7.4	1	Quadratic Patterns, Fibonacci & Other Patterns
8.1 and 8.2	1	Assigning a Measure to Likelihood, Estimating Likelihood
8.3 and 8.4	1	Expected Value, Expecting the Unexpected
Review	1	Review Chapters 7 and 8
Assess	1	Test Chapters 7 and 8
9.1 and 9.2	1	Information Design, Describing "Average"
9.3 and 9.4	1	Describing Dispersion, Describing by Sampling
10.1 and 10.2	1	Health & Fitness, The Olympics
10.3 and 10.4	1	Professional Sports, Outdoor Sports
Review	1	Review Chapters 9 and 10
Assess	1	Test Chapters 9 and 10

Course Total: 30 Days

High School

Chapter 1	16 Days
1.1	3 days
1.2	3 days
Review/Quiz	1 day
Chapter Project	1 day
1.3	2 days
1.4	3 days
Review/Quiz	1 day
Chapter Review	1 day
Chapter Test	1 day

Chapter 4	16 Days
4.1	2 days
4.2	3 days
Review/Quiz	1 day
Chapter Project	1 day
4.3	3 days
4.4	3 days
Review/Quiz	1 day
Chapter Review	1 day
Chapter Test	1 day

Chapter 2	15 Days
2.1	2 days
2.2	3 days
Review/Quiz	1 day
Chapter Project	1 day
2.3	2 days
2.4	3 days
Review/Quiz	1 day
Chapter Review	1 day
Chapter Test	1 day

Chapter 5	15 Days
5.1	2 days
5.2	3 days
Review/Quiz	1 day
Chapter Project	1 day
5.3	2 days
5.4	3 days
Review/Quiz	1 day
Chapter Review	1 day
Chapter Test	1 day

Chapter 3	17 Days
3.1	3 days
3.2	3 days
Review/Quiz	1 day
Chapter Project	1 day
3.3	3 days
3.4	3 days
Review/Quiz	1 day
Chapter Review	1 day
Chapter Test	1 day

Chapter 6	16 Days
6.1	2 days
6.2	3 days
Review/Quiz	1 day
Chapter Project	1 day
6.3	3 days
6.4	3 days
Review/Quiz	1 day
Chapter Review	1 day
Chapter Test	1 day

High School (continued)

Chapter 7	15 Days
7.1	2 days
7.2	3 days
Review/Quiz	1 day
Chapter Project	1 day
7.3	2 days
7.4	3 days
Review/Quiz	1 day
Chapter Review	1 day
Chapter Test	1 day

Chapter 9	15 Days
9.1	2 days
9.2	3 days
Review/Quiz	1 day
Chapter Project	1 day
9.3	2 days
9.4	3 days
Review/Quiz	1 day
Chapter Review	1 day
Chapter Test	1 day

Chapter 8	15 Days
8.1	2 days
8.2	3 days
Review/Quiz	1 day
Chapter Project	1 day
8.3	2 days
8.4	3 days
Review/Quiz	1 day
Chapter Review	1 day
Chapter Test	1 day

Chapter 10	16 Days
10.1	3 days
10.2	3 days
Review/Quiz	1 day
Chapter Project	1 day
10.3	2 days
10.4	3 days
Review/Quiz	1 day
Chapter Review	1 day
Chapter Test	1 day

Chapter Pre/Post Tests

Pre-Tests and Post-Tests are available for Chapters 1–10 in PDF format at *Math.andYou.com/IRG*.

Name_____   Date _____

Chapter 1 Post-Test

1. You and your friend participate in a charity run. For every mile run, $2 is donated to the charity. You run 4 miles and your friend runs 3 miles. How much money, in dollars, do you and your friend raise for the charity?

2. A store has a buy-one-get-one-half-off sale on laundry detergent. The regular price of the laundry detergent is $2.60 per bottle. You buy two bottles. What is the total cost, in dollars, before taxes?

3. The price of admission to a World War I history museum is $8.29 for adults and $6.47 for children. A family of 2 adults and 4 children visits the museum. What is the total cost, in dollars, of admission?

4. You and your friend vacation in France and share the cost of transportation and lodging. You and your friend pay $119.78 for transportation and $758.46 for lodging. What is your share of the total cost, in dollars?

5. You are tiling the floor of a 6-foot by 8-foot bathroom. The sink occupies a 3-foot by 2-foot area and the bathtub occupies a 5-foot by 3-foot area. You do not need to tile the area occupied by the sink or bathtub. How much of the floor, in square feet, do you need to tile?

(Area of a rectangle $=$ base $\times$ height)

6. Your backyard is 60 feet long and 50 feet wide. You install a circular pool with a 10-foot radius. What is the area of the backyard, in square feet, that can be planted with grass? Round your answer to the nearest whole number.

(Area of a rectangle $=$ base $\times$ height)

(Area of a circle $= 3.14 \times (\text{radius})^2$)

Answers

1. _____14_____
2. _____3.90_____
3. _____42.46_____
4. _____439.12_____
5. _____27_____
6. _____2686_____

Date _____

...d add about
...flour in the

...rson's speed,

...number in

...is number in

...ficant digits does

Answers

7. _____151.8_____
8. _____600_____
9. _____0.0000002_____
10. _____4,900,000_____
11. _____1_____
12. _____5_____
13. _____3_____
14. _____560_____
15. _____40_____
16. _____92_____

---

12. The area of a park is 10,047 square feet. How many significant digits does this number have?

13. You leave a 12% tip for a $25 meal. How much is the tip, in dollars?

14. You are 70% of the way through an 800-page novel. How many pages have you read?

15. About 800 of the 2000 stamps in your collection are foreign. About what percent of the stamps in your collection are foreign?

16. You receive 23 out of 25 points on an exam. What is your score as a percent?

Date _____

...45 miles per hour.

...n weekdays you
...ds you use about
...ease?

...s does it take you

...years. In how many
...?

...ch do the contents

...long, in minutes,
does it take you to run 2 miles?

(1 hour $=$ 60 minutes)

Answers

17. _____50_____
18. _____75_____
19. _____20_____
20. _____7_____
21. _____20,000_____
22. _____24_____
23. _____203_____
24. _____15.2_____

23. Your friend in Spain sends you a recipe. The directions say to pre-heat the oven to 95°C. What is the temperature in degrees Fahrenheit?

($F = 1.8C + 32$)

24. A building is 50 feet tall. How tall is the building in meters? Round your answer to the nearest tenth.

(1 m $\approx$ 3.28 feet)

Chapter 1   The Mathematics of Calculation

Section Topics

1.1 Order of Operations & Formulas   Use the order of operations to evaluate a numerical expression. Use a calculator to evaluate a numerical expression. Use the order of operations to evaluate a formula.

1.2 Rounding & Calculators   Round numbers in a real-life context. Read large and small numbers. Understand the concept of "garbage in, garbage out."

1.3 Using Percent   Understand and find a percent of a number. Determine what percent one number is of another number. Use percent to represent change.

1.4 Units & Conversions   Use unit analysis to "balance" both sides of a formula. Convert within a given system of measure. Convert between different systems of measure.

Chapter Comments

Section 1.1 begins with the order of operations. The point of Example 3 is that students should not assume that their calculators use the PEMDAS order of operations; they should use parentheses to force the PEMDAS order. You may want to provide examples of keystrokes specific to the various calculators used in your class.

The problems in Examples 4, 5, and 6 may cause "math anxiety" in some of your students. Emphasize that unit analysis will help them to organize their thoughts and avoid confusion. Encourage students to begin by writing down a relevant formula and then substituting known values into the formula, including units. Seeing how the units relate will help students to discover a way to solve the problem. Unit analysis is given full attention in Section 1.4, but spending time on it here will benefit students as well.

Section 1.2 emphasizes the importance of using reasoning to determine when and how to round. It teaches students to examine the accuracy of estimates with a critical eye and cautions students against introducing more accuracy when performing computations. Examples 3 and 4 discuss scientific or exponential notation and its usefulness when comparing quantities.

The examples and exercises in Section 1.3 give straightforward practice with percents. The Extending Concepts exercises provide opportunity to interpret percents on a deeper level.

Section 1.4 is dedicated to unit analysis. This topic has already been introduced but now receives more attention here. It is worth taking the extra time to make sure that your students grasp this concept and are comfortable using it. Consider assigning every exercise in this section. Make sure students understand that when converting units, the "forms of one" must be chosen so that the units cancel out; you may want to point out the Study Tip on page 37.

Chapter 2   The Mathematics of Consumption

Section Topics

2.1 Unit Prices   Find the unit price of an item. Compare the unit prices of two or more items. Find the annual cost of an item.

2.2 Markup & Discount   Find the markup on an item. Find the discount on an item. Find the final price after multiple discounts.

2.3 Consumption Taxes   Find the sales tax on an item. Find the excise tax on an item. Find the value-added tax on an item.

2.4 Budgeting   Create and balance a monthly budget. Write checks and balance a checkbook. Analyze a budget.

Chapter Comments

The insights in Section 2.1 should encourage students to be smart shoppers. You may want to work through several examples like Example 3. Point out that some products are intentionally marked with differing units to prevent obvious comparisons. For instance, two rolls of wrapping paper cost the same, but one is labeled in square feet and the other is labeled with length in yards and width in feet. Or, a particular brand of candy is available in two size bags, one labeled in ounces and the other labeled in pounds. Additional practice with unit conversion is available in Exercises 5, 7–9, 12, 13, and 20.

Section 2.2 gives perspective on the retail industry. Examples 1, 2, and 3 explain markup terminology from the perspective of a retailer. Examples 4, 5, and 6 help students gain an understanding of discounts as a consumer.

In Section 2.3, students will learn the differences between sales tax, excise tax, and value-added tax. The section also addresses complications that arise when a country's sales tax laws vary greatly depending on the jurisdiction where a person resides.

In Section 2.4, the first two examples show just one of many ways to create a spreadsheet for a personal budget. Examples 3 and 4 emphasize that the term "balancing a checkbook" encompasses more than keeping a record of checks written. It means documenting all transactions in a checking account. Remind students that even if they make all their payments electronically, overdrafts can still occur. In Example 6, note that qualifying for a mortgage does not necessarily mean that it is a financially wise decision.

Chapter 3   The Mathematics of Logic & the Media

Section Topics

3.1 Sets & Set Diagrams   Use a union of two sets to represent *or*. Use an intersection of two sets to represent *and*. Use the complement of a set to represent *not*.

3.2 Statements & Negation   Analyze statements that have the term *all*. Analyze statements that have the term *some* or *many*. Analyze negations of statements.

3.3 Deductive & Inductive Reasoning   Use deductive reasoning with syllogisms. Know how a deductive reasoning system is created. Use inductive reasoning.

3.4 Fallacies in Logic   Recognize deductive fallacies. Use set diagrams to detect fallacies. Recognize fallacies in advertisements.

Chapter Comments

In Section 3.1, the concepts of union and intersection in Examples 1–4 can be confusing for students. A common stumbling block is the use of *and* and *or* with set diagrams. Students often think that the phrase "*A* and *B*" means everything that is in both sets, but it actually represents only the intersection. Similarly, the phrase "*A* or *B*" would seem to indicate a smaller subset, when in actuality it represents everything that is in *A*, *B*, and the intersection. Emphasize the set diagrams that accompany the definitions of union and intersection on pages 102 and 104.

Understanding set diagrams is critical before moving on to Section 3.2, which shows how set diagrams can be used to analyze statements. This is especially helpful when negating statements involving *and* and *or*, as shown in Examples 5 and 6.

Section 3.3 gives rules for writing logical arguments. The goal of the first two examples is that students grasp the pattern for a syllogism. Visual learners will benefit from using set diagrams to analyze syllogisms. Consider asking students to draw a set diagram with the Checkpoint following Example 1 to enrich their understanding. The three concerns at the top of page 125 are important; emphasize with point #3 that a syllogism can be valid even if one or both of its premises are not true. Remind students that the inductive reasoning in Examples 5 and 6 is the most common type of reasoning because it usually involves uncertainty.

Section 3.4 shows how to recognize illogical arguments, or fallacies. The Study Tips throughout this section contain a wealth of helpful descriptions of various fallacies; spending significant class time on them would be worthwhile. The set diagrams in Examples 3 and 4 can be challenging for students to set up on their own. Point out that there is often more than one way to draw a set diagram for a particular argument; it is just a tool to help you conclude whether the argument is valid. Throughout this section, make sure students understand that just because a syllogism is a fallacy does not mean that the conclusion is false.

Chapter 4   The Mathematics of Inflation & Depreciation

Section Topics

4.1 Exponential Growth   Make a table showing exponential growth. Draw a graph showing exponential growth. Find an exponential growth rate.

4.2 Inflation & the Consumer Price Index   Use a consumer price index. Use a graph to interpret a consumer price index. Compare inflation to the value of the dollar.

4.3 Exponential Decay   Make a table and graph showing exponential decay. Calculate and use half-life. Find an exponential decay rate.

4.4 Depreciation   Use straight-line depreciation. Use double declining-balance depreciation. Use sum of the years-digits depreciation.

Chapter Comments

In Section 4.1, be sure students see the basic characteristic of exponential growth: for each successive period of time, a quantity grows by the same percent. Example 5 shows the difference between linear growth (increase by the same *amount*) and exponential growth (increase by the same *percent*). Students can read more about linear, exponential, and quadratic growth in Chapter 7.

Note that logistic growth is introduced in the 4.1 Extending Concepts exercises. A logistic growth pattern starts off like exponential growth. At a certain point, however, the rate of growth begins to decrease, and eventually the population reaches a maximum size and is barely growing.

The consumer price index (CPI) is introduced in Section 4.2. Be sure students understand that the numbers in the CPI are not dollar values, but measures of the change over time relative to their reference base of 100. The term *inflation rate* appears in Example 3 (and elsewhere in this section) but its definition appears only in the Math Help for page 164 at *Math.andYou.com*. You may want to reiterate the formula to your students:

$$\text{Inflation rate in year A} = \frac{\text{CPI in year A} - \text{CPI in preceding year}}{\text{CPI in preceding year}} \times 100.$$

Section 4.3 discusses exponential decay. A useful explanation of half-life is given in the Study Tip prior to Example 3. Some algebra is necessary to find the rate of decay in Example 6; students can review the Math Help for page 179 at *Math.andYou.com*.

Section 4.4 presents three classic types of depreciation. Students can find definitions of *useful life* and *salvage value* in the Math Help for page 184 at *Math.andYou.com*. Example 6 compares the three types of depreciation and gives a useful graphical comparison. The Extending Concepts exercises introduce a fourth type of depreciation that begins with double declining-balance depreciation and switches to straight-line depreciation.

Chapter 5   The Mathematics of Taxation

Section Topics

5.1 Flat Tax & Political Philosophy   Calculate a flat income tax. Identify types of taxes. Analyze an indirect tax.

5.2 Graduated Income Tax   Calculate a graduated income tax. Analyze a graduated income tax system. Compare a graduated income tax with a flat income tax.

5.3 Property Tax   Calculate a property tax. Analyze assessments and tax credits. Analyze exemptions for property tax.

5.4 Social Security & Payroll Taxes   Calculate Social Security & Medicare taxes. Evaluate the benefits of Social Security. Analyze the viability of Social Security.

Chapter Comments

As an introduction to the first two sections, point out that there are three types of income tax that people pay: federal, state, and local. The first paragraph of Section 5.1 mentions that federal income tax is not a flat tax but that seven states do have a flat income tax. If income tax is new to some of your students, you may want to clarify that federal income tax laws are consistent across the board for all states, whereas state and local income tax laws vary. Also, emphasize that the graph above Example 3 is important for students to understand in order to grasp the concepts throughout Sections 5.1 and 5.2.

Section 5.2 gives students an excellent overview of a graduated income tax system. Examples 1 and 2 illustrate how graduated income tax is calculated. Make sure students understand that a person's taxable income is broken down into brackets and *each portion* is taxed according to a different rate. Consider working through the spreadsheets in Example 1 to show how the amounts on each line are determined. After Examples 1 and 2, the remainder of the section is dedicated to analyzing the federal graduated income tax system: how the money is distributed, and how the tax system could be changed to preserve the same result or to balance the budget. Note: The circle graph in Checkpoint 3 is complicated; the table in the Checkpoint Solution at *Math.andYou.com* provides students with helpful insight on the meaning of the categories.

In Section 5.3, the *assessed value* and the *market value* of a property can be confusing. The definitions at the top of page 226 are very helpful. To further complicate matters, the terms tax rate, assessment level, and market value tend to have different interpretations in different tax districts. This section was written and reviewed carefully to explain property tax in a way that coincides with how it is most commonly applied. Some students may benefit from a math review prior to Example 5, as its solution involves some algebra.

Section 5.4 can enlighten your students on a number of issues: payroll from the perspectives of the employer and the employee, how Social Security works, when to retire, and the future viability of Social Security for this country. True to form for this text, the examples, checkpoints, and exercises ask thought-provoking questions that require students to think about the philosophical and political issues behind the math.

Chapter 6   The Mathematics of Borrowing & Saving

Section Topics

6.1 Introduction to Lending   Read promissory notes and find due dates. Find the cost of credit for a loan. Find the annual percentage rate for a loan.

6.2 Buying Now, Paying Later   Create an amortization table. Analyze the cost of buying on credit. Analyze credit in the United States.

6.3 Home Mortgages   Compare rates and terms for a home mortgage. Analyze the effect of making principal payments. Compare the costs of buying and renting.

6.4 Savings & Retirement Plans   Find the balance in a savings account. Find the balance in an increasing annuity. Analyze a decreasing annuity.

Chapter Comments

Section 6.1 is an introduction to the terms connected with loans, credit, and interest. This section makes sense of what can be a daunting and confusing world of terms that people can face when borrowing money or financing a purchase. As students encounter new terms, encourage them to write definitions of these terms in their own words to help them better understand and be able to use them.

Section 6.2 discusses in greater detail the topics of Section 6.1. Students will benefit from going through each line of the spreadsheet in Example 1 to see how the entries are calculated. Explain why the interest paid each month is decreasing. Make sure students understand why the balance after each monthly payment does not decrease by $203.51 each month. Example 3 has been simplified for illustrative purposes; students are not expected to know how to calculate the interest on a credit card (they would need to know the average daily balance, the number of days in the billing period, and when any payments are made). Point out that the graph in Example 6 does not include home mortgages; to see the history of mortgage debt compared with consumer credit, refer to the graph in Exercise 18. This section's Extending Concepts exercises offer students valuable "life skills" by helping them to understand credit card statements.

The examples in Section 6.3 point out some important lessons about home mortgages. Home buyers can potentially save a lot of money by negotiating for a smaller purchase price and a lower interest rate, by making a larger down payment, by choosing a shorter term for the mortgage, and by making extra principle payments.

Working through the examples and exercises of Section 6.4 will give students an appreciation for the value of saving and investing.

Throughout this chapter, encourage your students not to get so mired in the details of spreadsheets and formulas that they miss the overriding lessons. The purpose is to give students enough knowledge of the math to enable them to make wise financial decisions.

Chapter 7   The Mathematics of Patterns & Nature

Section Topics

7.1 Linear Patterns   Recognize and describe a linear pattern. Use a linear pattern to predict a future event. Recognize a proportional pattern.

7.2 Exponential Patterns   Recognize and describe an exponential pattern. Use an exponential pattern to predict a future event. Compare exponential and logistic growth.

7.3 Quadratic Patterns   Recognize and describe a quadratic pattern. Use a quadratic pattern to predict a future event. Compare linear, quadratic, and exponential growth.

7.4 Fibonacci & Other Patterns   Recognize and describe the Fibonacci pattern. Analyze geometric Fibonacci patterns. Recognize and describe other patterns in mathematics.

Chapter Comments

Before beginning this chapter, you may want to give your students an overview by showing them graphs of linear, exponential, quadratic, logistic growth, and other patterns. Keep in mind that this chapter was written to give students the tools to determine patterns and make predictions without actually manipulating mathematical equations.

In Checkpoint 1 of Section 7.1, instead of using an algebraic formula with variables representing height and femur length, the relationship is given in words, and students use a spreadsheet to perform the computations. This approach is used throughout this chapter and should build confidence in your students because, instead of being overwhelmed by algebra and formulas, they can let the spreadsheet do the work. It puts the emphasis on understanding the relationships, not the mathematical computation. Emphasize that many linear patterns in real life are not *exactly* linear, but they are close enough to allow for educated predictions.

In Section 7.2, point out the Study Tip on page 312, which notes the difference between linear and exponential patterns. In Examples 2, 3, and 4, the ratios of consecutive terms are not equal, but they are close enough to indicate a roughly exponential pattern: each successive number increases (or decreases) by roughly the same percent. Examples 5 and 6 discuss the pattern of logistic growth conceptually without analyzing any data. A formula for the logistic growth rate is given in Extending Concepts Exercises 21–24.

In Section 7.3, students look at second differences to find quadratic patterns. Example 3 uses a regression program to model the data and make predictions. The exercises, however, do not require this. It is up to you how much emphasis to give this technique. Examples 5 and 6 (and related Exercises 13–16) are cumulative in that they ask students to determine whether a pattern is linear, exponential, or quadratic.

Section 7.4 presents a collection of interesting patterns found in the world around us, including Fibonacci patterns, the golden ratio, Kepler's Third Law, sine waves, triangular numbers, and the Lucas sequence.

Chapter 8   The Mathematics of Likelihood

Section Topics

8.1 Assigning a Measure to Likelihood   Use probability to describe the likelihood of an event. Analyze the likelihood of a risk. Use likelihood to describe actuarial data.

8.2 Estimating Likelihood   Find a theoretical probability. Find an experimental probability. Estimate a probability using historical results.

8.3 Expected Value   Find an expected value involving two events. Find an expected value involving multiple events. Use expected value to make investment decisions.

8.4 Expecting the Unexpected   Find the probability of independent events. Find the probability that an event does not occur. Find counterintuitive probabilities.

Chapter Comments

The topics in this chapter are cumulative; they build upon one another as the chapter progresses. So, you should teach the sections in order.

The goal of Section 8.1 is for students to become familiar with the concept of assigning a measure to the likelihood of an event. This measure is a number between 0 and 1 and it is called the probability that the event will occur. Exercises 1 and 2 give students practice converting among fractions, decimals, and percents. Extending Concepts Exercises 21–23 would be good to assign as preparation for the upcoming topic of theoretical probability in the next section.

In Section 8.2, students learn how to calculate basic probabilities. Make sure your students understand theoretical, experimental, and historical probability, and when each is appropriate.

Section 8.3 shows that using expected value as a decision guideline can provide helpful insight. For instance, in Example 3, suppose each parent is willing to pay the child's weekly allowance using the offered method. Because the expected value of the mother's offer is greater, the child has a greater chance of earning more over the long run with her offer. Example 5 shows that, in some situations, people do not tend to make choices based on the best expected value. In Example 6, remind students that expected value represents the average payoff when making a great number of speculative investments.

In Section 8.4, students learn how to calculate the probability of two or more independent events. Point out that the words "at least" in Examples 3 and 4 can give students a clue about which technique to use. When you want to find the probability that *at least* so many people or things do something, you can begin by finding the probability that *none* of them do and then subtract the result from 1. The probabilities in Examples 5 and 6 are *counterintuitive* because they contradict what seems right according to common sense.

Chapter 9 The Mathematics of Description

Section Topics

9.1 Information Design   Use stacked area graphs to represent the changing parts of a whole. Use a radar graph and an area graph to represent data. Graphically represent data sets that have several variables.

9.2 Describing "Average"   Use mean, median, and mode to describe the average value of a data set. Read and understand box-and-whisker plots and histograms. Understand the effect of outliers on averages.

9.3 Describing Dispersion   Use standard deviation to describe the dispersion of a data set. Use standard deviation to describe a data set that is normally distributed. Compare different types of distributions.

9.4 Describing by Sampling   Use a randomly chosen sample to describe a population. Determine whether a sample is representative of a population. Determine a sample size to obtain valid inferences.

Chapter Comments

The emphasis in Section 9.1 is on drawing conclusions from graphical presentations of data. Types of graphs include stacked area graphs, radar graphs, area graphs, and graphs with several variables such as animated bubble charts and stream graphs. In Example 6, students can view the complete stream graph by using the link provided in the Checkpoint Solution at *Math.andYou.com*. The exercises introduce a candlestick chart, which is another type of graph having several variables.

Section 9.2 introduces mean, median, mode, and population pyramids in Examples 1 and 2. Note that the corresponding exercises use stem-and-leaf plots; some of your students may benefit from a review of these before beginning the exercises. Other topics in this section include box-and-whisker plots, histograms, and outliers. Refer your students to the Math Help for Example 5 at *Math.andYou.com* for additional insight on outliers.

In Section 9.3, students learn about distributions of data and how to use standard deviation to describe the data. A common source of confusion is misunderstanding what the vertical axis represents in distribution histograms. Emphasize that these are frequency diagrams; the horizontal axis represents the measurements and the vertical axis shows the frequency of those measurements. A bell-shaped graph has the most frequent occurrences of a measurement in the middle of the data with the frequencies diminishing in each direction from there. In Example 2, you can clarify moving averages by pointing students to the Math Help at *Math.andYou.com*.

Section 9.4 presents the idea of inferring from a sample. To introduce this topic, you may find it helpful to review with your students the diagram in the Math Help for Example 1 at *Math.andYou.com*, which gives a visual illustration of sampling and confidence levels. This section also addresses sampling issues such as representative sampling, biased and unbiased samples, market research and sample size, and biased survey questions.

Chapter 10   The Mathematics of Fitness & Sports

Section Topics

10.1 Health & Fitness   Compare a person's weight, height, and body fat percentage. Interpret and use a person's heart rate and metabolism. Determine factors for cardiovascular health.

10.2 The Olympics   Analyze winning times and heights in the Summer Olympics. Analyze winning times in the Winter Olympics. Understand Olympic scoring.

10.3 Professional Sports   Use mathematics to analyze baseball statistics. Use mathematics to analyze football statistics. Use mathematics to analyze statistics in other professional sports.

10.4 Outdoor Sports   Use mathematics to analyze hiking and mountain climbing. Use mathematics to analyze kayaking and sailing. Use mathematics to analyze bicycling and cross-country skiing.

Chapter Comments

Section 10.1 offers insight and formulas relating to an assortment of health issues. Encourage your students to read these topics introspectively, considering their own personal health decisions.

Section 10.2 analyzes some of the trends in winning Olympic statistics and how they may be related to changes in techniques, equipment, or other factors. Example 1 points out a linear pattern in the data; if your students need a refresher on this, you can refer them to Section 7.1. The last two examples in the section give the math behind some subjective Olympic scoring.

The topics in Section 10.3 give students a glimpse of some statistics used in professional sports. Each example covers a different aspect of a professional sport. Your students' general sports knowledge will dictate whether you need to spend more or less time on terminology. For instance, the Checkpoint 4 solution available at *Math.andYou.com* gives some discussion in terms of third and fourth quarter; you may want to point out that each quarter in the NFL lasts 15 minutes. This section's Extending Concepts exercises use a bubble graph, one of the information designs featured in Section 9.1.

Section 10.4 contains a miscellaneous collection of statistics about outdoor sporting activities. Each one shows how mathematics and graphs can enhance a person's understanding of the information.

Chapter 1

Section 1.1   Order of Operations & Formulas

Example 1 Instructor Notes

Help students understand the importance of order of operations by drawing a parallel between math and verbal languages. Rules set language apart from simpler forms of communication. These rules help the reader or listener understand the writer or speaker. In natural languages, like English or Spanish, rules that deal with the order of the parts of language are called syntax. In mathematics, these rules are called **order of operations.**

Have students consider the following sentence.

My friends and I are going to dinner and a movie later.

How many ways can this sentence be understood? What common rules help us to understand what the writer probably means? In the same way, it is important to understand what the expression

$$100.00 + 14.50 \times 0.06$$

actually means. Have the students try calculating from left to right and then multiplying before adding. Are their answers the same? Ask them why order of operations is important.

Checkpoint Solution

Add the 12 monthly usage amounts and subtract the 11 equal payments already made to find the amount you owe in May.

$$(112.90 + 120.97 + 122.58 + 106.45 + 98.39 + 95.16 + 112.90 + 116.13$$
$$+ 103.23 + 100.00 + 91.94 + 108.06) - 11(95)$$

$= 1288.71 - 11(95)$	Add inside parentheses.
$= 1288.71 - 1045$	Multiply.
$= 243.71$	Subtract.

You owe $243.71 in May.

Here is another way to find this solution. For each month, subtract the payment you made from the amount you owe. Then use a spreadsheet to find the balance due in May.

Download the following spreadsheet and try entering different amounts as your equal monthly payment. Try finding an amount so that you owe nothing in May.
http://math.andyou.com/content/01/01/data/mthu_data_0101_002_01.xls

Example 2 Instructor Notes

Food calories are known as "large calories" or "kilocalories" because one food calorie represents 1000 "small calories." Kilocalories are usually abbreviated Cal or Calorie, but when referring to food, it has become common practice to use a lowercase "c."

Notice that we do not add the calories for every ingredient in the recipe. Many of the ingredients, such as the mustard, cayenne pepper, and white vinegar have calories, but they occur in such small amounts that the number of calories is very small. In contrast, the main ingredients, such as the egg yolks, salad oil, and sugar have a relatively large number of calories. There is a variation in the number of calories every time you make the recipe. For example, eggs come in different sizes, and the oil measurement is difficult to measure precisely. If the oil varies by half a teaspoon, then the number of calories in the recipe varies by

$$0.5 \text{ tsp} \times 40.625 \text{ calories/tsp} = 20.3125 \approx 20 \text{ calories.}$$

So, the variation in the recipe is more than the calories in the minor ingredients. Calculating the main ingredients is "good enough."

Point out to students that the answer to this multiplication problem includes both the number and the units: "20 calories." Stress that remembering to list the units is one of the best ways students can improve their math skills. Review the multiplication problem again, explaining unit analysis. Point out that the "tsp" and "cups" units cancel out in the multiplication.

$$0.5 \text{ tsp} \times \frac{1 \text{ cup}}{48 \text{ tsp}} \times \frac{1950 \text{ calories}}{1 \text{ cup}} = 20.3125 \approx 20 \text{ calories}$$

Have the students find a favorite recipe. Then have them find the number of calories in the recipe and the number of calories in a single serving.

Checkpoint Solution

a. Add the number of teaspoons for each ingredient in the recipe.

$$2(3) + 0.5 + 1.5(48) + 0.75 + 0.25 + 4.5 + 4$$

$$= 6 + 0.5 + 72 + 0.75 + 0.25 + 4.5 + 4 \qquad \text{Multiply.}$$

$$= 88 \qquad \text{Add.}$$

There are 88 teaspoons in the recipe.

b. Divide the number of calories in the recipe by the number of teaspoons to get calories per teaspoon.

$$\frac{3039 \text{ calories}}{88 \text{ tsp}} \approx 35 \text{ calories per tsp}$$

There are 35 calories in each teaspoon.

Example 3 Instructor Notes

Calculators use a variety of symbols to represent the mathematical operations. For example, some calculators have the symbol ($\pm$) rather than ($-$) to enter a negative number.

Calculators also vary on how they interpret "order of operations." There are three basic types:

1. PEMDAS: Use the conventional order of operations that is accepted in math.

2. Operation Activated: Each operation activates the equal key.

$2 + 3 \times 4$

3. RPN: Reverse Polish Notation is used by some technical calculators.

$2 + 3 \times 4$

Checkpoint Solution

Using the standard order of operations, you need to add the numbers in parentheses before dividing. So, (d) is a correct way to find the average.

Have the students try confirming this by estimating the answer and then trying both ways with their calculator. The average of 50, 62, and 73 is about 60. Some calculators give $136.33 for (c) while all calculators give $61.67 for (d). The keystrokes for (d) are closest to the estimate, so (d) is a correct way to find the average.

Example 4 Instructor Notes

Although *Math & YOU* does not take the view that mathematics is a collection of formulas that need to be memorized, there are some formulas that are used so commonly that it saves time to memorize them. The area of a rectangle and the area of a circle are two such formulas.

$$A = bh \qquad\qquad A = \pi r^2$$
$$\text{Rectangle} \qquad\qquad \text{Circle}$$

Remind students to write the units of measurement. Unit analysis enables you to tell whether the units you are using make sense in the context of the problem. Examples:

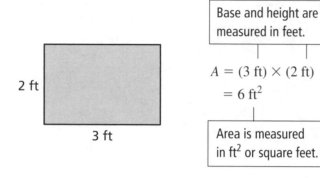

Base and height are measured in feet.

$$A = (3 \text{ ft}) \times (2 \text{ ft})$$
$$= 6 \text{ ft}^2$$

Area is measured in ft^2 or square feet.

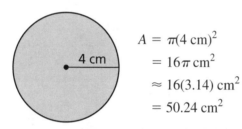

$$A = \pi (4 \text{ cm})^2$$
$$= 16\pi \text{ cm}^2$$
$$\approx 16(3.14) \text{ cm}^2$$
$$= 50.24 \text{ cm}^2$$

Units for Pi

Note that π is the ratio of the circumference of a circle to the diameter of the circle. Because it is a ratio, it has no units.

Checkpoint Solution

One room is 8.5 feet square. The other room is 9 feet by 10 feet. Start by finding the area of the two rooms.

$$(8.5 \text{ ft})^2 + (9 \text{ ft}) \times (10 \text{ ft}) = 72.25 \text{ ft}^2 + (9 \text{ ft}) \times (10 \text{ ft}) \qquad \text{Evaluate exponent.}$$
$$= 72.25 \text{ ft}^2 + 90 \text{ ft}^2 \qquad \text{Multiply.}$$
$$= 162.25 \text{ ft}^2 \qquad \text{Add.}$$

The two rooms have a combined area of 162.25 square feet. Each tile is one square foot, and 20 extra tiles are required. So, you should order at least 183 tiles.

c. Each box has 12 tiles. Because $\dfrac{183}{12} = 15.25$, you should order 16 boxes.

d. Each tile is $7.65, there are 12 tiles per box. The total cost for 16 boxes is

$$16 \text{ boxes} \times \frac{12 \text{ tiles}}{1 \text{ box}} \times \frac{\$7.65}{1 \text{ tile}} = \$1468.80.$$

Unit Analysis: Note how "box" and "tile" cancel out and you are left with $.

Example 5 Instructor Notes

When calculations involve rates, unit analysis will help solve the problems. For instance, if the problem asks for an answer in miles per hour, then the solution should include a quantity in miles divided by a quantity in hours.

Similarly, if the problem asks for an answer in calories and the rate is in calories per hour, the solution should include multiplying by hours to end up with just calories. Example:

$$\text{Calories burned} = 0.75 \text{ hr} \times \frac{1126}{1 \text{ hr}} = 844.5 \text{ Cal}$$

Checkpoint Solution

The total number of calories in your lunch is

$590 + 210 + 510 = 1310$ calories.   Total calories for lunch

At 155 pounds, running 10 miles per hour, you burn 1126 calories. At this rate you have to run

$1310 \text{ Cal} \times \dfrac{1 \text{ hr}}{1126 \text{ Cal}} \approx 1.16 \text{ hours}$ Hours needed to work off lunch calories

to burn the calories you eat. This is about 70 minutes.

How to Write a Rate

In the Math Help, the rate is written as $\dfrac{1126 \text{ Cal}}{1 \text{ hr}}$.

In the Checkpoint Solution, the rate is written as $\dfrac{1 \text{ hr}}{1126 \text{ Cal}}$.

Review with students how to know which one to use.

1. You know the units that are given.

2. You know the units you need for the answer.

3. Use unit analysis. That is, use the version of the rate that will convert the given units into the desired units.

Instructor Notes and Checkpoint Solutions   **15**

Example 6 Instructor Notes

Notice the similarities between the formulas on this page and the formulas on page 6. Both are of the form

$$\text{Amount} = \text{Rate} \times \text{Unit}.$$

In such formulas, the only difference is the unit of measure for Amount. Here are some examples.

$$\text{Miles} = \frac{\text{Miles}}{\text{Hour}} \times \text{Hours} \qquad \text{Cost} = \frac{\text{Cost}}{\text{Pound}} \times \text{Pounds} \qquad \text{Earnings} = \frac{\text{Earnings}}{\text{Month}} \times \text{Months}$$

Checkpoint Solution

There are 12 months in a year. Your yearly earnings are

$$4800 \frac{\$}{\text{month}} \times \frac{12 \text{ months}}{\text{yr}} = \$57{,}600 \text{ per year.}$$

4% of this is $2304. So, your total compensation before sales commission is

$$\$57{,}600 + \$2304 + 12(\$1200) = \$74{,}304.$$

This is more than your guaranteed total compensation in (a) $72,720 and (b) $73,340.

Here is the summary of the three job offers.

Total Compensation	Profit Sharing	Maximum Total with Bonus
$72,720	$0	$72,720
$73,340	$20,000	$93,340
$74,304	$36,000	$110,304

So, the third job offer has the greatest potential.

Section 1.2   Rounding & Calculators

Example 1 Instructor Notes

It seems that people often want math to have rules. The point of this lesson, however, is not in learning how to apply rules, but learning to apply common sense when communicating about numbers.

One communication standard to use when making statements about numbers is to list only as many significant digits as you are confident are correct.

Tell students when they are uncertain about the accuracy of the numbers, to use phrases such as "about 210 inches" or "approximately 3.7 inches." Including statistical jargon can make a statement more precise, such as

"At a 95% confidence level, the average height is 5′7″, plus or minus 1 inch."

Checkpoint Solution

In 2010, the population of the United Kingdom was about 62 million. The country's defense department spent about $70 billion.

$$\frac{\$70 \text{ billion}}{62 \text{ million}} \approx \$1129.032258 \text{ per person}$$

Defense spending in the United Kingdom is about $1129 per person.

Example 2 Instructor Notes

When using unit analysis, the rules for "canceling" units are the same as they are for simplifying fractions. For instance, you can simplify $\frac{4}{6}$ as follows.

$$\frac{4}{6} = \frac{\cancel{2} \times 2}{\cancel{2} \times 3} = \frac{2}{3}$$

Similarly, when you multiply "tanks" by "gallons per tank," the "tanks" cancel out of the numerator and the denominator, leaving the answer as gallons.

$$(27.985 \; \cancel{tanks}) \times \left(\frac{11.9 \text{ gallons}}{\cancel{tank}}\right) = 333.0215 \text{ gallons}$$

To see why "miles" cancel out when you divide "miles" by "miles per tank," tell students to think back to a rule for dividing fractions. The rule states that "to divide by a fraction, invert and multiply."

$$\frac{15,000 \text{ miles}}{536 \text{ miles per tank}} = 15,000 \text{ miles} \div \frac{536 \text{ miles}}{1 \text{ tank}} \qquad \text{"per" means divide.}$$

$$= 15,000 \text{ miles} \times \frac{1 \text{ tank}}{536 \text{ miles}} \qquad \text{Invert and multiply.}$$

$$= 15,000 \; \cancel{miles} \times \frac{1 \text{ tank}}{536 \; \cancel{miles}} \qquad \begin{array}{l} \text{Cancel out "miles" from} \\ \text{numerator and denominator.} \end{array}$$

$$\approx 27.985 \text{ tanks} \qquad \text{The answer is in tanks.}$$

Review this concept with students often, and provide ample opportunities for practice. Once they master unit analysis for both multiplying and dividing, they will have the power to make simple work out of the math in dozens of types of real-life problems.

Checkpoint Solution

To find the "miles per gallon" for each type of car, use the given information and divide.

c. A 2011 Toyota Prius: $\dfrac{536 \text{ miles}}{11.9 \text{ gal}} \approx 45$ miles per gallon

d. A 2011 Infiniti EX35: $\dfrac{360 \text{ miles}}{20 \text{ gal}} = 18$ miles per gallon

Example 3 Instructor Notes

Exponential (or scientific) notation is based on rules for multiplying by powers of 10. Examples:

$3.25 \times 10 = 32.5$ To multiply by 10 (or 10^1), move the decimal point 1 digit to the right.

$3.25 \times 100 = 325.0$ To multiply by 100 (or 10^2), move the decimal point 2 digits to the right.

$3.25 \times 1000 = 3250.0$ To multiply by 1000 (or 10^3), move the decimal point 3 digits to the right.

$3.25 \times 0.1 = 0.325$ To multiply by 0.1 (or 10^{-1}), move the decimal point 1 digit to the left.

$3.25 \times 0.01 = 0.0325$ To multiply by 100 (or 10^{-2}), move the decimal point 2 digits to the left.

$3.25 \times 0.001 = 0.00325$ To multiply by 1000 (or 10^{-3}), move the decimal point 3 digits to the left.

Checkpoint Solution

The diameter of a virus is

3×10^{-8} meter $= 0.00000003$ meter.

In Example 3, students saw that the length of a bacteria cell is 0.000003 meter. This means that viruses are roughly 100 times smaller than bacteria. In other words, if you were the size of a bacteria cell, your cell phone would be the size of a virus.

Another difference between viruses and bacteria is that viruses need living cells in order to reproduce. Once a virus is inside a living cell, it takes over the cell's resources and begins producing more virus particles. Bacteria do not need living cells to reproduce. In fact, bacteria live and produce in almost every environment on Earth, including water, ice, and soil.

Example 4 Instructor Notes

When trying to make sense of the magnitude of very large numbers, it helps to remember that each "number name" is 1000 times more than the previous number name.

- 1 million is 1000 times more than 1 thousand
- 1 billion is 1000 times more than 1 million
- 1 trillion is 1000 times more than 1 billion

Although we listed the "byte system" as powers of 10, the same names are sometimes interpreted as powers of 2. This is especially true in computer programming because computers work on a "base 2" system. In that system, 1 kilobyte is considered to be 1024 bytes. The table at the right compares the two systems.

Byte System		
Name (symbol)	Power of 10 Value (in bytes)	Power of 2 Value (in bytes)
kilobyte (kB)	10^3	2^{10}
megabyte (MB)	10^6	2^{20}
gigabyte (GB)	10^9	2^{30}
terabyte (TB)	10^{12}	2^{40}
petabyte (PB)	10^{15}	2^{50}
exabyte (EB)	10^{18}	2^{60}
zettabyte (ZB)	10^{21}	2^{70}
yottabyte (YB)	10^{24}	2^{80}

Checkpoint Solution

To find the storage for one Apple iPad, divide the total amount of stored digital information by 50 billion Apple iPads.

$$\frac{0.8 \text{ zettabytes}}{50 \text{ billion iPads}} = \frac{0.8 \times 1,000,000,000,000,000,000,000 \text{ bytes}}{50,000,000,000 \text{ iPads}}$$

$$= \frac{800,000,000,000 \text{ bytes}}{50 \text{ iPads}}$$

$$= 16,000,000,000 \text{ bytes per iPad}$$

$$= 16 \text{ gigabytes per iPad}$$

So, one Apple iPad can store 16 gigabytes of information.

Example 5 Instructor Notes

The phrase "garbage in, garbage out" is often used by computer programmers. Basically, it means that if the information you input is wrong (garbage), then the resulting output will also be wrong (garbage). This same principle applies to any type of calculation.

Here is an example. Suppose someone claims that the population of Chicago is 2,725,418 and the population of San Francisco is 803,548. Such a claim has to be "garbage." No one could know these populations with this amount of accuracy. So, if you use these numbers to claim that the combined population of the two cities is

$$2,725,418 + 803,548 = 3,528,966$$

your claim is also "garbage." A more reasonable claim would be to say that the populations are about 2.7 million and 0.8 million, implying that the combined population is about 3.5 million.

Checkpoint Solution

In rewriting these statements, remember that when you are communicating significant digits, you have two considerations.

1. Do not list more digits than you know are correct.

2. Do not list more digits than your audience needs.

d. **Original Statement:** The weight of an athlete is 213.6 pounds. Perhaps this statement could be valid, provided it was made minutes before a wrestling match, in which exact weight is important. In most contexts, however, this level of accuracy is inappropriate for listing a person's weight. After all, in any 24-hour period weight can easily vary by 2 or 3 pounds.

   Rewritten Statement: The weight of an athlete is about 215 pounds.

e. **Original Statement:** The record time for a 100-meter dash is 9.58 seconds. For many years, track events have commonly measured times to the nearest hundredth of a second. So, this statement does not need to be rewritten.

f. **Original Statement:** The distance between Earth and the Sun is 92,955,819 miles. This statement is in the field of science, so precise accuracy could be appropriate. Even so, when you think about the statement, you wonder what it means. Is it the distance between the centers or the surfaces? Moreover, Earth orbits the Sun in an elliptical path, not a circular path. So, the "distance" between Earth and the Sun is not constant. For this reason, the statement would be better rewritten.

   Rewritten Statement: The distance between Earth and the Sun is about 93 million miles.

Example 6 Instructor Notes

Review the formulas from Section 1.1 that students should memorize:

Rectangle   **Circle**

$A = bh$ $A = \pi r^2$

Point out that when you need to find the area of other geometric shapes, you can usually use one or both of these formulas to derive a formula for the area of the other shape. For example, to find the area of a right triangle whose base is 4 feet and whose height is 3 feet, you can imagine that the triangle is half of a rectangle.

Because the area of the rectangle is $A = bh$, it follows that the area of the triangle is

$$A = \frac{1}{2}bh = \frac{1}{2}(4 \text{ ft}) \times (3 \text{ ft}) = 6 \text{ ft}^2.$$

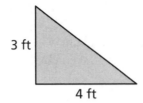

3 ft

4 ft

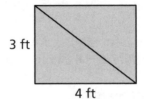

3 ft

4 ft

Remind students to always check their calculations for correct units. In the above product,

- $\frac{1}{2}$ has no units. Like π, it is a ratio—in this case, the ratio of the area of a triangle to the area of its corresponding rectangle.

- 4 is the base. The base has feet as its units.

- 3 is the height. The height has feet as its units.

- 6 is the area. The area has square feet as its units.

Use the Lunar Eclipse Computer to find information about the next total eclipse of the moon in your area. (See *http://www.usno.navy.mil/USNO/astronomical-applications/data-services/lunar-ecl-us*.)

Checkpoint Solution

One way to estimate the average number of characters in the names is to assume that the people who died have the same types of names as people in a typical metropolitan phone book. You could randomly select 50 or 60 names and count the characters. When we did this, we found the average number of letters in last names to be 7 and the average number of letters in first names to be 5. So, one estimate for the number of characters is

(First Name) (space) (Middle Initial) (space) (Last Name)

  5   + 1 +   1   + 1 +   7   = 15.

Remember, this number is an estimate. Most of the names on the memorial would have a different number of characters, as in GARY W ERICSON, which has 14 characters counting the two spaces.

Section 1.3   Using Percent

Example 1 Instructor Notes

This section introduces another critical skill that students must develop for success in mathematics: knowing how to find and how to interpret percent. You can use the following review exercises to check your students' familiarity with percent.

1. Write 0.5 as a percent.

2. Write 0.5% as a decimal.

3. What is 20% of 48?

4. 30 is what percent of 90?

5. What is 25% of 500?

Answers

1. 0.5 is one-half, or 50%. (Move decimal point 2 places to the right.)

2. 0.5% is less than 1%. In decimal form, it is 0.005.

3. 10% of 48 is 4.8. So, 20% is 9.6.

4. 30 is one-third of 90. So, 30 is $33\frac{1}{3}\%$ of 90.

5. 25% is one-fourth. So, 25% of 500 is 125.

Checkpoint Solution

Alaska has a land area of 571,951 square miles. According to the table on page 24, 69.1% of this is owned by the federal government.

$$69.1\% \text{ of } 571,951 = 0.691 \times 571,951$$
$$\approx 395,218 \text{ mi}^2$$

So, the federal government owns about 395,200 square miles of Alaska.

In Example 1, we found that the federal government owns about 92,800 square miles of Nevada. So, the federal government owns much more land in Alaska than it does in Nevada.

There are about 3.5 million square miles of land in the United States. About 67% of that land is owned by individuals, corporations, and states. The remaining land is owned by the federal government and is administered for the most part by four federal agencies:

1. The Bureau of Land Management (BLM)

2. The National Park Service (NPS) (U.S. Department of Interior)

3. The Fish and Wildlife Service (FWS) (U.S. Department of Interior)

4. The Forest Service (FS) (U.S. Department of Agriculture)

Example 2 Instructor Notes

There are 3 things that students should notice about Example 2.

1. The parts of a circle graph always total 100%. In this case, you have

   $$61.0\% + 26.1\% + 9.4\% + 3.5\% = 100.0\%$$

2. You should take statistics, like the ones in Example 2, as rough estimates. After all, how could anyone know how many dogs live in the United States?

3. The solution in Example 2 produced an estimate of 73 million dogs in the United States. The American Veterinary Medical Association puts the estimate at about 72 million. Using a spreadsheet like the one in Example 2, students can change the estimate for the average number of dogs owned by households with 3 or more dogs to see if they can get a total that agrees with the AVMA.
   (See *http://math.andyou.com/content/01/03/data/mthu_data_0103_025_02.xls*.)

	A	B	C	D	
1	**Households**	**Number of Dogs**	**Percent**	**Dogs**	
2	117,000,000	0	61.0%	0	
3	117,000,000	1	26.1%	30,537,000	
4	117,000,000	2	9.4%	21,996,000	
5	117,000,000	5	3.5%	20,475,000	
6			100.0%	73,008,000	
7					
8					

Checkpoint Solution

$$\frac{2.45 \text{ cats}}{1 \text{ household}} \times 0.33 \times 117,000,000 \text{ households} = 94,594,500 \text{ cats}$$

There are about 95 million pet cats in the United States.

As you might imagine, sources disagree on this number. The American Veterinary Medical Association claims that 32.4% of households own cats, with an average ownership of 2.2 cats. This puts the AVMA's estimate for the total number of cats in the United States at about 83 million.

Unit Analysis Using Percent

When using unit analysis with percent, remember that a percent is a ratio that has the same units in the numerator and denominator. Because these "same units" cancel each other, we usually say that a percent has no units.

Example 3 Instructor Notes

Make sure students understand the following facts about percent.

1. A percent is the **ratio of two numbers.**

2. The numerator and denominator are measured in the **same units.**

3. The numerator is the **part.**

4. The denominator is the **base.**

5. Dividing the numerator by the denominator produces the **decimal form** of a percent.

Examples:

a. Of 16 coins, 4 are nickels.

$$\frac{\text{Number of nickels}}{\text{Number of coins}} = \frac{4 \text{ coins}}{16 \text{ coins}} = 0.25$$

So, 25% of the coins are nickels.

b. Your hourly wage of $9.50 will be increased by $2.15.

$$\frac{\text{Amount of raise}}{\text{Salary}} = \frac{\$2.15}{\$9.50} \approx 0.226$$

So, you will receive a 22.6% raise.

Checkpoint Solution

There are 103 letters in this Spanish version of SCRABBLE.

Number of A's:	11
Number of E's:	11
Number of I's:	6
Number of O's:	8
Number of U's:	6
Total:	42

$$\boxed{\text{Part}} \!\!-\!\! \frac{42 \text{ letters}}{103 \text{ letters}} \approx 0.41 = 41\%$$
$$\boxed{\text{Base}} \!\!-\!\!$$

So, in this Spanish version of SCRABBLE, about 41% of the tiles are vowels. Note that a different Spanish version of SCRABBLE is sold outside of North America and has 100 letter tiles, including 12 A's, 12 E's, 6 I's, 9 O's, and 5 U's.

$$\boxed{\text{Part}} \!\!-\!\! \frac{44 \text{ letters}}{100 \text{ letters}} \approx 0.44 = 44\%$$
$$\boxed{\text{Base}} \!\!-\!\!$$

So, in this Spanish version of SCRABBLE, exactly 44% of the tiles are vowels.

Example 4 Instructor Notes

Explain that a percent is a ratio, which means that the numerator and denominator must have the same units. Fractions in which the numerator and denominator have different units are called rates, as in "dollars per hour" or "miles per gallon."

Same units	$\dfrac{44 \text{ lb}}{210 \text{ lb}} \approx 0.2095 \approx 20.1\%$	Ratio (no units)
Same units	$\dfrac{20 \text{ kg}}{95.5 \text{ kg}} \approx 0.2094 \approx 20.1\%$	Ratio (no units)
Different units	$\dfrac{20 \text{ kg}}{210 \text{ lb}} \approx 0.095 \text{ kg per lb}$	Rate (different units)

Checkpoint Solution

In each case, divide the number of pounds by the total weight (in pounds). When doing this with a spreadsheet, you can specify how many digits you want displayed in the result. (See *http://math.andyou.com/content/01/03/data/mthu_data_0103_027_04.xls.*)

	A	B	C	
1	**Substance**	**Pounds**	**Percent**	
2	Water	111	61.7%	
3	Protein	30	16.7%	
4	Fat	27	15.0%	
5	Other	12	6.7%	
6	**Total**	**180**		
7				

Example 5 Instructor Notes

Point out that when working with percent increase, it is important to keep track of whether the numerator is the "increase" or the "increased amount."

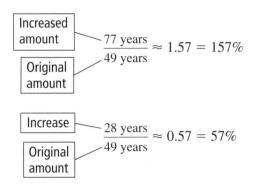

$$\dfrac{77 \text{ years}}{49 \text{ years}} \approx 1.57 = 157\%$$

When the numerator is the "increased amount," the percent represents the new amount, including the original amount.

$$\dfrac{28 \text{ years}}{49 \text{ years}} \approx 0.57 = 57\%$$

When the numerator is the "increase," the percent represents only the increase, and does not include the original amount.

Checkpoint Solution

Here is one way to describe the changes in life expectancy.

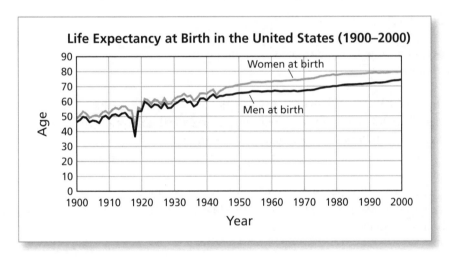

a. In 1900, a woman's life expectancy at birth was about 50 years. During the next 100 years, this rose by about 30 years, which was an increase of about 60%. The two major reasons for the increase were the discovery of antibiotics and the improved survival rates (for mothers and for babies) during childbirth.

b. In 1900, a woman's life expectancy at birth was about 50 years. During the next 100 years, life expectancy rose to about 80 years—or about 160% of the life expectancy in 1900. The two major reasons for the increase were the discovery of antibiotics and the improved survival rates (for mothers and for babies) during childbirth.

Example 6 Instructor Notes

When dealing with increases, markups, or profits that are greater than 100%, there is a good chance that your communication will be misunderstood. For example, ask students how they would interpret the following statement.

"The retailer has a markup of 200%."

It's not that this statement is ambiguous in mathematics. It clearly means that an item is sold for 3 times the wholesale price. For instance, if you buy an item for $50 and sell it for $150, then you marked it up $100, which is 200% of your wholesale price.

Even so, the problem is that many people think that marking up a wholesale price of $50 to $100 is a 200% markup. So, when talking about percents that are greater than 100%, you need to decide whether it is more important to be understood or to be correct.

To increase your chance of being understood, you should talk about the actual increases, not just the percent increases.

Checkpoint Solution

The graph in Example 6 shows the price of gold from 1972 to 2010.

In the early 1980s, there was a short period of time in which speculation in the price of gold was rampant. The price of gold quadrupled in just a few years.

In 1971, President Richard Nixon ended the U.S. dollar convertibility to gold, and the central role of gold in world currency systems ended. The dollar and gold floated. In January, 1980 gold price hit a record of $850 per ounce. This meant that the price of gold had quadrupled in just a few short years.

The price quickly dropped back down to around $400 per ounce, where it stayed for about 15 years. After falling even more in the early 2000s, it started to rise again. In early 2011, the price of gold had hit a record high of more than $1200 per ounce.

Section 1.4   Units & Conversions

Example 1 Instructor Notes

Review the unit analysis rules on page 34 and discuss the following example:

Consider a rectangle that is 3 feet high and 4 feet wide.

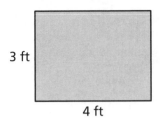

3 ft

4 ft

- The perimeter of the rectangle is

    3 ft + 4 ft + 3 ft + 4 ft = 14 ft.   Addition preserves units.

- The area of the rectangle is

    4 ft × 3 ft = 12 ft^2.   Multiplication changes units.

Checkpoint Solution

Show students how writing the units helps keep track of the calculations.

$$52 \text{ wk} \times \frac{55 \text{ hr}}{1 \text{ wk}} \times \frac{\$413}{1 \text{ hr}} = \$1,181,180$$

See that "weeks" and "hours" cancel out and you are left with "dollars."

Although the result may seem unreasonable, you can check the history of some famous cases to see that litigation bills can run up to several million dollars.

Example 2 Instructor Notes

The beautiful thing about "the unit analysis approach to math" is that it reduces so many problems in mathematics to the same strategy.

The more students practice using unit analysis, the more they will build their intuition for knowing when to multiply, when to add, when to subtract, and when to divide.

Ask students to think about this example.

You are tutoring a young student who is trying to solve the following problem. "An employee at a fast-food restaurant is paid $8.50 per hour. The employee works 32 hours in a week. How much does the employee earn in the week?"

For you, it is intuitive to multiply $8.50 per hour by 32 hours. But how would you explain to a 3rd or 4th grader why you multiply?

$$\frac{\$8.50}{1 \text{ hr}} \times 32 \text{ hr} = \$272$$

Checkpoint Solution

c. You can estimate the number of species of mammals that will become extinct during the next 100 years as follows.

$$\frac{60 \text{ species}}{410 \text{ years}} \times 100 \text{ years} \approx 14.6$$

During the next 100 years, perhaps 15 species of mammals will become extinct.

d. You can estimate the number of years in which 40 more species of birds will have become extinct as follows.

$$\frac{40 \text{ species}}{\dfrac{125 \text{ species}}{410 \text{ years}}} = 40 \text{ species} \times \frac{410 \text{ years}}{125 \text{ species}} \qquad \text{To divide, invert and multiply.}$$

$$= 131.2 \text{ years}$$

So, you might expect it to take about 130 years for 40 additional species of birds to become extinct. Remember, however, that this type of prediction is quite rough. It assumes that the rate of extinction of new species will be the same as it was during the past 410 years.

Example 3 Instructor Notes

Although most countries use the metric system, Americans have resisted switching from the customary system to metric. Perhaps one reason is that the customary system evolved naturally in accord with the human body. The metric system is patterned after "base 10" and the circumference of Earth. Here are some examples.

Length	Historical Beginning
Inch	The width of a human thumb
Foot	The length of a human foot
Yard	The distance from a human nose to the end of an outstretched human arm
Mile	The distance a human can walk in 1000 paces (two steps)

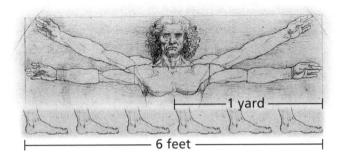

Pounds, ounces, quarts, gallons, and other measures in the U.S. customary system have similar connections to humans and human activities, such as measuring food, precious metals, and grain.

Checkpoint Solution

From Example 3, you know that there are

31,536,000 seconds

in a calendar year. Because there are 365.24218967 days in a solar year, there are

$$1 \text{ solar year} = (365.24218967 \text{ days})\left(\frac{24 \text{ hr}}{1 \text{ day}}\right)\left(\frac{60 \text{ min}}{1 \text{ hr}}\right)\left(\frac{60 \text{ sec}}{1 \text{ min}}\right)$$

$$= 31,556,925.19 \text{ seconds}$$

in a solar year. So, there are about $31,556,925 - 31,536,000 = 20,925$ more seconds in a solar year than in a calendar year.

Example 4 Instructor Notes

You can roughly convert between feet per second and miles per hour as follows.

1. To *approximately* convert from mph to ft/sec, multiply by 1.5.

$$110 \text{ mph} \approx (110 \times 1.5) \text{ ft/sec} = 165 \text{ ft/sec}$$

2. To *approximately* convert from ft/sec to mph, multiply by $\frac{2}{3}$.

$$15 \text{ ft/sec} \approx \frac{2}{3} \times 15 \text{ mph} = 10 \text{ mph}$$

For instance, the speed of sound is roughly 1100 ft/sec and a normal commercial jet travels at about 500 mph. Is a normal commercial jet faster than the speed of sound?

500 mph is roughly 750 ft/sec. So, a normal commercial jet is not faster than the speed of sound.

Checkpoint Solution

c. From the graph, the parachutist jumps from the airplane at a time of 0 seconds. He accelerates for about 20 seconds. Then for another 20 seconds, his speed is constant at about 110 miles per hour. So, he is in free fall for a total of about 40 seconds.

d. At the end of 40 seconds, the parachutist's speed abruptly drops to about 10 miles per hour. This must have been the time when he opened his parachute. When the time is 70 seconds, his speed drops to zero. So, he must have spent about 30 seconds with the parachute open.

Example 5 Instructor Notes

If you need to make frequent conversions between U.S. Customary units and metric units, the quick approximations on page 38 are helpful.

Quick Approximations:

$1 \text{ mi} \approx \dfrac{8}{5} \text{ km}$ Multiply by 8, then divide by 5.

$F \approx 2C + 30$ Multiply by 2, then add 30.

$1 \text{ gal} \approx 4 \text{ L}$ Multiply by 4.

$1 \text{ lb} \approx \dfrac{2}{5} \text{ kg}$ Multiply by 2, then divide by 5.

Examples:

1. You are visiting Canada. You want to set the thermostat in your hotel room to 70°F. Is setting it to 20°C correct?

    Multiply 20 by 2 to get 40. Then add 30 to get 70.

    So, a temperature of 20°C is approximately 70°F.

2. You are visiting Canada. You buy 500 grams of ground beef to make five grilled hamburgers. Are you making quarter-pound hamburgers?

    Multiply $\dfrac{1}{4}$ by 2 to get $\dfrac{1}{2}$. Divide by 5 to get $\dfrac{1}{10}$ kg or 100 grams.

    So, a quarter pound is about 100 grams. You are making quarter-pound hamburgers.

Checkpoint Solution

c. When gas is 105.9 cents per liter in Canada, it is about

    4×105.9 cents per liter $= 423.6$ cents per gallon $\approx \$4.24$ per gallon.

    So, it is about $4.24 per gallon. So, it seems to be more expensive than in the United States.

d. Of course, to make an exact comparison, you would also need to account for the exchange rate in Canadian and American currencies. During the past 10 years, the Canadian dollar has been as low as $0.62 U.S. and as high as $1.09 U.S. Students may view a graph of the fluctuating exchange rates in the Checkpoint Solution at *Math.andYou.com.*

Example 6 Instructor Notes

A good way for students to build familiarity and intuition about conversions is to make their own spreadsheets and look at the results. To do this, students will have to have some familiarity with writing algebraic expressions.

Give students the opportunity to create the following spreadsheet using the six steps provided. (See *http://math.andyou.com/content/01/04/data/mthu_data_0104_039_06.xls*).

1. Enter the titles "Celsius" and "Fahrenheit" into Row 1.

2. Enter 100 into cell A2.

3. Enter the formula = A2-10 into cell A3.

4. Copy this formula into cells A4 through A17.

5. Enter the formula = (9/5)*A2+32 into cell B3.

6. Copy this formula into cells B4 through B17.

Encourage students who are not used to working with spreadsheets to familiarize themselves with their computer software and practice using the programs. Discuss ways that spreadsheets could benefit them outside the classroom.

	A Celsius	B Fahrenheit	C
1	Celsius	Fahrenheit	
2	100	212	
3	90	194	
4	80	176	
5	70	158	
6	60	140	
7	50	122	
8	40	104	
9	30	86	
10	20	68	
11	10	50	
12	0	32	
13	-10	14	
14	-20	-4	
15	-30	-22	
16	-40	-40	
17	-50	-58	

Checkpoint Solution

a. From the spreadsheet in Example 6, you can see that a temperature of 20°C is equal to a temperature of 68°F.

b. You need to find a temperature in degrees Celsius so that

$$77 = \frac{9}{5}C + 32.$$

Using the spreadsheet in Example 6, a temperature of 77°F will fall between 20°C and 30°C. By trial and error, you can see that 77°F is equal to 25°C.

Chapter 2

Section 2.1   Unit Prices

Example 1 Instructor Notes

Point out that a unit price is a type of rate. This means that it is a fraction that has different units in the numerator and denominator. Here are some other examples of rates.

$$\frac{\$1.20}{1 \text{ lb}} \qquad \frac{25 \text{ mi}}{1 \text{ gal}} \qquad \frac{75 \text{ mi}}{1 \text{ hr}}$$

Of these, the first rate is a unit price because it gives the price (in dollars) per unit of length, area, volume, weight, quantity, or time. Here are some other examples.

Unit price for ribbon ($3.20 per foot)	$\dfrac{\$3.20}{1 \text{ ft}}$	Length
Unit price for carpet ($32 per square yard)	$\dfrac{\$32}{1 \text{ yd}^2}$	Area
Unit price for gas ($3.20 per gallon)	$\dfrac{\$3.20}{1 \text{ gal}}$	Volume
Unit price for peanuts ($3.20 per pound)	$\dfrac{\$3.20}{1 \text{ lb}}$	Weight
Unit price for eggs ($3.20 per dozen)	$\dfrac{\$3.20}{1 \text{ doz}}$	Quantity
Unit price for car rental ($32 per day)	$\dfrac{\$32}{1 \text{ day}}$	Time

Checkpoint Solution

a. Caviar: $\dfrac{\$853.65}{8 \text{ oz}} \approx \dfrac{\$106.71}{1 \text{ oz}}$

b. Wrinkle cream: $\dfrac{\$119.00}{1.7 \text{ fl oz}} = \dfrac{\$70.00}{1 \text{ fl oz}}$

c. Honey: $\dfrac{\$10.50}{8 \text{ oz}} \approx \dfrac{\$1.31}{1 \text{ oz}}$

Remember that fluid ounce is a measure of volume, while ounce is a measure of weight. The use of the term "ounce" for both measures stems from the fact that one fluid ounce of water weighs about one ounce. This relationship is summarized in the saying "A pint's a pound the world around."

There are 16 fluid ounces in a pint. And there are 16 ounces in a pound.

Example 2 Instructor Notes

In part (a) of the solution, be sure that students notice how unit analysis is used to come up with the answer. Here is what you are given.

$$\frac{\$16.50}{100\text{ lb}}$$

When simplified, this fraction will give a unit price in *dollars per pound*, but you want to know the unit price in *dollars per gallon*. To accomplish this, you can multiply by a conversion factor that relates pounds and gallons, as follows.

$$\text{Unit price} = \frac{\$16.50}{100\text{ lb}} \times \frac{8.6\text{ lb}}{1\text{ gal}} = \frac{\$1.419}{1\text{ gal}}$$

Conversion factor

Make sure students understand how this conversion works. Students who master the concept of unit analysis will find many "math windows" opened to them as they stop viewing math as a collection of rules and formulas to be memorized and see it as a way to provide answers to questions in everyday life.

Checkpoint Solution

c. In 2010, a dairy farmer earned about $25 for every 100 pounds of milk produced organically.

$$\text{Unit price} = \frac{\$25}{100\text{ lb}} \times \frac{8.6\text{ lb}}{1\text{ gal}} = \frac{\$2.15}{1\text{ gal}}$$

A dairy farmer earned $2.15 per gallon of milk.

d. The price of a gallon of organic milk was about $ 5.25.

Amount earned by farmer

$$\frac{\$2.15}{\$5.25} \approx 0.4095$$

Grocery price

The dairy farmer received about 41.0% of the grocery store price.

Example 3 Instructor Notes

A *unit price* is sometimes called a unit cost. In either case, remind students that it is customary to write the dollar amount in the numerator.

$$\frac{\$1.50}{1 \text{ lb}} \qquad \text{Dollar amount in numerator}$$

$$\frac{1 \text{ lb}}{\$1.50} \qquad \textbf{Not} \text{ dollar amount in denominator}$$

Point out two things in Example 3:

1. To compare unit prices, you should write each unit price using the same units.

2. To convert dollars per gallon to dollars per fluid ounce, multiply by a conversion factor.

$$\text{Part (b) unit price} = \frac{\$17.99}{2 \text{ gal}} \times \frac{1 \text{ gal}}{128 \text{ fl oz}} \approx \frac{\$0.07}{1 \text{ fl oz}}$$

Conversion factor

Checkpoint Solution

Each of the detergents in Example 3 recommends 2 fluid ounces for a load of wash. The cost per load is as follows.

Brand A: $(2 \text{ fl oz}) \times \dfrac{\$0.13}{1 \text{ fl oz}} = \$0.26$ Cost per load

Brand B: $(2 \text{ fl oz}) \times \dfrac{\$0.07}{1 \text{ fl oz}} = \$0.14$ Cost per load

Brand C: $(2 \text{ fl oz}) \times \dfrac{\$0.16}{1 \text{ fl oz}} = \$0.32$ Cost per load

For the homemade laundry soap, use 1 gallon = 16 cups to figure out the amount of soap produced in one batch.

$$\frac{1}{3} \text{ bar} + \frac{1}{2} \text{ cup} + \frac{1}{2} \text{ cup} + 6 \text{ cups} + 4 \text{ cups} + 16 \text{ cups} + 6 \text{ cups} \approx 33 \text{ cups}$$

Assuming there is no cost for water, the cost of the recipe is $\$0.40 + \$0.17 + \$0.14 = \$0.71$.

Each load of laundry needs $\dfrac{1}{2}$ cup of soap.

Homemade: $(0.5 \text{ cup}) \times \dfrac{\$0.71}{33 \text{ cups}} \approx \$0.01$ Cost per load

So, the cost per load is roughly $0.01.

Example 4 Instructor Notes

There is an important subtlety in Example 4.

"When you are finding a unit price, how do you know the units for the denominator?"

For pizza, should the units be length (inches), area (square inches), or volume (cubic inches)? Make sure you understand that using "length" is not valid. In the example, "area" is used because it is assumed that the pizzas have a uniform thickness. If the thickness is significantly different, then it would be better to use "volume" as the denominator for the unit price.

In the solution, notice that we used the formula for the area of a circle.

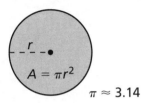

$\pi \approx 3.14$

The area of a circle is pi times radius squared.

Checkpoint Solution

e. Area $\approx 3.14(12 \text{ in.})^2 \approx 452.2 \text{ in.}^2$

Unit price $\approx \dfrac{\$24.99}{452.2 \text{ in.}^2} \approx \$0.055 \text{ per in.}^2$ Jumbo

So, the jumbo pizza has the least unit price. It is slightly less than the unit price for a large pizza.

Example 5 Instructor Notes

The first paragraph on page 56 states an important concept: saving a modest amount daily can result in saving a significant amount annually.

For instance, in Example 5(b), saving only $0.85 per pound on all meat purchases can result in an annual savings of over $600 for a family of four. Remember also that this amount is "after taxes." For many families, this represents a savings of about $1000 in gross income.

Checkpoint Solution

The annual amount of wheat flour and sugar consumed (per person) is

$$136.6 + 65.7 = 202.3 \text{ lb.}$$

For a family of four, this amounts to

$$4(202.3) = 809.2 \text{ lb.}$$

If the family were able to save $0.67 per pound, the total annual savings would be

$$809.2 \, \cancel{\text{lb}} \times \frac{\$0.67}{1 \, \cancel{\text{lb}}} = \$542.16.$$

So, the family could save about $540 in a year buying discounted flour and sugar. This, of course, assumes that someone in the family does "home cooking." If the family's consumption of flour and sugar consists primarily of processed food or food at restaurants, then the savings would be far less.

Example 6 Instructor Notes

Review with students the overall strategy in the solution for Example 6.

The cost of 6 homemade cheeseburgers is $9.67.

↓

The cost of 6 restaurant cheeseburgers is $20.94.

↓

The savings for 6 cheeseburgers is $11.27.

↓

The annual savings is about $586.

Checkpoint Solution

d. The cost of the ingredients is

$$1.59 + 1.89 + 3.49 + 2.89 + 0.35 + 0.79 = \$11.00.$$

The unit price per serving of spaghetti is

$$\text{Unit price} = \frac{\$11.00}{4 \text{ servings}} = \$2.75 \text{ per serving.}$$

e. The cost of four restaurant spaghetti meals at $7.95 each is

$$4(\$7.95) = \$31.80.$$

So, it would cost $31.80 − $11.00 = $20.80 more to buy four spaghetti dinners at a restaurant than to make them at home.

On average, Americans eat out between four and five times a week. The point of this example is that eating out costs significantly more than buying raw materials, cooking yourself, and eating at home.

Section 2.2 Markup & Discount

Example 1 Instructor Notes

The terms "markup" and "markup percent" are technical terms that are used in business. Both terms are commonly misused and misunderstood.

Markup: Technically this term only applies to retail (or reselling) businesses. If a retail business buys an item for $10 and sells it for $15, then the markup is $5. The term markup is not applied to businesses that manufacture (or significantly alter) items. For instance, it is not fair to say that a pharmaceutical company that pays $0.10 for the ingredients in a pill and sells the pill for $1.10 has a markup of $1.

Markup Percent: When using the term markup percent, remind students that the numerator is the markup and the denominator is the wholesale price. Refer to page 64 to show how this differs from the term "discount percent." When calculating discount percent, the denominator is the retail price.

Checkpoint Solution

To find the markup percent for each item, divide the markup by the wholesale price.

c. **Automobile:**

$$\frac{\text{Markup}}{\text{Wholesale price}} = \frac{\$27{,}990 - \$25{,}450}{\$25{,}450} = \frac{\$2540}{\$25{,}450} \approx 0.0998$$

The markup percent is about 10%. This is a typical markup rate for a new car. For used cars, the markup rate is often higher.

d. **Leather Chair:**

$$\frac{\text{Markup}}{\text{Wholesale price}} = \frac{\$799 - \$235}{\$235} = \frac{\$564}{\$235} = 2.40$$

The markup percent is about 240%. This is a typical markup rate for new furniture. Having a very high markup rate is what allows furniture stores to have high discount sales.

Example 2 Instructor Notes

Example 2 illustrates a correct use of the word "markup." Notice that the transaction involves only buying the handbag and reselling it. Remind students that the term "markup" should not be used when a business adds something to the product. That process is called "value added." For instance, when a custom van company buys the shell of a new van for $5000, adds a luxury interior, and resells the van for $25,000, the increase in price is not called "markup."

In Example 2, there are two important points for people who run small business ventures such as this one.

1. Be sure to keep a record of all of your expenses. In this example, notice how incorrect it would be to tell someone that you bought the handbag for $195 and sold it for a profit of $200. It sounds really nice, but it simply doesn't take into account all of your expenses.

2. Anytime you earn money, whether it is babysitting, tips, mowing lawns, or having a yard sale, you are responsible for claiming the income on your state and federal income tax returns. Failure to do this is a punishable crime. No one knows the extent of the lost tax revenue from unreported income, but the U.S. Treasury Department has estimated that the problem costs the government about $250 billion per year.

Checkpoint Solution

This is a common error in business. The problem is that the business is using the wrong denominator.

$$\text{Markup} = \$200 - \$140$$
$$= \$60$$

Correct Denominator:

$$\frac{\$60}{\$140} \approx 0.429 = 42.9\%$$

Wholesale price

Incorrect Denominator:

$$\frac{\$60}{\$200} = 0.3 = 30\%$$

Retail price

So, the bookstore is actually using a markup of about 42.9%, not 30%. Although this could be an innocent error, because the error results in claiming a smaller markup percent, one is tempted to suspect that the error is sometimes intentional.

Example 3 Instructor Notes

As is true of the terms "markup" and "markup percent," the terms "discount" and "discount percent" are technical terms that are used in business.

Discount: Technically this term only applies to retail (or reselling) businesses. An item is discounted when its normal retail price is lowered. The discount is the difference between the "Regular Price" and the "Discounted Price." You can see the potential for abuse with this definition. It is common that a retailer artificially inflates the "Regular Price" for the sake of being able to claim a larger discount.

Discount Percent: When using the term discount percent, be sure that the numerator is the discount and the denominator is the regular retail price.

Checkpoint Solution

As is shown in Example 3, a spreadsheet works well to organize the problem. In the spreadsheet provided at *Math.andYou.com*, students can change the values in the yellow cells to answer the Checkpoint.

(See *http://math.andyou.com/content/02/02/data/mthu_data_0202_064_03.xls*.)

	A	B	C	D	E	F
1	**Wholesale**	**Regular**	**Discount**	**Discount**	**Quantity**	
2	**Price**	**Price**	**Percent**	**Price**	**Sold**	**Revenue**
3	$8.37	$24.99	0.0%	$24.99	11	$274.89
4	$8.37	$24.99	25.0%	$18.74	7	$131.20
5	$8.37	$24.99	50.0%	$12.50	3	$37.49
6	$8.37	$24.99	75.0%	$6.25	4	$24.99
7						**$468.56**
8						

You paid $25(8.37) = \$209.25$ for the shirts. Your total markup was $468.56 - 209.25 = \$259.31$.

$$\frac{\text{Total markup}}{\text{Total wholesale price}} = \frac{\$259.31}{\$209.25} \approx 1.239 = 123.9\%$$

The average markup percent for selling the 25 shirts is about 124%, even though the last 4 shirts were sold at a loss.

Note About Round-Off Error: In the spreadsheet, note that some of the amounts shown in column F are not the product of columns D and E. This result is due to round-off error. You can avoid this type of error by using a "greatest integer function (INT)" when listing the prices in column D. The spreadsheet provided at *Math.andYou.com* has an alternate table that uses the greatest integer function.

Example 4 Instructor Notes

A generic drug is a drug that is produced and distributed without patent protection. A generic must contain the same active ingredients as the original formulation. The original drug is given patent protection for several years before a generic drug can be sold in its place. It is far less expensive to develop a generic drug than to develop an original drug. For this reason, generic drugs are often sold at significantly discounted prices.

	A	B	C	D	E
1	Condition	Brand	Generic	Discount	Percent
2	High Blood Pressure	$128.00	$13.00	$115.00	89.8%
3	High Cholesterol	$95.00	$37.00	$58.00	61.1%
4	Depression	$103.00	$37.00	$66.00	64.1%
5	Arthritis Pain	$135.00	$30.00	$105.00	77.8%
6	Heartburn	$179.00	$24.00	$155.00	86.6%
7					

Checkpoint Solution

The simplest way to solve this problem is to use a spreadsheet.
(See *http://math.andyou.com/content/02/02/data/mthu_data_0202_065_04b.xls.*)

	A	B	C	D	E
1	Condition	U.S.	Canada	Discount	Percent
2	Stomach Acid Medication	$129.00	$53.00	$76.00	58.9%
3	Antihyperglycemic Agent	$52.00	$12.00	$40.00	76.9%
4	Conjugated Estrogens	$26.00	$7.00	$19.00	73.1%
5					

Example 5 Instructor Notes

Discounts commonly come in two forms: (1) a percent or (2) a dollar amount.

Ask students, when there are two or more discounts that can be applied to a sale, whether the final price is affected by the order in which the discounts are applied. Discuss the following situations.

a. **Both Discounts are Percents:** If both discounts are percents, then the final price you pay is not affected by the order in which the discounts are given.

b. **Both Discounts are Dollar Amounts:** If both discounts are dollar amounts, then the final price you pay is not affected by the order in which the discounts are given.

c. **One Discount is Percent and One is a Dollar Amount:** Example 5 shows that when you mix the types of discounts, the order in which they are applied does make a difference in the final price that you pay.

Checkpoint Solution

When both discounts are percents, the order in which you apply the discounts does not affect the final price you pay.

A 10% discount followed by a 25% discount:

Take 10% off.

$$\$40 - 0.1(\$40) = \$40.00 - \$4.00$$
$$= \$36.00$$

Then, take 25% more off.

$$\$36 - 0.25(\$36) = \$36 - \$9$$
$$= \$27$$

A 25% discount followed by a 10% discount:

Take 25% off.

$$\$40 - 0.25(\$40) = \$40.00 - \$10.00$$
$$= \$30.00$$

Then, take 10% more off.

$$\$30 - 0.1(\$30) = \$30 - \$3$$
$$= \$27$$

With either order, the final price of the jeans is $27. This is a total discount percent of 32.5%.

Notice that $(0.9)(0.75) = 0.675$, which is the same as a total discount percent of 32.5%.

Example 6 Instructor Notes

Discounts commonly come in two forms: (1) a percent or (2) a dollar amount.

Ask students, when there are two or more discounts that can be applied to a sale, whether the final price is affected by the order in which the discounts are applied. Discuss the following situations.

a. **Both Discounts are Percents:** Example 6 shows that the order in which two discount percents are applied does not affect the final price that you pay.

b. **Both Discounts are Dollar Amounts:** If both discounts are dollar amounts, then the final price you pay is not affected by the order in which the discounts are given.

c. **One Discount is Percent and One is a Dollar Amount:** Example 5 shows that when you mix the types of discounts, the order in which they are applied does make a difference in the final price that you pay.

Checkpoint Solution

If you spend 20 minutes a week clipping coupons, that amounts to

$$\frac{20 \text{ min}}{1 \text{ week}} \times \frac{1 \text{ hr}}{60 \text{ min}} \times \frac{52 \text{ weeks}}{1 \text{ year}} \approx 17.3 \text{ hr per year.}$$

By saving \$1000 per year, this represents an hourly wage of

$$\frac{\$1000}{17.3 \text{ hr}} \approx \$57.80 \text{ per hour}$$

which isn't a bad hourly wage. It looks like clipping coupons is worth the effort.

Use the *Universal Currency Converter* to determine how many Euros you will receive for \$2000 (USD). (See *http://www.xe.com/ucc/.*)

Section 2.3 Consumption Taxes

Example 1 Instructor Notes

Remind students that it is best to perform all calculations involving percent with the decimal form of the percent.

Change "of" to "times"

$$8\% \text{ of } \$214{,}000 = 0.08 \times \$214{,}000$$

Change 8% to decimal form

Also point out that the percent form can easily have decimal places. Whether it does or not, to change to decimal form, move the decimal two places to the left.

Percent Form	Decimal Form
8%	0.08
1.5%	0.015
100%	1.0
1.0%	0.0001

Checkpoint Solution

c. High heel shoes: $6\% \text{ of } \$250 = 0.06 \times \$250$
$$= \$15.00$$

d. Watch: $7.4\% \text{ of } \$1350 = 0.074 \times \$1350$
$$= \$99.90$$

Example 2 Instructor Notes

The two most common forms of percent problems are:

(1) What is 20% of $80?

(2) 50 is what percent of 200?

Help students through examples and enough practice to master both types of problems. Encourage them that their efforts will pay off. They may be surprised at how many types of real-life problems become easier for them.

(1) What is 20% of $80?

Strategy: (a) Write percent in decimal form and (b) multiply.

$$0.20 \times \$80 = \$16$$

(2) 50 is what percent of 200?

Strategy: (a) Divide and (b) write in percent form.

$$50/200 = 0.25 = 25\%$$

Checkpoint Solution

a. To answer this question, you need to estimate the retail price of a major appliance. Let's say that this is $1000.

$$6.5\% \text{ of } \$1000 = 0.065 \times 1000$$
$$= \$65$$

This is the estimated lost sales tax per appliance. With 10,000 appliances, the total lost sales tax per year would be around $650,000.

b. The population of the United States is about 310 million. With untaxed purchases of $500 per person per year, the annual total of untaxed purchases is about

$$\frac{\$500}{1 \text{ person}} \times 310,000,000 \text{ people} = \$155,000,000,000. \qquad \$155 \text{ billion}$$

Suppose that the average sales tax rate is 6%. This would be a total lost sales tax revenue of about $9.3 billion for one year.

Example 3 Instructor Notes

When you make broad estimates like the one in Example 3, explain to students that your estimate is only as good as your assumptions. It is a good idea to explicitly write your assumptions down and then to list them whenever you communicate your estimate.

For instance, one of the assumptions is that roughly 20% of adults in the United States smoke cigarettes. If the true percent is closer to 15%, then your final estimate will be roughly one-third greater than it should have been.

Checkpoint Solution

The United States uses about 140 billion gallons of gasoline in a year. Federal excise tax is about $0.18 per gallon and state excise tax ranges from $0.08 to $0.45. Let's estimate the average to be $0.45 per gallon (including state and federal taxes).

This means that the total excise tax revenue on gasoline is about

$$\frac{\$0.45}{1 \text{ gal}} \times 140{,}000{,}000{,}000 \text{ gallons} = \$63{,}000{,}000{,}000. \qquad \$63 \text{ billion}$$

Example 4 Instructor Notes

Check to make sure students understand how the conclusion in part (a) of Example 4 is made.

a. From 2006 to 2009, the revenue declined by

$$\$73,961,000,000 - \$62,483,000,000 = \$11,478,000,000.$$

This is a decline of about 15.5%.

When you talk about a "decline," the comparison should always use the original number as the base.

Correct: $73,961,000,000 as the base

$$\frac{\$11,478,000,000}{\$73,961,000,000} \approx 0.155 = 15.5\%$$

Incorrect: $62,483,000,000 as the base

$$\frac{\$11,478,000,000}{\$62,483,000,000} \approx 0.184 = 18.4\%$$

Checkpoint Solution

c. The revenue was projected to rise from $62.483 billion to $87.829 billion. This is an increase of

$$\$87,829,000,000 - \$62,483,000,000 = \$25,346,000,000.$$

d. This is a percent increase of

$$\frac{\$25,246,000,000}{\$62,483,000,000} \approx 0.404 = 40.4\%.$$

e. A plan could include an increase in the excise taxes for alcohol, gasoline, cigarettes, and gambling. An appropriate increase in these taxes could raise the necessary tax revenue because people are still going to pay for these items even if the prices increase.

Example 5 Instructor Notes

For the spreadsheet in Example 5(b), point out that the 10% tax at each stage is only for the value-added and not for the new value at that stage.
(See *http://www-staging.mathandyou.com/content/02/03/data/mthu_data_0203_078_05.xls.*)

After all, that is the whole point of a "value-added" tax—to tax only the value that is added at that stage of production.

	A	B	C	D
	Current Value	Value Added	10% Value-Added Tax	New Value
1				
2	$0.00	$10.00	$1.00	$11.00
3	$11.00	$25.00	$2.50	$38.50
4	$38.50	$150.00	$15.00	$203.50
5	$203.50	$210.00	$21.00	$434.50
6	Total	$395.00	$39.50	
7				

Checkpoint Solution

a. If the sales tax rate is 8%, then the sales tax is

$$\text{Sales tax} = 0.08 \times \$395$$

$$= \$31.60.$$

b. For a value-added tax of 8%, use a spreadsheet.
(See *http://www-staging.mathandyou.com/content/02/03/data/mthu_data_0203_078_05.xls.*)

	A	B	C	D
1	Current	Value	8% Value-	New
2	Value	Added	Added Tax	Value
3	$0.00	$10.00	$0.80	$10.80
4	$10.80	$25.00	$2.00	$37.80
5	$37.80	$150.00	$12.00	$199.80
6	$199.80	$210.00	$16.80	$426.60
7	Total	$395.00	$31.60	
8				

Notice that in both cases, the total tax is $31.60.

Example 6 Instructor Notes

The graph in Example 6 provides students with an example of a stacked area graph. It shows five sources of tax revenue for the federal government. From bottom to top:

- Individual income tax
- Corporate income tax
- Payroll tax
- Excise tax
- Other

To determine the percent of each tax, you need to estimate the height of its shaded area.

Checkpoint Solution

a. The total taxes represented by the circle graph are

$$\$52 + \$45 + \$42 + \$20 + \$11 = \$170 \text{ billion.}$$

The percent represented by individual income tax is

$$\frac{\$52}{170} \approx 0.306 = 30.6\%.$$

This is less than the percent for individual income taxes for the federal government.

b. The percent represented by corporate income tax is

$$\frac{\$11}{\$170} \approx 0.065 = 6.5\%.$$

This is less than the percent for corporate income taxes for the federal government.

Section 2.4 Budgeting

Example 1 Instructor Notes

One would think that all budget systems are set up the same way. If you check several different systems on the Internet, however, you will see that they vary. Make sure students understand that in the system presented, an expense is money you spend. So a difference of $-\$12.40$ is an expense of $\$12.40$ that you did not have to make. This means that your actual expense on groceries is 12.40 less than you budgeted.

In this budget system, a red (or negative) entry for income is "bad" because you didn't get as much income as you budgeted.

A red (or negative) entry for expense is "good" because you didn't spend as much as you budgeted.

Checkpoint Solution

Subtract the amount in the second column from the amount in the first column.

CATEGORY	MONTHLY ACTUAL AMOUNT	–	MONTHLY BUDGETED AMOUNT	=	DIFFERENCE
Utilities					
Electricity	$121.46		$125.00		−$3.54
Water and sewer	$62.30		$58.00		$4.30

You spent *less* than you budgeted.

You spent *more* than you budgeted.

In some budget systems, the entry $-\$3.54$ is listed as ($3.54).

Example 2 Instructor Notes

Remind students that in this budget system, a red (or negative) entry for income is "bad" because you didn't get as much income as you budgeted. A red (or negative) entry for expense is "good" because you didn't spend as much as you budgeted.

Checkpoint Solution

The totals are shown in the following spreadsheet.

(See *http://math.andyou.com/content/02/04/data/mthu_data_0204_085_02.xls*.)

CATEGORY	MONTHLY ACTUAL AMOUNT	MONTHLY BUDGETED AMOUNT	DIFFERENCE
INCOME	$5500.00	$5500.00	$0.00
Income Taxes Withheld			
Federal income tax	$1100.00	$1100.00	$0.00
State and local income tax	$225.00	$225.00	$0.00
Social Security/Medicare tax	$412.50	$412.50	$0.00
Spendable Income	$3762.50	$3762.50	$0.00
EXPENSES			
Home			
Mortgage or rent	$455.00	$455.00	$0.00
Homeowners/renters insurance	$95.00	$95.00	$0.00
Property taxes	$234.00	$234.00	$0.00
Utilities			
Electricity	$121.46	$125.00	−$3.54
Water and sewer	$62.30	$58.00	$4.30
Natural gas	$158.16	$200.00	−$41.84
Telephone (landline, cell)	$138.92	$125.00	$13.92
Food			
Groceries	$287.60	$300.00	−$12.40
Eating out, lunches, snacks	$234.86	$200.00	$34.86
Health and Medical			
Insurance (medical, dental, vision)	$165.00	$165.00	$0.00
Medical expenses, co-pays	$0.00	$200.00	−$200.00
Transportation			
Car payments	$175.00	$175.00	$0.00
Gasoline/oil	$48.23	$60.00	−$11.77
Auto repairs/maintenance/fees	$0.00	$50.00	−$50.00
Auto insurance	$125.00	$125.00	$0.00
Debt Payments	$253.48	$253.48	$0.00
Entertainment/Recreation	$124.50	$150.00	−$25.50
Clothing	$0.00	$50.00	−$50.00
Investments and Savings	$125.00	$125.00	$0.00
Miscellaneous	$93.50	$200.00	−$106.50
Total Expenses	$2,897.01	$3345.48	−$448.47

The total of the difference column is −$448.47, which means that you spent $448.47 less than you budgeted.

Example 3 Instructor Notes

Emphasize the importance of keeping personal financial records. For example, when balancing a checkbook, show how to subtract debits (expenses) and add credits (deposits).

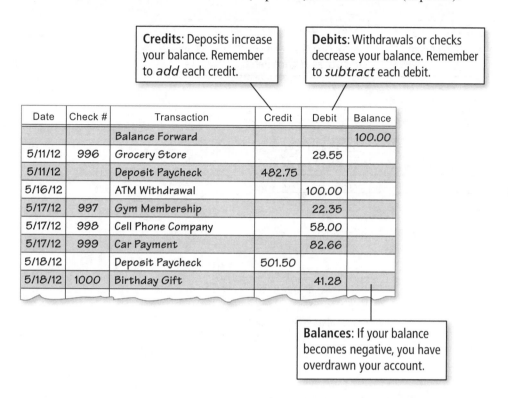

Credits: Deposits increase your balance. Remember to *add* each credit.

Debits: Withdrawals or checks decrease your balance. Remember to *subtract* each debit.

Date	Check #	Transaction	Credit	Debit	Balance
		Balance Forward			100.00
5/11/12	996	Grocery Store		29.55	
5/11/12		Deposit Paycheck	482.75		
5/16/12		ATM Withdrawal		100.00	
5/17/12	997	Gym Membership		22.35	
5/17/12	998	Cell Phone Company		58.00	
5/17/12	999	Car Payment		82.66	
5/18/12		Deposit Paycheck	501.50		
5/18/12	1000	Birthday Gift		41.28	

Balances: If your balance becomes negative, you have overdrawn your account.

Checkpoint Solution

The balances are shown in the following spreadsheet.

(See *http://math.andyou.com/content/02/04/data/mthu_data_0204_086_03.xls.*)

	A	B	C	D	E	F
1	**Date**	**Check #**	**Transaction**	**Credit**	**Debit**	**Balance**
2			Balance Forward			$100.00
3	5/11/2012	996	Grocery Store		$29.55	$70.45
4	5/11/2012		Deposit Paycheck	$482.75		$553.20
5	5/16/2012		ATM Withdrawal		$100.00	$453.20
6	5/17/2012	997	Gym Membership		$22.35	$430.85
7	5/17/2012	998	Cell Phone Company		$58.00	$372.85
8	5/17/2012	999	Car Payment		$82.66	$290.19
9	5/18/2012		Deposit Paycheck	$501.50		$791.69
10	5/18/2012	1000	Birthday Gift		$41.28	$750.41
11						

Example 4 Instructor Notes

Remind students when balancing a checkbook to subtract debits (expenses) and add credits (deposits).

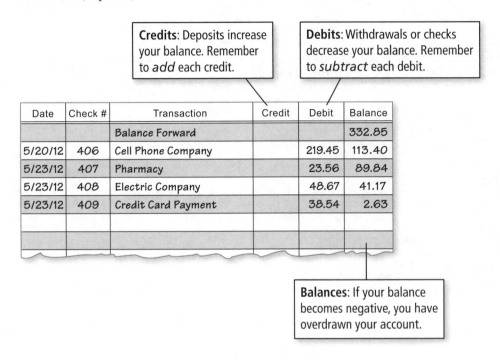

Credits: Deposits increase your balance. Remember to *add* each credit.

Debits: Withdrawals or checks decrease your balance. Remember to *subtract* each debit.

Date	Check #	Transaction	Credit	Debit	Balance
		Balance Forward			332.85
5/20/12	406	Cell Phone Company		219.45	113.40
5/23/12	407	Pharmacy		23.56	89.84
5/23/12	408	Electric Company		48.67	41.17
5/23/12	409	Credit Card Payment		38.54	2.63

Balances: If your balance becomes negative, you have overdrawn your account.

Checkpoint Solution

If each one of the vendors charged you a $25 penalty, you would end up with the following charges:

Insufficient funds penalty	$50.00
Pharmacy penalty	$25.00
Insufficient funds penalty	$50.00
Electric company penalty	$25.00
Insufficient funds penalty	$50.00
Credit card company penalty	$25.00
Total	**$225.00**

Example 5 Instructor Notes

If students enter this budget into a spreadsheet, then they can program the spreadsheet to calculate the percent for each category.
(*See http://math.andyou.com/content/02/04/data/mthu_data_0204_088_05.xls.*)

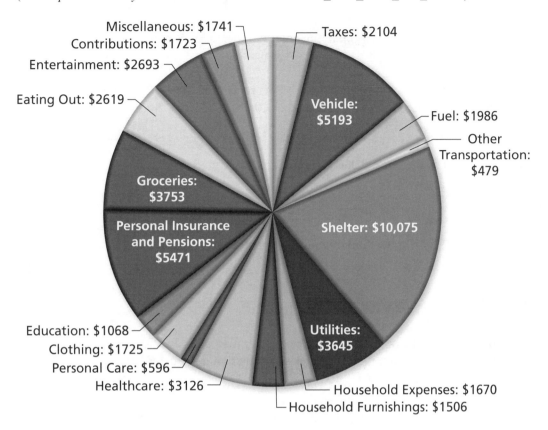

Checkpoint Solution

The percent for transportation is

$$\frac{5193 + 1986 + 479}{51{,}173} = \frac{7658}{51{,}173} \approx 0.150 = 15\%.$$

The percent for food is

$$\frac{2619 + 3753}{51{,}173} = \frac{6372}{51{,}173} \approx 0.125 = 12.5\%.$$

Students can use the spreadsheet to confirm answers by adding the individual percents for each category.

Example 6 Instructor Notes

Explain that the math symbol ≤ is read, "Less than or equal to." This means that the inequality

$$\frac{\text{Monthly mortgage}}{\text{Gross monthly income}} \leq 28\%$$

is read, "The ratio of your mortgage to your gross monthly income should be less than or equal to 28%."

If you check on the Internet, you will see that many financial advisers regard the 28/36 Rule as being too risky. More conservative rules are in the neighborhood of 20/28, rather than 28/36.

Checkpoint Solution

Your gross annual income is $73,000, which means that your gross monthly income is

$$\frac{\$73,000}{12} \approx \$6083.33.$$

Your monthly mortgage would be $1950. So, the ratio of your mortgage to your monthly income is

$$\frac{\$1950}{\$6083.33} \approx 0.321 = 32.1\%.$$

At this point, you have failed the 28/36 Rule because this ratio is greater than 28%. Just for the sake of curiosity, you can check the ratio of your mortgage plus your other monthly debts.

$$\frac{\$1950 + \$450}{\$6083.33} = \frac{\$2300}{\$6083.33} \approx 0.395 = 39.5\%$$

So, by the 28/36 Rule, you also fail to qualify for the mortgage.

Chapter 3

Section 3.1   Sets & Set Diagrams

Example 1 Instructor Notes

This text does not use formal Venn diagrams or Euler diagrams. The diagrams we are using are informal and are intended only to help students understand relationships between sets or statements.

If the set diagram on page 102 were a formal Venn diagram, it would have 4 regions.

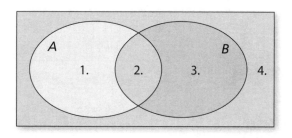

1. In A but not in B.
2. In both A and B.
3. In B but not in A.
4. Not in A or B.

The outer rectangle, the universal set, contains all the objects that are being considered. For instance, in Example 1, the universal set could be the set of all households in the United States.

Checkpoint Solution

For this question, point out that it helps to start by summarizing the given information.

- 120 million women in the United States
- 5.7 million of these rode a motorcycle in the past year
- 25 million Americans rode motorcycles in the past year

Here are two ways to draw the same information.

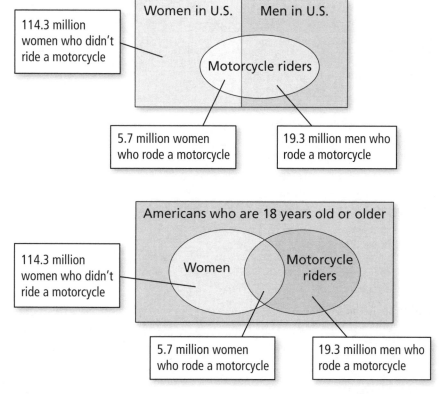

Example 2 Instructor Notes

In formal set theory, 3 sets determine $2^3 = 8$ regions. In general, n sets determine 2^n regions. To see that the three sets in Example 2 determine 8 regions, you need to define a universal set that contains all three sets. For instance, the universal set could be "all people."

Checkpoint Solution

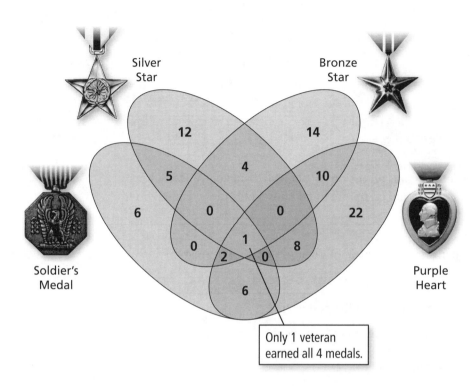

Only 1 veteran earned all 4 medals.

Purple Heart: Wounded or killed in action

Bronze Star: Fourth highest combat award (bravery)

Silver Star: Third highest combat award (bravery)

Soldier's Medal: Highest noncombat award (heroism)

h. Number of veterans who earned a purple heart:

$$22 + 8 + 0 + 6 + 2 + 1 + 0 + 10 = 49$$

i. Number of veterans who earned a purple heart or a bronze star:

$$22 + 8 + 0 + 6 + 2 + 1 + 0 + 10 + 0 + 0 + 4 + 14 = 67$$

j. Number of veterans who earned a purple heart and a bronze star:

$$2 + 1 + 0 + 10 = 13$$

k. There was one veteran who earned all four medals.

Example 3 Instructor Notes

The intersection and union of two sets can be drawn as follows.

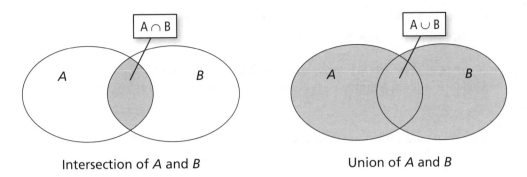

Intersection of *A* and *B*   Union of *A* and *B*

Checkpoint Solution

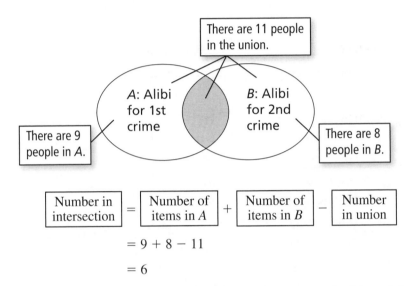

$$\boxed{\begin{array}{c}\text{Number in}\\\text{intersection}\end{array}} = \boxed{\begin{array}{c}\text{Number of}\\\text{items in } A\end{array}} + \boxed{\begin{array}{c}\text{Number of}\\\text{items in } B\end{array}} - \boxed{\begin{array}{c}\text{Number}\\\text{in union}\end{array}}$$

$$= 9 + 8 - 11$$

$$= 6$$

So, you can be certain that 6 of 11 people did *not* commit either of the two crimes.

Example 4 Instructor Notes

Example 4 is for illustration only. The numbers used in the example are hypothetical.

The goal of the example is to illustrate that a 6-point match between two fingerprints is not sufficient to conclude that the fingerprints came from the same person.

There is no agreement on how many points need to match to conclude that two fingerprints come from the same individual. The United Kingdom requires a 16-point minimum and Australia requires a 12-point minimum.

In the United States, states set their own minimum point standards. The FBI has no minimum number that must be identified to declare an absolute match, but it does rely on a 12-point quality assurance standard.

Checkpoint Solution

You can continue the pattern in Example 4 as follows.

1 billion people have Point 1	1,000,000,000 people	1-point match
20% of these also have Point 2	200,000,000 people	2-point match
20% of these also have Point 3	40,000,000 people	3-point match
20% of these also have Point 4	8,000,000 people	4-point match
20% of these also have Point 5	1,600,000 people	5-point match
20% of these also have Point 6	320,000 people	6-point match
20% of these also have Point 7	64,000 people	7-point match
20% of these also have Point 8	12,800 people	8-point match
20% of these also have Point 9	2,560 people	9-point match
20% of these also have Point 10	512 people	10-point match
20% of these also have Point 11	102 people	11-point match
20% of these also have Point 12	20 people	12-point match

So, using the hypothesis that any two people have a 20% likelihood of matching one and two fingerprint points, there are up to 20 people out of a billion that have a 12-point match.

If you continue this pattern for 16 points, you can see why the United Kingdom requires a 16-point match to conclude that two fingerprints "absolutely" came from the same person.

Example 5 Instructor Notes

Notice the spelling of "complement." You can remember that complement is spelled with an "e" by remembering that the word is related to "complete."

Complement:

- a word or phrase used to complete a grammatical construction
- a complete number or quantity; "a full complement"
- something added to complete or embellish or make perfect
- make complete or perfect; supply what is wanting or form the complement to
- either of two parts that mutually complete each other

Compliment:

- say something to someone that expresses praise
- express respect or esteem for
- a remark (or act) expressing praise and admiration

Checkpoint Solution

The unemployment rate for the year shown in Example 5 is

$$\frac{\text{Number unemployed}}{\text{Number employed or unemployed}} = \frac{8{,}923{,}000}{154{,}286{,}000} \approx 0.058 = 5.8\%.$$

The Department of Labor and Statistics defines the unemployment rate as the ratio of unemployed to the number of people who are employed or unemployed, but seeking employment.

- People with jobs are employed.
- People who are jobless, looking for jobs, and available for work are unemployed.
- People who are neither employed nor unemployed are not in the labor force.

To be counted as unemployed, you must be available for work and be actively seeking work. People who choose to not work (stay-at-home parents, retired, in school) are not considered unemployed.

Example 6 Instructor Notes

In the set diagram on page 107, the fish class is drawn as the complement of the union of birds, amphibians, mammals, and vertebrates.

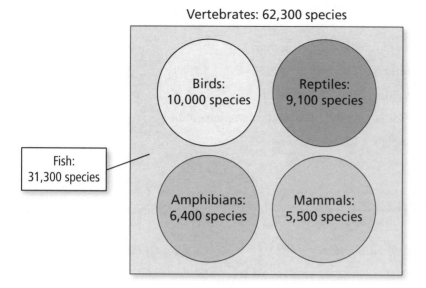

Vertebrates: 62,300 species

Birds: 10,000 species

Reptiles: 9,100 species

Fish: 31,300 species

Amphibians: 6,400 species

Mammals: 5,500 species

Checkpoint Solution

Here is one possible set diagram for this information.

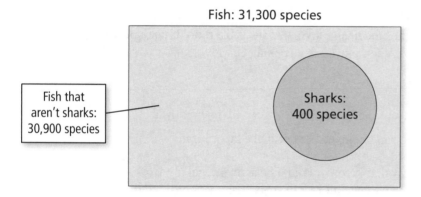

Fish: 31,300 species

Fish that aren't sharks: 30,900 species

Sharks: 400 species

Note that for the purpose of illustration, we have classified fish (like sharks) that have cartilage skeletons as vertebrate. Sharks and other cartilaginous fish (skates and rays) have skeletons made of cartilage and connective tissue. Cartilage has about half the density of bone. This reduces the skeleton's weight, saving energy.

Section 3.2   Statements & Negations

Example 1 Instructor Notes

To understand a statement, it is helpful to shorten it and write it in outline form.

All people have equal rights, which include:

a. the right to Life

b. the right to Liberty

c. the right to Pursue Happiness.

Here is an alternative way to draw a set diagram for this information.

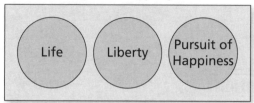

Rights of all people

Note that different set diagrams help you see different aspects of a statement. The set diagram in Example 1 points out that creatures other than humans (such as dogs) may have these rights. The set diagram above points out that there may be other rights that all humans have (such as the right to worship).

Checkpoint Solution

The 10th Amendment in the Bill of Rights is often quoted to defend "state rights." When you examine the statement, however, you can see other implications. The amendment basically states that all power falls into four categories: power given to federal government, power denied to anyone, power given to a state, and power given to an individual. One would wish that the amendment was more precise . . . with examples.

All Powers

Powers given to the federal government	Powers denied anyone	Powers given to each state	Powers given individuals
Example: print money	Example: own a slave	Example: license marriage	Example: speak freely

Note that the amendment does not specify which powers are clearly given to individuals. This is a matter of great political debate. For instance, simply because you live in a state, does this give the state the power to insist that you pay sales tax on items purchased in other states?

Example 2 Instructor Notes

A set diagram for the rental policy in Example 2 can be drawn in many ways. Emphasize that the point of the example is not to learn to draw a specific type of set diagram. The point is to learn to use some means, either a set diagram or some other graphic or outline, to help analyze a statement. Some students may prefer other graphics or outlines to help them see events and plan strategies. Here is an example using a decision tree.

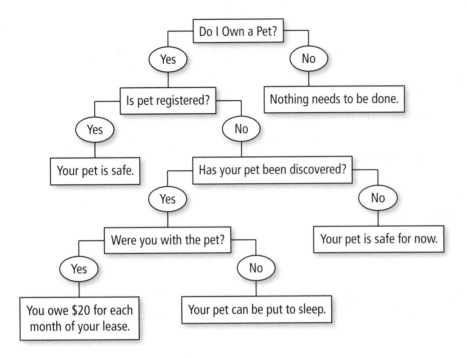

Checkpoint Solution

Any number of diagrams or graphics could help people understand this clause. Whatever diagram is used, it should be clear that the clause is one-sided and greatly favors the owner. Here is one way to draw a set diagram to represent the court cost portion of the clause.

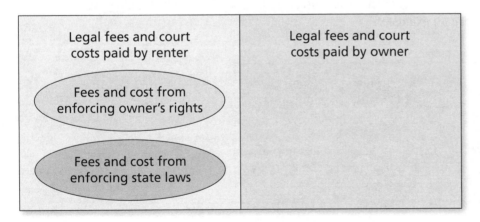

Note that you might have to pay for other legal fees, in addition to the ones specified by your renter's agreement.

Example 3 Instructor Notes

The word "some" means "at least one." In Example 3, there were four presidential candidates who won the popular vote, but still lost the election. However, even if there were only one such person, the following statement would be true.

> *In the United States, some presidential candidates have won the popular vote, but still lost the election.*

The set diagram shown in Example 3 is a classic use of a formal Venn diagram. There are two basic sets.

> Set A: Candidates who won the popular vote

> Set B: Candidates who won the election

These two basic sets determine four regions in the diagram. Moreover, each of the four regions has historical members.

Checkpoint Solution

"In the United States, 14 presidents served as vice presidents: J. Adams, Jefferson, Van Buren, Tyler, Fillmore, A. Johnson, Arthur, T. Roosevelt, Coolidge, Truman, Nixon, L. Johnson, Ford, and George H.W. Bush. Of these, Fillmore, A. Johnson, Arthur, and Ford did not win a presidential election."

Here is one way to draw a set diagram showing this information.

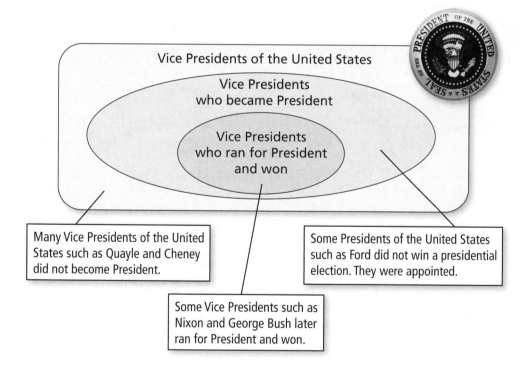

Example 4 Instructor Notes

Point out to students that when you draw a set diagram and set A is inside set B, you are saying that "All A are B."

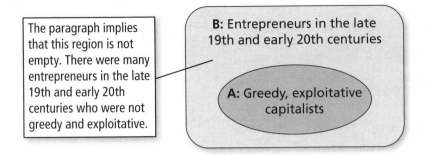

The paragraph implies that this region is not empty. There were many entrepreneurs in the late 19th and early 20th centuries who were not greedy and exploitative.

B: Entrepreneurs in the late 19th and early 20th centuries

A: Greedy, exploitative capitalists

The diagram, however, does not necessarily imply that there are some members of B who are not members of A. If you want to make that point, you should annotate or label your diagram to make that clear.

Checkpoint Solution

Here is one way to draw a set diagram showing this information.

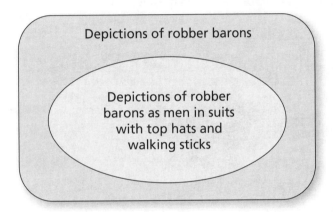

Depictions of robber barons

Depictions of robber barons as men in suits with top hats and walking sticks

Example 5 Instructor Notes

Here is a nice way to think about the negation of statements that have *and*.

And Statements: Spot is a member of set A and of set B.

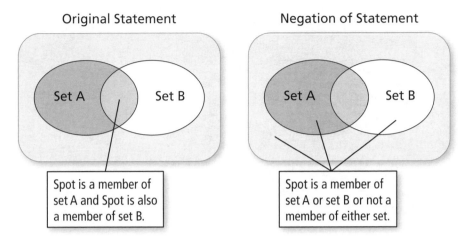

Original Statement

Negation of Statement

Set A Set B

Set A Set B

Spot is a member of set A and Spot is also a member of set B.

Spot is a member of set A or set B or not a member of either set.

Checkpoint Solution

In the game of Clue, there are three playing cards in an envelope. One card is a weapon, one is a room, and one is a person. All of the other cards are dealt to the players. If someone guesses that it was "Miss Scarlet with the wrench in the kitchen", and you have one or more of these cards, then you must show the person who guessed one of the cards.

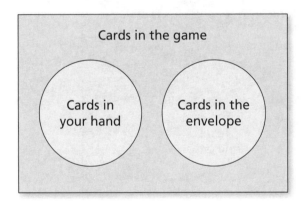

Cards in the game

Cards in your hand

Cards in the envelope

Original Statement: "The three cards in the envelope are Miss Scarlet, the Wrench, and the Kitchen."

Negation of Statement: "One of the cards, either Miss Scarlet or the Wrench or the Kitchen, is in my hand or another player's hand."

Example 6 Instructor Notes

Here is a nice way to think about the negation of statements that have *or*.

Or Statements: Fido is a member of set A or set B.

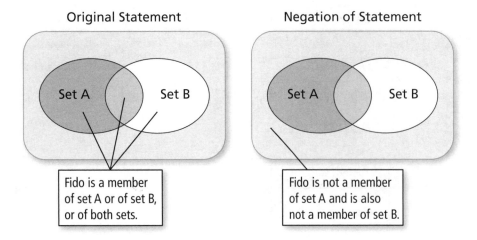

Original Statement	Negation of Statement

Fido is a member of set A or of set B, or of both sets.

Fido is not a member of set A and is also not a member of set B.

Checkpoint Solution

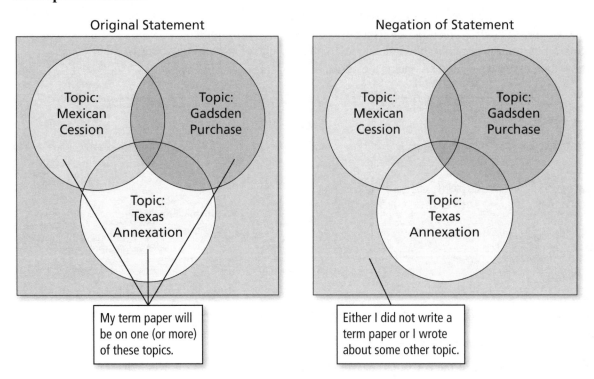

Original Statement	Negation of Statement

Topic: Mexican Cession

Topic: Gadsden Purchase

Topic: Texas Annexation

My term paper will be on one (or more) of these topics.

Either I did not write a term paper or I wrote about some other topic.

The original statement will be false if I do not write a term paper or I write about some other topic.

Section 3.3   Deductive & Inductive Reasoning

Example 1 Instructor Notes

The brief survey of logic in this chapter is intended to show the importance of using logic to analyze arguments in order to determine whether the reasoning is valid.

In Aristotle's type of categorical syllogism, a syllogism is of the following form.

- Premise: All B are A   All men are mortal.
- Premise: All C are B   All Greeks are men.
- Premise: All C are A   All Greeks are mortal.

The premises and conclusion must be of the form "All A are B," "Some A are B," "No A are B," or "Some A are not B." The difference between this form and the modern "If P, then Q" form is one of wording. For instance, the above syllogism can be rewritten as follows.

- Premise: If a being is a man, then the being is mortal.
- Premise: If a being is a Greek, then the being is a man.
- Conclusion: If a being is a Greek, then the being is mortal.

Suggest that students may consider taking an entire course on logical reasoning, or search the Internet and find an introductory book on the subject.

Checkpoint Solution

Here is one possible syllogism.

- Premise: Any physical theory is always provisional, in the sense that it is only a hypothesis; you can never prove it.
- Premise: Any theory of gravity is a physical theory.
- Conclusion: You can never prove any theory of gravity.

This syllogism may be surprising to students, especially when they consider that Stephen Hawking is considered to be one of the most brilliant physicists who ever lived.

Example 2 Instructor Notes

Example 2 is a wonderful example of the use of logical analysis to help clearly understand arguments. When you casually read Daniel Defoe's statement, you might come up with the conclusion that he is saying that without education, women are guilty of more offenses than men. On more careful examination, however, you can see that is not implied. It is entirely possible that women are simply guilty of fewer offenses than men . . . with or without education.

- Premise: If women had the same opportunity for education as men, then they would be guilty of fewer offenses than men.

- Premise: Women have the same opportunity for education as men.

- Conclusion: Women are guilty of fewer offenses than men.

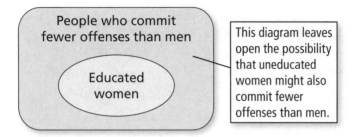

This example points out the need for careful logical analysis of arguments in all parts of life, but certainly in fields such as law, business, and contractual negotiations.

Checkpoint Solution

Here is a possible syllogism that involves this quote.

- Premise: All men are innocent in their own eyes.

- Premise: John is a man.

- Conclusion: John claims to be innocent.

Here is another possible syllogism and a set diagram that involves this quote.

- Premise: Everyone arrested for a crime claims to be innocent.

- Premise: John was arrested for a crime.

- Conclusion: John claims to be innocent.

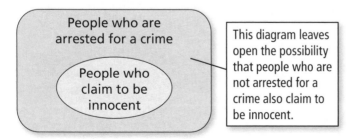

Example 3 Instructor Notes

Explain that while applied geometry, the geometry of measurement used in some careers or hobbies, is derived from Euclidean geometry, Euclidean geometry puts a lot of emphasis on derivations and proofs. It is a formal logical system.

Checkpoint Solution

Here is Euclid's 5th Postulate:

5. Parallel Postulate: At most one line can be drawn through any point not on a given line parallel to the given line in a plane.

Here is one way to write it as a syllogism.

- Premise: Given a line and a point not on the line, there is at most one line that passes through the point and is parallel to the given line.

- Premise: You are given a line and a point not on the line.

- Conclusion: There is at most one line that passes through the point and is parallel to the given line.

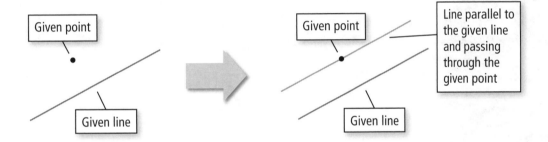

Example 4 Instructor Notes

It is doubtful that many of your students will ever have a use for any type of non-Euclidean geometry. The author of the book, however, wanted to give your students an example of two perfectly good logical systems that disagree with each other, and yet are perfect for modeling their own worlds.

Euclidean Geometry: Is a perfect model for people who live in a plane or in normal 3-dimensional space.

Spherical Geometry: Is a perfect model for people who live on the surface of a sphere.

These two geometries are inconsistent with each other. Both can't be "true" at the same time in the same place, but being "true" isn't really the point.

Checkpoint Solution

In spherical geometry, it is also true that a triangle is determined by three intersecting lines (great circles).

One such triangle is pictured below.

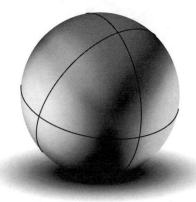

The question is, is the sum of the three angle measures less than 180 degrees, equal to 180 degrees, or greater than 180 degrees? You might try conducting an experiment to measure the three angles. To do this, you must be sure that each of the three sides is a great circle. You also need to take very careful measurements of the angles.

If you perform this experiment, you will discover that the sum of the angles measures greater than 180 degrees.

Example 5 Instructor Notes

Inductive reasoning is the most common type of reasoning used by humans. Moreover, it is likely the only type of reasoning used by animals other than humans. For instance, a horse in a pasture might observe that "every time I touch my nose to the electric fence, it shocks me." This is a pattern that the horse has observed and from the experiences has formed a conclusion that touching an electric fence is unpleasant.

Although inductive reasoning is necessary and common, we should still realize that it is not infallible. Here is an example. From every observation you (and most everyone else) has made, you might conclude that all dairy calves have exactly one head.

And yet, years ago in the United States, a traveling circus had a two-headed calf on display. This unusual calf proved that the statement "All calves have exactly one head" is false. For information on this unusual phenomena, look up "polycephaly" on the Internet.

Checkpoint Solution

You can draw a set diagram of the inductive reasoning as follows.

- All the tigers I have seen are orange with black stripes.

- Therefore, all tigers are orange with black stripes.

Although this is valid inductive reasoning, the conclusion is not correct. Some tigers are white with black stripes. Others are pure white.

Example 6 Instructor Notes

In statistics, you see that statistical inference is almost always based on inductive reasoning. The only cases in which this is not true are when you are able to sample an entire population.

In most cases, the sample taken is small compared to the population, and the inference is stated with a degree of uncertainty. For instance, you might say, "I am 95% certain that the mean height of men in the United States is 70 inches, plus or minus 1 inch."

The point is that inductive reasoning does not generally provide us with certainty. And yet, as humans, we are all comfortable living with uncertainty. It exists, often unsaid but understood, in almost all of our conversations.

For instance, when you tell someone "I'll be there in about 10 minutes," both you and the person listening to you understand that something could happen to make the statement false.

Checkpoint Solution

One can hardly pick up a newspaper or news magazine without reading about other examples of inductive reasoning related to environmental issues. Here are a few examples.

- Overpopulation by humans, which many environmentalists agree is the primary problem.

- Global warming, which is a result of overpopulation.

- Indirect threatening of animal species by destruction of habitat.

- Direct threatening of animal species by fishing and hunting.

- Poisoning of the environment through garbage, plastics, and toxic waste.

Section 3.4   Fallacies in Logic

Example 1 Instructor Notes

Be sure students understand that just because a syllogism is a fallacy, it does not mean that the conclusion is false. Consider the following fallacy.

- Premise: When it rains, the ground gets wet.

- Premise: The ground is wet.

- Conclusion: Therefore, it must have rained. ☹

This is a fallacy because the conclusion does not follow logically from the two premises. And yet, common sense tells you that most of the time, the conclusion would be true. After all, if you woke up in the morning and walked outside and saw that the ground was wet, wouldn't you assume that it had rained during the night?

Deduction of a fallacy is especially important in legal matters. Think about the situation described in Example 1. How would you feel if you were accused of a crime, given a polygraph test in which you truthfully proclaimed your innocence, and then told that the polygraph indicated that you lied?

Ask students to explain why the type of fallacy in Example 1 is called affirming the consequent.

- Premise: When people lie, their heart rate increases and they sweat.

- Premise: This man has an increased heart rate and is sweating.

- Conclusion: Therefore, he is lying. ☹

The second part of the first premise is called the consequent. The second premise is affirming that the consequent is true.

Checkpoint Solution

To help see that this argument is a fallacy, students can write it as a syllogism.

- Premise: When a large meteor hits Earth, it forms a large crater.

- Premise: The diameter of Crater Lake in Oregon is about 5 miles.

- Conclusion: So, Crater Lake must have been formed by a huge meteor. ☹

In this form, the logic is not correct. This is another example of affirming the consequent. In this particular case, the reasoning is not only incorrect, the conclusion is actually false. Crater Lake was formed about 7700 years ago when an ancient volcano collapsed. It is not the result of a meteor striking Earth.

Example 2 Instructor Notes

In logic, the premise

    If P, then Q

is logically equivalent to its contrapositive

    If not Q, then not P.

The contrapositive, however, is not what is involved in denying the antecedent.

- Premise: When it rains, the ground gets wet.   If P, then Q.
- Premise: It isn't raining.   Not P.
- Conclusion: Therefore, the ground is not wet. ☹   Therefore, not Q.

Ask students to explain why the type of fallacy is called denying the antecedent.

Checkpoint Solution

Here is the original statement.

The buyer of a new vehicle brought claims against a manufacturer under Ohio's Lemon Law and for breaches of a warranty act. The trial court ruled in favor of the defendant on both claims. The court of appeals analyzed the trial court's logic. The trial court first addressed the plaintiff's Lemon Law claim and determined that it was invalid. Next, the trial court concluded that since the Lemon Law claim was not valid, the warranty act claim was not valid. The court of appeals rejected the trial court's reasoning, based on the fallacy of *denying the antecedent*.

Summarized from *"Conventional Logic: Using the Logical Fallacy of Denying the Antecedent as a Litigation Tool,"* Stephen Rice

Here is a possible rewriting as a syllogism.

- Premise: If the Lemon Law claim is valid, then the automobile warranty is valid.
- Premise: The Lemon Law claim is not valid.
- Conclusion: Therefore, the automobile warranty is not valid. ☹

In this form, you can see that the syllogism is a fallacy and that it is of the form denying the antecedent.

Example 3 Instructor Notes

The fallacy of "non sequitur" or "false cause" is common.

- Premise: P implies Q.   Government funding for police, schools, and roads is necessary.

- Premise: P implies R.   Government funding for police, schools, and roads comes from taxes.

- Conclusion: R implies Q.   Therefore, taxes are necessary. ☹

Ask students to explain why this type of fallacy is called "It does not follow."

The point of Example 3 is that a set diagram can help when trying to analyze a syllogism.

Oddly enough, when you believe that a syllogism has reached a valid conclusion, it is tempting to not think as clearly. Remind students when they are analyzing a syllogism, to try to divorce themselves from whether the conclusion is true or false.

Checkpoint Solution

Here is the original statement.

Our society is filled with violence, and there is a lot of violence on TV. It follows that the violence in society is caused by people watching TV.

Here is a possible set diagram for this argument.

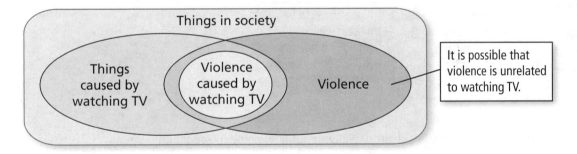

Example 4 Instructor Notes

Like all fallacies, the fallacy of the undistributed middle carries with it a terrible sense of injustice. This fallacy is summed up in the phrase "guilty by association."

- Premise: All A are B.

- Premise: Jeffrey is a B.

- Conclusion: Therefore, Jeffrey is an A.

One shudders to think of how many innocent people have been judged guilty in situations involving "guilty by association."

This type of incident has occurred throughout history. One famous example is described in a 1940 western novel by Walter Van Tilburg Clark. It is called The Ox-Bow Incident. In the story two drifters join a lynch mob to find and hang three men presumed to be rustlers and the killers of a local man.

Checkpoint Solution

Here is a description of the situation in Salem, Massachusetts.

In 1692, as part of the Salem witch trials, several people were arrested and accused of witchcraft. Their accusers claimed that young girls were having fits whenever the accused were present.

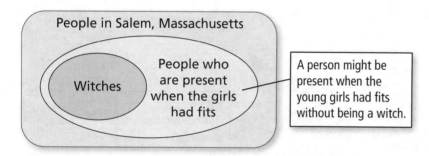

As the Salem witch trials continued, the residents of Salem gradually came to see that the young girls were not having fits because of a supernatural power, but because they were relishing in the power and attention that circumstance had given them.

Example 5 Instructor Notes

In Example 5, notice that the syllogism is valid. The problem with the argument is not that the conclusion does not follow from the two premises. The problem is that the first premise is not valid. With many celebrity endorsements, it is also quite possible that the second premise is also not valid.

- Premise: If Marilyn Monroe uses a product, then you should use it.

- Premise: Marilyn Monroe uses Lustre-Creme shampoo.

- Conclusion: Therefore, you should use Lustre-Creme shampoo. ☺

Appeal to authority can be a valid form of logical argument. It is less often true that an appeal to celebrity is a valid form of logical argument. Notice that to be valid, an appeal to authority or celebrity should pass the following criteria.

1. The authority has competence in the area, not just popularity.

2. The judgement must be within the authority's expertise.

3. The authority must be interpreted correctly.

4. Direct evidence is available.

5. A technique is needed to settle disagreements between equally qualified authorities.

Whether you agree or disagree with this policy depends on your political philosophy.

If you believe that it is the government's responsibility to protect citizens from making bad decisions or bad choices, then you probably agree with the policy. Just because something is foolish or harmful, is it the responsibility of the government to make it illegal?

On the other hand, if your political philosophy is that the primary responsibility for making good decisions and good choices lies with the individual, then you probably disagree with this policy. Historically, the philosophy of "Buyer Beware" was part of early America. As the country grew, however, the government felt more and more compelled to protect citizens. One small instance of this is the rules and regulations that a restaurant must comply with to be licensed to prepare and sell food.

Example 6 Instructor Notes

It is sad that one of the greatest culprits in the use of all sorts of fallacies is in political campaign. This occurs because the United States is not, nor has it ever been, a true democracy. In a true democracy, as was practiced in Ancient Athens, each citizen is given one vote.

Rather than being a democracy (one citizen one vote), the United States type of government is called a republic. In a republic, like ancient Rome, there is a select group of people who are elected to represent the citizenry of the country. For all of its benefits, this type of government has the side effect of placing vast power into the hands of a few (or a few hundred) people. Because of this power, it has become cost effective to spend millions (and occasionally hundreds of millions) of dollars to ensure that the candidate of your choice is elected.

With this much at stake, logic is generally the driving force in a campaign. It was this realization that caused Americans to be shocked by the marketing and selling of Richard Nixon.

Checkpoint Solution

The Veronica advertisement is blatantly illogical.

- It associates the candidate with the American flag.

- It portrays a glamorous view of the candidate. (Oddly, better looking candidates have an advantage over candidates who are not as good looking.)

- It begs the question by assuming that "they" don't want Veronica in Congress.

- It also begs the question by assuming that Veronica is honest.

Of the four political advertisements on page 139, the Jones advertisement has the greatest appeal to logic.

- It appears to direct the reader to a Web site, presumably in which issues are discussed.

- It does not picture the American flag or other symbols of patriotism.

To see why political campaign managers tend to use patriotic red-white-blue advertisements, try showing the four political ads on page 139 to several people. Ask each person which ad is the most appealing. Given no additional information, which of the four candidates would each person be most likely to vote for? If you find that the red-white-blue ads are chosen more often, then you can see why campaign managers choose this style.

Chapter 4

Section 4.1   Exponential Growth

Example 1 Instructor Notes

In Example 1, students found a formula for the exponential growth of a bacteria culture. While this model is helpful for determining the number of bacteria after an elapsed time, it may be difficult to get a sense of the speed of the rate of exponential growth. Even a graph of the model might not be enough to communicate this. (Students will learn more about graphing exponential growth later in Section 4.1.) The video in the Example 1 Math Help, however, is a powerful demonstration of the rate of exponential growth. Before watching the video, note that

- the initial population is one.

- the growth rate is 100% every 20 minutes.

- the video shows the growth during a 12-hour period, but the video is about 16 seconds in length.

In the formula for exponential growth, $A = P(1 + r)^n$, the expression $(1 + r)$ is sometimes referred to as the **growth factor.** To see why, let $P = 1$ and $r = 300\% = 3$. Then evaluate $A = 1(1 - 3)^n$ for several values of n, where n is the time in years.

Years, n	Formula	Value
0	$A = 1(4)^0$	$A = 1$
1	$A = 1(4)^1$	$A = 4$
2	$A = 1(4)^2$	$A = 16$
3	$A = 1(4)^3$	$A = 64$

After the initial value, each value is 4 times the previous value. So, when the growth factor is 4, the value quadruples every year. Knowing that $(1 + r)$ is the growth factor can help answer questions such as, "What annual rate of growth will result in an amount tripling every year?" or "What annual rate of growth will result in an amount doubling every two years?" To answer the first question, have students find a value of r so that $1 + r = 3$, which is a growth factor of 3 (tripling the value every year). Refer students to the Example 6 Math Help in Section 4.1 for a method of solving the second question.

Checkpoint Solution

There are 24 hours in one full day. The formula for this exponential growth is

$$A = P(1 + r)^n = 2(1 + 0.52)^{24}. \qquad P = 2, r = 52\% = 0.52, n = 24$$

So, the number of bacteria in the culture after one full day is $A = 46{,}267$.

Explain that because you cannot have a part of a bacterium, the decimal part of the number of bacteria is left off and the number of bacteria is given as a whole number.

Example 2 Instructor Notes

To make a spreadsheet similar to the one in Example 2, students can use the steps below. [Note that Step 6 uses the exponential growth formula given in Example 2, $A = 1(1 + 1)^n = 2^n$.]
(See *http://math.andyou.com/content/04/01/data/mthu_data_0401_153_02.xls.*)

1. Enter the titles "Foldings, *n*" and "Number of Noodles" into Row 1.
2. Enter 0 into cell A2.
3. Enter the formula =A2 + 1 into cell A3.
4. Select cell A3. From the **Edit** menu, choose **Copy**.
5. Select cells A4 through A14. From the **Edit** menu, choose **Paste**.
6. Enter the formula = 2^A2 into cell B2.
7. Select cell B2. From the **Edit** menu, choose **Copy**.
8. Select cells B3 through B14. From the **Edit** menu, choose **Paste**.

Checkpoint Solution

Using the Internet, you can find that the greatest possible distance from Earth to Pluto is about 4.5 trillion miles.

For simplicity, assume Chef Mark is 6 feet tall and that his arm span is equal to his height. Then the length of each noodle is 6 feet. To convert feet to miles, multiply by the unit conversion factor (1 mile/5280 feet).

$$\text{Length of one noodle} = 6 \text{ feet} \times \frac{1 \text{ mile}}{5280 \text{ feet}} = \frac{6}{5280} \text{ mile}$$

Students can use the steps shown in the Checkpoint Solution at *Math.andYou.com* to extend the spreadsheet from the Example 2 Math Help to 46 foldings and add a third column to track the length of the noodles.
(See *http://math.andyou.com/content/04/01/data/mthu_data_0401_153_02a.xls.*)

	A	B	C
1	**Foldings, *n***	**Number of Noodles**	**Length of Noodles (in miles)**
42	40	1,099,511,627,776	1,249,445,032
43	41	2,199,023,255,552	2,498,890,063
44	42	4,398,046,511,104	4,997,780,126
45	43	8,796,093,022,208	9,995,560,253
46	44	17,592,186,044,416	19,991,120,505
47	45	35,184,372,088,832	39,982,241,010
48	46	70,368,744,177,664	79,964,482,020
49			

From the spreadsheet, you can see that at 42 foldings the length of the noodles is 4,997,780,126 miles, which is greater than the greatest possible distance from Earth to Pluto. So, the claim is true, 46 doublings of the noodles are "long enough to stretch to Pluto and beyond."

Example 3 Instructor Notes

To use a spreadsheet to make a column graph similar to the one in Example 3, have students use the following steps. [Note that Step 6 uses the exponential growth formula given in Example 3, $A = 2(1 + 0.3)^n$.]

(See *http://math.andyou.com/content/04/01/data/mthu_data_0401_154_03.xls.*)

1. Enter the titles "Week, *n*" and "Number of Mice" into Row 1.
2. Enter 0 into cell A2.
3. Enter the formula =A2 + 1 into cell A3.
4. Select cell A3. From the **Edit** menu, choose **Copy.**
5. Select cells A4 through A44. From the Edit menu, choose **Paste.**
6. Enter the formula = 2*(1 + 0.3)^A2 into cell B2.
7. Select cell B2. From the **Edit** menu, choose **Copy.**
8. Select cells B3 through B44. From the **Edit** menu, choose **Paste.**
9. Select cells in Rows 1-44, Columns A and B.
10. From the **Insert** menu, choose **Chart . . ..**
11. In the **Chart Wizard,** select **Column** from the **Chart type:** list. Then click **Next.**
12. Select the **Series** tab.
13. From the **Series** list, select "Week, *n*." Then click **Remove.**
14. From the **Series** list, select "Number of mice." Enter =Sheet1!$A$2:$A$44 into **Category (X) axis labels.** Click **Finish.**

Checkpoint Solution

Instead of one breeding pair (2 mice) there are 1000 breeding pairs (2000 mice) for the initial value. So the formula becomes

$$A = P(1 + r)^n = 2000(1 + 0.3)^{42}.$$

So, 1000 breeding pairs and their offspring can produce about 122,081,763 mice in just 42 weeks.

You can check this answer by entering 2000 in the spreadsheet for the initial number of mice.

Example 4 Instructor Notes

An integrated circuit is a microscopic array of electronic circuits and components that has been etched onto the surface of a semiconducting material such as silicon. It is called an integrated circuit because the components, circuits, and base material are all made from a single piece of silicon. An integrated circuit, more commonly known as a microchip, can be very complex, containing millions of elements. To learn more about the integrated circuit, read the article "The History of the Integrated Circuit" at *Nobelprize.org*. (*Source: Encyclopedia.com*)

Checkpoint Solution

One integrated circuit has an area of about one square centimeter. It would take forty million atoms placed side by side to make a row about 1 centimeter in length. An integrated circuit that is one square centimeter could hold $40{,}000{,}000^2 = 1{,}600{,}000{,}000{,}000{,}000$ or 1.6 quadrillion atoms.

Suppose that a transistor became as small as a single atom. Moore's Law would be valid until at least 2050, as shown in the spreadsheet.
(See *http://math.andyou.com/content/04/01/data/mthu_data_0401_155_04a.xls*.)

	A	B
1	Year	Number of Transistors
35	2042	124,554,051,584,000
36	2044	249,108,103,168,000
37	2046	498,216,206,336,000
38	2048	996,432,412,672,000
39	2050	1,992,864,825,344,000
40		

Advances in science, particularly the discovery of subatomic particles, could allow for even smaller transistors and integrated circuits in the future.

Example 5 Instructor Notes

In the definition of exponential growth rate, note that A_0 occurs before the occurrence of A_1. Also, the numbers in the study tip,

$$A_0, A_1, A_2, \ldots, A_{n-1}, A_n$$

are listed in the order of their occurrence. Another way to think of this list of numbers is that the numbers occur in chronological order; that is, as a sequence of events. That is why the list of numbers is referred to as a sequence.

Checkpoint Solution

Linear Growth: If the stock continues to increase by $0.20 per month, each share will be worth $4.35 + 48(0.2) = \$13.95$. So, your investment will be worth $100(13.95) = \$1395.00$. Students can use a spreadsheet to graph the linear growth.
(See *http://math.andyou.com/content/04/01/data/mthu_data_0401_156_05a_1.xls.*)

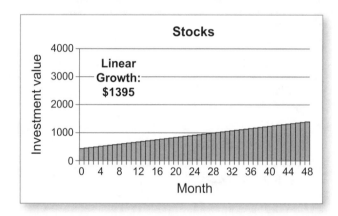

Exponential Growth: If the stock continues to grow at a rate of 4.6% in 4 years each share will be worth $4.35(1.046)^{48} \approx \$37.67$. So, your investment will be worth about $100(37.67) = \$3767.00$. Students can use a spreadsheet to graph the exponential growth.
(See *http://math.andyou.com/content/04/01/data/mthu_data_0401_156_05a_2.xls.*)

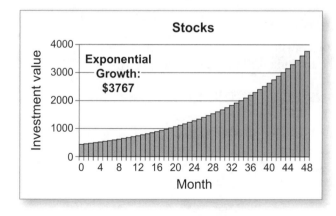

Example 6 Instructor Notes

Here is another way to solve Example 6. (You may want to review the Example 1 Math Help before continuing.) First, consider the exponential growth of an amount that doubles *every* year. The growth factor for this amount is equal to 2 and can be written as

$(1 + r)^1 = 2.$ The amount doubles after one year, so the exponent is 1.

In Example 6, you want to determine the annual rate of growth represented by Moore's Law. Moore's Law states that the number of transistors that can be placed inexpensively on an integrated circuit will double every *two years*. Because the amount doubles every *two years*, the square of the growth factor is equal to 2 and is written as

$(1 + r)^2 = 2.$ The amount doubles after two years, so the exponent is 2.

To find the annual rate of growth, substitute a few values for r and evaluate.

r	$(1 + r)^2$	Value
0.1	$(1 + 0.1)^2$	1.21
0.2	$(1 + 0.2)^2$	1.44
0.3	$(1 + 0.3)^2$	1.69
0.4	$(1 + 0.4)^2$	1.96
0.5	$(1 + 0.5)^2$	2.25

So, the value of r must be between 0.4 and 0.5. Next, try values of r starting with $r = 0.40$.

r	$(1 + r)^2$	Value
0.40	$(1 + 0.40)^2$	1.96
0.41	$(1 + 0.41)^2$	1.99
0.42	$(1 + 0.42)^2$	2.02

You now have a better estimate of r, which is 0.41 or 41%. You can continue this process of guessing, checking, and revising to obtain $r \approx 0.4142$, which corresponds to a growth factor of $(1 + 0.4142)^2 \approx 2.0000$ every two years. So, the annual rate of growth is about 41.42%.

Checkpoint Solution

You are given the initial value, $A = 29,000$, and the rate of growth, $r = 41.42\%$ The elapsed time is the difference in the years, $n = 2010 - 1978 = 32$. The formula for this exponential growth is

$A = P(1 + r)^n = 29,000(1 + 0.4142)^{32}.$ $P = 29,000, r = 41.42\%, n = 32$

So, about 1,899,960,845 transistors could be placed on an integrated circuit in 2010.

Section 4.2　Inflation & the Consumer Price Index

Example 1 Instructor Notes

The United States Bureau of Labor Statistics (BLS) publishes more than one consumer price index (CPI). For instance, BLS keeps track of the changes in the prices for milk, bedroom furniture, clothing, airline fares, hospital services, televisions, college tuition, and haircuts. The CPI used in Section 4.2 measures the average change in prices paid for consumer goods and services by urban consumers. Point out that the numbers in the CPI are not dollar values, but measures of the change over time relative to their reference base of 100.

Most of the specific consumer price indexes have a 1982–84 reference base, or "base year." (Note: For the sake of simplicity, we use 1983 as the base year in the text.) That is, BLS sets the average index level equal to 100. You can check this for the table given in Section 4.2 by using the values 96.5, 99.6, and 103.9 (the index values for 1982, 1983, and 1984, respectively).

$$\frac{96.5 + 99.6 + 103.9}{3} = \frac{300}{3} = 100$$

BLS then measures changes in relation to the reference base. An index of 110, for instance, means there has been a 10% increase in price since the reference base. Similarly, an index of 90 means a 10% decrease.

In 2007, the BLS began to publish its consumer price indexes rounded to three decimal places rather than one. For simplicity, the CPI given in Section 4.2 lists the numbers rounded to one decimal place. To learn more about the CPI, students can go to the United States Bureau of Labor Statistics Frequently Asked Questions at *http://www.bls.gov/cpi/cpifaq.htm*.

Checkpoint Solution

Assuming that each decade begins and ends on years that are multiples of ten, you can determine the percent increase for each decade by using the formula

$$\text{Percent change in CPI} = \frac{\text{new CPI} - \text{old CPI}}{\text{old CPI}}.$$

Students can use a spreadsheet to see that the greatest percent increase of

$$\frac{82.4 - 38.8}{38.8} \approx 1.124 = 112.4\%$$

happened during the 1970s.

(See *http://math.andyou.com/content/04/02/data/mthu_data_0402_162_01a.xls*.)

Example 2 Instructor Notes

The United States Bureau of Labor Statistics (BLS) has an online calculator called the "CPI inflation calculator" at *http://stats.bls.gov/data/inflation_calculator.htm*. (Image shown below.) The calculator uses the average consumer price index for a given year. This data represents changes in prices of all goods and services purchased for consumption by urban households. For the current year, the latest monthly index value is used.

To use the calculator, follow the steps given below.

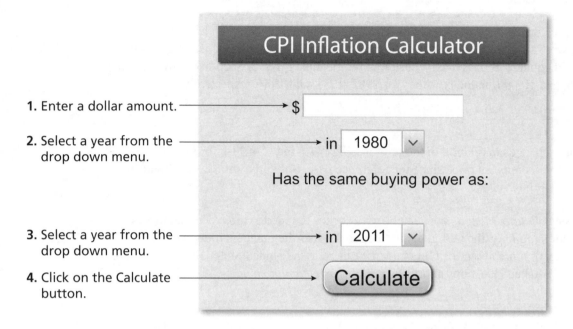

Note that for the years 2007 and later, the calculator uses index values rounded to three decimal places. Because the CPI given in Section 4.2 lists the numbers rounded to one decimal place, answers obtained using the calculator may differ from those shown in the text. For more information on the CPI, see the Example 1 Math Help for page 162.

Checkpoint Solution

The CPI was 16.3 in 1942 and 218.1 in 2010. If the value of the washing machine kept up with inflation, it would be worth

$$\text{Value in 2010} = \frac{\text{CPI in 2010}}{\text{CPI in 1942}} (\text{value in 1942})$$

$$= \frac{218.1}{16.3}(\$150)$$

$$\approx \$2007.$$

Example 3 Instructor Notes

The annual inflation rate is the percent change from one year to the next in the general level of prices. The CPI can be used to estimate the inflation rate using the formula

$$\text{Inflation rate in year A} = \frac{\text{CPI in year A} - \text{CPI in preceding year}}{\text{CPI in preceding year}} \times 100.$$

For instance, to estimate the inflation rate in 2006, use the CPI in 2006, 201.6, and the CPI in 2005, 195.3.

$$\text{Inflation rate in year 2006} = \frac{201.6 - 195.3}{195.3} \times 100 \approx 3.2$$

The graph in the Example 3 Math Help shows the inflation rate from 1931 through 2010.

Students can download a spreadsheet of the data used to create the inflation rate graph and the CPI graph in Example 3.
(See *http://math.andyou.com/content/04/01/data/mthu_data_0401_156_05a_2.xls*.)

Checkpoint Solution

Based on this graph, it is hard to associate either party with inflation more than the other. We had Democratic presidents during most of the 1930s (no inflation) and 1940s (increasing inflation), a Republican president during the 1950s (stable inflation), and a Democratic president for most of the 1960s (rising inflation). During the 1970s, when inflation was at its worst, we had a Republican president during the early and middle part of the decade and a Democrat for the last few years. From the 1980s through the 2000s, when inflation was gradually decreasing, we had Republican, then Democratic, then Republican presidents. If you had to pick one, you could say the Democratic party has been associated with inflation slightly more the Republican party, but we haven't taken into account control of Congress, which belonged to the Democrats for most of the 1930s through the 1980s and has shifted back and forth since.

Example 4 Instructor Notes

In the graph of the CPI from 1774 through 2010, note that the dates reflect the years that the U.S. was involved in the indicated war. For instance, World War I started before 1917, so the years listed are only those in which the U.S. officially participated in the war.

Checkpoint Solution

Using deductive reasoning (Chapter 3), the argument makes sense as long as the following premises are correct.

- Premise 1:   Inflation occurs when the monetary base grows faster than the amount of goods and services.

- Premise 2:   Deficit spending adds money to the economy without adding goods or services.

- Conclusion: Deficit spending results in inflation.

Example 5 Instructor Notes

According to *The Economist*, devaluation is "a sudden fall in the value of a currency against other currencies. Strictly, devaluation refers only to sharp falls in a currency within a fixed exchange rate system." (An exchange rate is the price at which one currency can be converted into another.) "Also, devaluation usually refers to a deliberate act of government policy, although in recent years reluctant de valuers have blamed financial speculation. Most studies of devaluation suggest that its beneficial effects on competitiveness are only temporary; over time they are eroded by higher prices."

Students can download the spreadsheet used in Example 5 to see how the value of the dollar has changed since 1931.
(See *http://math.andyou.com/content/04/02/data/mthu_data_0402_166_05.xls*.)

Checkpoint Solution

Devaluation of the dollar causes inflation and causes people's possessions and companies' assets to be worth more nominally. Most economists agree that some inflation is necessary and some think that intentionally devaluing the dollar will help improve the economy.

Example 6 Instructor Notes

A budget deficit occurs when spending exceeds revenue, and a surplus occurs when revenue exceeds spending. The U.S. federal government deficits (or surpluses) are shown in the graph below. (A value less than $0 represents a deficit, and a value greater than $0 is a surplus.). Since 1980, the government has had a surplus in only four fiscal years. Ask students to compare the graph to the one of the U.S. Federal Debt in Example 6 on page 167.

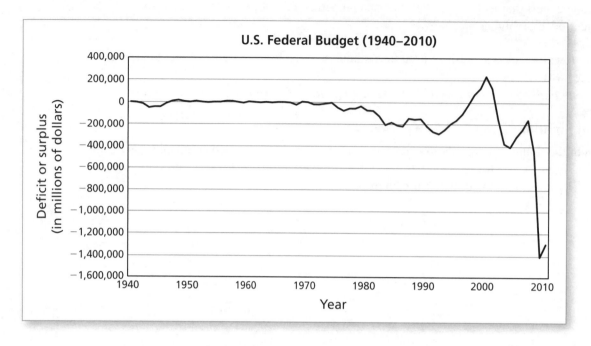

Note on the Fiscal Year

The Federal fiscal year begins on October 1 and ends on the subsequent September 30. It is designated by the year in which it ends; for example, fiscal year 2010 began on October 1, 2009, and ended on September 30, 2010. Prior to fiscal year 1977 the Federal fiscal years began on July 1 and ended on June 30. In calendar year 1976 the July–September period was a separate accounting period (known as the transition quarter or TQ) to bridge the period required to shift to the new fiscal year. In the figure above, the receipts and outlays incurred during TQ were split evenly and added to those of 1976 and 1977. *(Source: Office of Management and Budget)*

Checkpoint Solution

This loan plan is not valid because it is not realistic to assume housing prices will increase by 10% annually. Housing prices often increase by less than 10% from year to year and have even decreased in recent years. It is also not realistic to assume a constant 4% annual inflation rate.

Section 4.3   Exponential Decay

Example 1 Instructor Notes

In Example 1, note that n represents the number of turbines and not elapsed time. The relationship between the numbers of turbines and salmon, however, can be modeled by the formula for exponential decay. Also, point out to students that the numbers of survivors are rounded *down* because it is not reasonable to count "half of a fish" as a survivor. So, when $n = 3$, the amount is $A = 100,000(1 - 0.15)^3 = 61,412.5 \approx 61,412$. For a further discussion on the rounding of numbers, see Section 1.2.

Students can make a spreadsheet using the steps below. [Note that Step 6 uses the exponential decay formula given in Example 1, $A = 100,000(1 - 0.15)^n = 100,000(0.85)^n$.] (See *http://math.andyou.com/content/04/03/data/mthu_data_0403_174_01.xls*.)

1. Enter the titles "Turbines, n" and "Survivors" into row 1.
2. Enter 0 into cell A2.
3. Enter the formula =A2 + 1 into cell A3.
4. Select cell A3. From the Edit menu, choose Copy.
5. Select cells A4 through A8. From the Edit menu, choose Paste.
6. Enter the formula =ROUNDDOWN(100000*0.85^A2, 0) into cell B2.
7. Select cell B2. From the Edit menu, choose Copy.
8. Select cells B3 through B8. From the Edit menu, choose Paste.
9. Select cells B2 through B8. From the Format menu, choose Cells . . ..
10. In the Format Cells dialog, select the Number tab.
11. From the Category: list, select Number.
12. For Decimal places:, enter 0. Check the Use 1000 Separator (,) box. Click OK.

	A	B
1	**Turbines, *n***	**Survivors**
2	0	100,000
3	1	85,000
4	2	72,250
5	3	61,412
6	4	52,200
7	5	44,370
8	6	37,714

Exponential decay formula

ROUNDDOWN(100000*0.85^A2, 0)

Number of digits to round the number

Checkpoint Solution

Use the formula for exponential decay.

$$A = P(1 + r)^n = 100,000(1 - 0.15)^{12} \qquad P = 100,000, r = 15\% = 0.15, n = 12$$

$$\approx 14,224.18$$

Because there can't be a fraction of a salmon left, 14,224 salmon will survive.

Example 2 Instructor Notes

Note in Example 2 that n represents the height (in thousands of feet) and not elapsed time. The relationship between the height and atmospheric pressure, however, can be modeled by the formula for exponential decay. Also, because n is the height in thousands of feet, point out to students that $n = 35$ corresponds to a height of 35,000 feet.

For more information about sea level, visit the National Oceanic and Atmospheric Administration at *http://tidesandcurrents.noaa.gov/sltrends/sltrends.shtml*.

Students may download a spreadsheet of the data used to make the graph in Example 2. (See *http://math.andyou.com/content/04/03/data/mthu_data_0403_175_02.xls*.)

Checkpoint Solution

The formula for this exponential decay is

$$A = P(1 - r)^n = 1(1 - 0.038)^n. \qquad P = 1, r = 3.8\% = 0.038$$

At 14,000 feet, the atmospheric pressure is

$$A = 1(1 - 0.038)^{14} \qquad\qquad n = 14$$
$$\approx 0.581 \text{ atm.}$$

At 20,320 feet, the atmospheric pressure is

$$A = 1(1 - 0.038)^{20.32} \qquad\qquad n = 20.32$$
$$\approx 0.455 \text{ atm.}$$

So, the atmospheric pressure decreases by about $0.581 - 0.455 = 0.126$ atmosphere as you climb from 14,000 to 20,320 feet.

Example 3 Instructor Notes

To make a spreadsheet similar to the one in Example 3, have students use the steps below.

[Note that Step 6 uses the half-life formula given in Example 3, $A = 500\left(\dfrac{1}{2}\right)^{t/3}$.]

(See *http://math.andyou.com/content/04/03/data/mthu_data_0403_176_03.xls*.)

1. Enter the titles "Time, t" and "Amount, A" into row 1.
2. Enter 0 into cell A2.
3. Enter the formula =A2 + 3 into cell A3.
4. Select cell A3. From the Edit menu, choose Copy.
5. Select cells A4 through A10. From the Edit menu, choose Paste.
6. Enter the formula =500*0.5^(A2/3) into cell B2
7. Select cell B2. From the Edit menu, choose Copy.
8. Select cells B3 through B10. From the Edit menu, choose Paste.
9. Select cells B2 through B10. From the Format menu, choose Cells . . ..
10. In the Format Cells dialog, select the Number tab.
11. From the Category: list, select Number.
12. For Decimal places:, enter 2. Then click OK.

Checkpoint Solution

Students can enter the half-life formula

$$A = P\left(\frac{1}{2}\right)^{t/T} = 500\left(\frac{1}{2}\right)^{t/3} \qquad P = 500,\ T = 3$$

into a spreadsheet.
(See *http://math.andyou.com/content/04/03/data/mthu_data_0403_176_03a.xls*.)

	A	B
1	Time, *t*	Amount, *A*
2	0	500.00
3	3	250.00
4	6	125.00
5	9	62.50
6	12	31.25
7	15	15.63
8	18	7.81
9	21	3.91
10	24	1.95
11	27	0.98
12	30	0.49
13	33	0.24
14	36	0.12

You can see that the amount of the drug drops to below 1 milligram after about 27 hours. About 2 milligrams were left after 24 hours, so this takes about 3 hours longer.

Example 4 Instructor Notes

Determining the age of ancient fossils or artifacts once was the job of paleontologists. By comparing the placement of an object with the age of the rock and silt layers in which it was found, scientists could usually make a general estimate of the object's age. This method is rather limited because many objects are found in areas whose ages are not known, such as a cave or frozen in ice.

In 1907, American chemist Bertram Boltwood (1870–1927) proposed that rocks containing radioactive uranium could be dated by measuring the amount of lead in the rock. (When uranium decays, it changes into lead over a long period of time.) So, the greater the amount of lead, the older the rock. This method is also limited because it only applies to objects containing uranium. The benefit of this discovery, however, was it showed that radioactive dating was possible.

The first method for dating organic objects, such as the remains of plants and animals, was developed by American chemist, Willard Libby (1908–1980). Libby began testing his carbon-14 dating procedure by dating objects whose ages were already known. He found that his methods, while not as accurate as he had hoped, were fairly reliable. He continued his research and was eventually able to determine the age of an object up to 50,000 years old with a precision of plus-or-minus 10%. (The accuracy of the estimate of the age depends upon assumptions concerning the past intensity of cosmic radiation, accuracy of the equipment used, and other factors.)

Scientists have developed other dating methods, including the uranium-thorium method, the potassium-argon method, and the rubidium-strontium method, all of which are based on the transformation of one element into another. (Source: *Encyclopedia.com*)

Checkpoint Solution

Use the formula for exponential decay using half-life.

$$A = P\left(\frac{1}{2}\right)^{t/T}$$

$$= 1\left(\frac{1}{2}\right)^{3000/5730} \qquad P = 1, t = 3000, T = 5730$$

$$= 0.696$$

So, the ratio of carbon-14 to carbon-12 in the soil samples was about 0.696.

Example 5 Instructor Notes

Review the algebraic steps for finding the exponential decay rate in Example 5.

$$\frac{A_t}{A_0} = 1 - r \qquad\qquad \text{Write formula.}$$

$$\frac{1710}{1800} = 1 - r \qquad\qquad \text{Substitute 1710 for } A_1 \text{ and 1800 for } A_2.$$

$$0.95 = 1 - r \qquad\qquad \text{Rewrite fraction as decimal.}$$

$$0.95 + r = 1 - r + r \qquad\qquad \text{Add } r \text{ to each side.}$$

$$0.95 + r = 1 \qquad\qquad \text{Simplify.}$$

$$0.95 - 0.95 + r = 1 - 0.95 \qquad\qquad \text{Subtract 0.95 from each side.}$$

$$r = 1 - 0.95 \qquad\qquad \text{Simplify.}$$

$$r = 0.05 \qquad\qquad \text{Subtract.}$$

So, $r = 0.05$. Note that in the context of the problem in Example 5, $r = 0.05$ corresponds to an exponential decay rate of 5% every decade.

Students may download a spreadsheet to access the data used in Example 5. (See *http://math.andyou.com/content/04/03/data/mthu_data_0403_178_05.xls*.)

Checkpoint Solution

Begin by finding the rate of exponential decay.

$$\frac{A_t}{A_0} = \frac{1764}{1800} = 0.98 = 1 - r \qquad\qquad A_1 = 1764, A_0 = 1800$$

This implies $r = 0.02$ and that the man's BMR decays by 2% every decade.

By using the formula for exponential decay

$$A = P(1 - r)^n = 1800(1 - 0.02)^n \qquad P = 1800, r = 0.02$$

and a spreadsheet, you can see that the man's BMR drops to about 1660 calories after 4 decades. (See *http://math.andyou.com/content/04/03/data/mthu_data_0403_178_05a.xls*.)

So, he will be about 60 years old.

Example 6 Instructor Notes

Review the algebraic steps for finding the exponential decay rate in Example 6.

$$\frac{A_1}{A_0} = 1 - r$$ Write formula.

$$\frac{7.5}{10} = 1 - r$$ Substitute 7.5 for A_1 and 10 for A_2.

$$0.75 = 1 - r$$ Rewrite fraction as decimal.

$$0.75 + r = 1 - r + r$$ Add r to each side.

$$0.75 + r = 1$$ Simplify.

$$0.75 - 0.75 + r = 1 - 0.75$$ Subtract 0.75 from each side.

$$r = 1 - 0.75$$ Simplify.

$$r = 0.25$$ Subtract.

So, $r = 0.25$. Note that in the context of the problem in Example 6, $r = 0.25$ corresponds to an exponential decay rate of 25% every 10,000 years.

Students may download a spreadsheet to access the data used in Example 6.
(See *http://math.andyou.com/content/04/03/data/mthu_data_0403_179_06.xls*.)

Checkpoint Solution

It took the plutonium 80,000 years to decay to $\frac{1}{10}$ its original size (from 10 grams to 1 gram).

Because it is decaying at a constant exponential rate, it will take 80,000 more years to decay to $\frac{1}{10}$ its size again (from 1 gram to $\frac{1}{10}$ gram.)

Students can check this result using the formula for exponential decay

$$A = P(1 - r)^n$$

$$= 10(1 - 0.25)^{16}$$ $P = 10, r = 0.25, n = 16$

$$\approx 0.100$$

or by using a spreadsheet.
(See *http://math.andyou.com/content/04/03/data/mthu_data_0403_179_06a.xls*.)

Section 4.4 Depreciation

Example 1 Instructor Notes

Note that the useful life of an item is an estimate of the number of years before the item must be replaced. It is an estimate because the useful life depends upon such things as frequency of use, care when in use, repair procedures, technology, and durability. The salvage value of an item is the estimated resale, trade-in, or scrap value of the item after its useful life.

To make a spreadsheet similar to the one in Example 1, have students use the steps below.
(See *http://math.andyou.com/content/04/04/data/mthu_data_0404_184_01.xls.*)

1. Enter the titles "Year," "Value before Depreciation," "Depreciation," and "Value after Depreciation" into Row 1.
2. Enter 1 into cell A2.
3. Enter the formula =A2 + 1 into cell A3.
4. Select cell A3. From the Edit menu, choose Copy.
5. Select cells A4 through A6. From the Edit menu, choose Paste.
6. Enter 25000 into cell B2 and 4000 into cells C2-C6.
7. Enter the formula = B2 – C2 into cell D2.
8. Select cell D2. From the Edit menu, choose Copy.
9. Select cells D3 through D6. From the Edit menu, choose Paste.
10. Enter the formula = D2 into cell B3.
11. Select cell B3. From the Edit menu, choose Copy.
12. Select cells B4 through B6. From the Edit menu, choose Paste.
13. Select cells B2 through B6, C2 through C6, and D2 through D6.
14. From the Format menu, choose Cells . . ..
15. In the Format Cells dialog, select the Number tab.
16. From the Category: list, select Currency.
17. For Decimal places: enter 0. For Symbol, choose $ from the drop down list. Then click OK.

Checkpoint Solution

The amount of depreciation each year is

$$\text{Annual depreciation} = \frac{(\text{purchase price}) - (\text{salvage value})}{\text{years of useful life}}$$

$$= \frac{25{,}000 - 4000}{7}$$

$$= \$3000.$$

Students may use a spreadsheet to compute a schedule.
(See *http://math.andyou.com/content/04/04/data/mthu_data_0404_184_01a.xls.*)

Example 2 Instructor Notes

An easy way to make a depreciation schedule is to enter the information into a spreadsheet. (See *http://math.andyou.com/content/04/04/data/mthu_data_0404_185_02.xls*.)

Also suggest that students use a scientific calculator to find the annual depreciation by the straight-line method, using these steps.

1. Subtract the salvage value from the purchase price.

2. Divide by the years of useful life.

3. Round to the nearest cent.

In Example 2, it was noted that in straight-line depreciation the same amount is expensed each year. Graphically, this creates a linear pattern, hence the name "straight-line depreciation." The figures below illustrate the linear pattern.

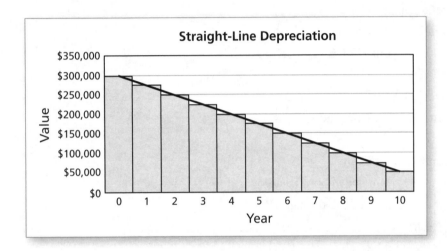

Checkpoint Solution

According to the depreciation schedule spreadsheet shown in Example 2, after five years, the combine was worth $175,000. If he sells it for $180,000, he should report the $5000 difference on his tax return. It will be taxed like regular income by the Internal Revenue Service. Taxing the difference on something sold for higher than its depreciated value is called "depreciation recapture."

Example 3 Instructor Notes

You have already seen that the annual depreciation in the straight-line method is the same each year. While relatively easy to calculate, straight-line depreciation is not really very representative of the way most items depreciate. Typically, depreciation is greatest in early years and levels off in later years. For instance, new cars usually depreciate more in the first year than in the second, more in the second than in the third, and so on. This feature of depreciation is built into double declining-balance depreciation, as shown in Example 3. Note in the spreadsheet and bar graph in Example 3 how the value depreciates the greatest in the first few years and levels off for the last few years.

(See *http://math.andyou.com/content/04/04/data/mthu_data_0404_186_03.xls*.)

Checkpoint Solution

Find the annual rate of depreciation.

$$\text{Annual rate of depreciation} = \frac{2}{\text{years of useful life}}$$

$$= \frac{2}{7}$$

A spreadsheet showing the depreciation schedule is shown below.
(See *http://math.andyou.com/content/04/04/data/mthu_data_0404_186_03a.xls*.)

	A	B	C	D
		Value before		Value after
1	Year	Depreciation	Depreciation	Depreciation
2	1	$25,000	$7,142.86	$17,857.14
3	2	$17,857.14	$5,102.04	$12,755.10
4	3	$12,755.10	$3,644.31	$9,110.79
5	4	$9,110.79	$2,603.08	$6,507.71
6	5	$6,507.71	$1,859.34	$4,648.36
7	6	$4,648.36	$648.36	$4,000.00
8	7	$4,000.00	$0.00	$4,000.00

Note that depreciation in the sixth and seventh years is adjusted so that the equipment depreciates to its salvage value, $4000.

Students can check their work using a *Depreciation Schedule Calculator* located in Tools.
(See *http://math.andyou.com/tools/depreciationcalculator.html*.)

Example 4 Instructor Notes

In Example 4, the salvage value is $25,000. From a practical standpoint, salvage value is often considered to be $0, because its valuation is often small and immaterial. For instance, after 5 years, a certain computer is considered obsolete. So, the computer has a salvage value of $0. (See *http://math.andyou.com/content/04/04/data/mthu_data_0404_187_04.xls*.)

Checkpoint Solution

Using the spreadsheet from Example 4, you can see that the value expensed during the first 4 years using double declining-balance depreciation was $200,000 − $81,920 = $118,080.

For straight-line depreciation, the annual depreciation would be

$$\frac{200,000 - 25,000}{10} = \$17,500.$$

After 4 years, the total depreciation expense is 4($17,500) = $70,000. The spreadsheet below confirms that the total depreciation during the first 4 years is $200,000 − $130,000 = $70,000. (See *http://math.andyou.com/content/04/04/data/mthu_data_0404_187_04a.xls*.)

	A	B	C	D
1	Year	Value before Depreciation	Depreciation	Value after Depreciation
2	1	$200,000.00	$17,500.00	$182,500.00
3	2	$182,500.00	$17,500.00	$165,000.00
4	3	$165,000.00	$17,500.00	$147,500.00
5	4	$147,500.00	$17,500.00	$130,000.00
6	5	$130,000.00	$17,500.00	$112,500.00
7	6	$112,500.00	$17,500.00	$95,000.00
8	7	$95,000.00	$17,500.00	$77,500.00
9	8	$77,500.00	$17,500.00	$60,000.00
10	9	$60,000.00	$17,500.00	$42,500.00
11	10	$42,500.00	$17,500.00	$25,000.00

So, using double declining-balance depreciation, we expensed $118,080 − $70,000 = $48,080 more during the first 4 years than we would have with straight-line depreciation.

Students can check their work using a *Depreciation Schedule Calculator* located in Tools. (See *http://math.andyou.com/tools/depreciationcalculator.html*.)

Example 5 Instructor Notes

Note that the numerator in the depreciation rate, $n + 1 - k$, is the number of years of useful life remaining at the beginning of the year. In Example 5, explain that the depreciation in Column C of the spreadsheet is found by multiplying the depreciation rate by the difference between the purchase price and the salvage value.

(See *http://math.andyou.com/content/04/04/data/mthu_data_0404_188_05.xls*.)

Because the difference between the purchase price and the salvage value is $60,000 - 15,000 = \$45,000$, you can calculate the depreciation for each year as shown.

Year	Value before Depreciation	Depreciation	Value after Depreciation
1	$60,000	$\left(\frac{5}{15}\right)(45,000) = \$15,000$	$45,000
2	$45,000	$\left(\frac{4}{15}\right)(45,000) = \$12,000$	$33,000
3	$33,000	$\left(\frac{3}{15}\right)(45,000) = \$9,000$	$24,000
4	$24,000	$\left(\frac{2}{15}\right)(45,000) = \$6,000$	$18,000
5	$18,000	$\left(\frac{1}{15}\right)(45,000) = \$3,000$	$15,000

In general, the depreciation in year k for the sum of the years-digits method is

Depreciation in year k = (Depreciation rate for year k)(Purchase price − Salvage value).

Checkpoint Solution

$$\text{Depreciation rate for year } k = \frac{n + 1 - k}{\text{sum of the years of useful life digits}}$$

$$= \frac{4 + 1 - k}{1 + 2 + 3 + 4}$$

$$= \frac{5 - k}{10}$$

Depreciation = (rate)(purchase price − salvage value)

$$= \frac{5 - k}{10}(60,000 - 15,000)$$

$$= \frac{5 - k}{10}(45,000)$$

A spreadsheet showing the sum of the years-digits depreciation schedule is available at *http://math.andyou.com/content/04/04/data/mthu_data_0404_188_05a.xls*. Students can check their work using a *Depreciation Schedule Calculator* located in Tools.
(See *http://math.andyou.com/tools/depreciationcalculator.html*.)

Example 6 Instructor Notes

According to the Internal Revenue Service (IRS), "depreciation is an income tax deduction that allows a taxpayer to recover the cost or other basis of certain property. It is an annual allowance for the wear and tear, deterioration, or obsolescence of the property."

"Most types of tangible property (except land), such as buildings, machinery, vehicles, furniture, and equipment are depreciable. Likewise, certain intangible property, such as patents, copyrights, and computer software is depreciable."

"Depreciation begins when a taxpayer places property in service for use in a trade or business or for the production of income. The property ceases to be depreciable when the taxpayer has fully recovered the property's cost or other basis or when the taxpayer retires it from service, whichever happens first." (See *http://www.irs.gov/businesses/small/article/0,,id=137026,00.html.*)

Checkpoint Solution

Sample answer:

I would choose an accelerated depreciation method. Depreciation counts as an expense, so depreciating more of the asset's value early will make it possible to maximize early tax deductions. Also, accelerated methods are usually more accurate. I would choose sum of the years-digits depreciation instead of double declining-balance depreciation to avoid having to make adjustments at the end of the asset's useful life. Note that although I chose sum of the years-digits depreciation, straight-line depreciation is often used for financial accounting (as opposed to managerial accounting) so that the company can report a higher net income in the earlier years for their investors.

Chapter 5

Section 5.1   Flat Tax & Political Philosophy

Example 1 Instructor Notes

It should be pointed out that each year the tax forms, tables, and laws may change slightly. So, some of the information in Chapter 5 will become outdated. However, the general procedures demonstrated in this chapter have been in existence for many years and are likely to be applicable for years to come. Furthermore, there are numerous deductions, exclusions, and exemptions that could be discussed, but the discussion in this chapter is limited to the more common ones. Also, we have kept the terms used in this chapter as simple as possible. For instance, we use the term "deductions" as an umbrella term for all amounts subtracted from gross income, but in a tax preparation course some of these "deductions" might be called "adjustments."

The current state tax rates can be found at the Federation of Tax Administrators website. (See *http://www.taxadmin.org/fta/rate/tax_stru.html*.)

Checkpoint Solution

Here is a sample answer for each argument.

The logic is valid:

The rich should pay higher taxes because they benefit more from taxpayer funded protections and projects more than any other group from:

>   U.S. Military, the nation's infrastructure, police, firemen, National Guard,
>   Coast Guard, Transportation Security Administration, FBI, CIA, education,
>   bailouts, federal loans for their corporations, tax cut loopholes, etc.

The logic is not valid:

A flat tax is fair because it treats all taxpayers equally, regardless of economic status. It is a simple system and would be good for growth. A flat tax would lower marginal tax rates and would not punish people for contributing to our nation's wealth by saving and investing their money. (Source: *The Heritage Foundation,*
http://www.heritage.org/research/reports/2005/07/a-brief-guide-to-the-flat-tax)

Example 2 Instructor Notes

According to Section 61 of the Internal Revenue Code, gross income is all income from whatever source derived, including (but not limited to) the following items.

- Compensation for services, including fees, commissions, fringe benefits, and similar items
- Gross income derived from business
- Gains derived from dealings in property
- Interest
- Rents
- Royalties
- Dividends
- Alimony and separate maintenance payments
- Annuities
- Income from life insurance and endowment contracts
- Pensions
- Income from discharge of indebtedness
- Distributive share of partnership gross income
- Income in respect of a decedent
- Income from an interest in an estate or trust

You can learn more about the Internal Revenue Code by visiting Cornell University Law School (*http://www.law.cornell.edu/uscode/26/61.html*) or the IRS website (*http://www.irs.gov/taxpros/article/0,,id=98137,00.html*).

Checkpoint Solution

Sample answer:

Repealing the 16th Amendment before creating an alternative form of government revenue is politically naive and fiscally irresponsible. While tax reform may be necessary, careful steps need to be followed in order to maintain or increase the standard of living in the United States.

Example 3 Instructor Notes

Tax evasion, which involves intentionally hiding income, falsely claiming deductions, or another means of not paying taxes owed, is illegal. Tax avoidance, however, means reducing taxes owed by legal means. For instance, you can reduce your tax liability by

- earning tax-free income from tax-exempt bonds or mutual funds.
- contributing to a qualified retirement account, such as a traditional IRA or 401(k).
- making a charitable contribution.

There are many other ways to legally reduce your tax burden. For instance, consider the itemized deductions for individual taxpayers in the Internal Revenue Code at Cornell University Law School.
(See *http://www.law.cornell.edu/uscode/html/uscode26/usc_sup_01_26_10_A_20_1_30_B_40_VI.html*.)

Checkpoint Solution

d. regressive tax; It takes a smaller proportion of an income as the income rises.

e. progressive tax; After certain deductions, a larger proportion of the taxable estate is paid in taxes as the value of the estate increases.

f. flat tax; A flat tax rate of 15% is applied to profit of the sale of a stock investment.

Example 4 Instructor Notes

Note in the solution to Example 4(b) that property tax for some Americans is regressive. For instance, this tax becomes regressive for older taxpayers with fixed incomes living in homes purchased many years earlier that currently have high reassessed real estate values.

Checkpoint Solution

Sample answer:

I disagree. Estate taxes are progressive taxes, not regressive taxes. Farms account for a small percentage of estates that exceed the exclusion amount. (Source: *Calculating Estate Tax Liability,* *http://www.nationalaglawcenter.org/assets/crs/RL33718.pdf*)

Example 5 Instructor Notes

On page 206, the common definitions of direct tax and indirect tax are given. According to United States constitutional law, however, a direct tax usually means a tax on property. An indirect tax is usually a tax imposed upon a right or privilege, such as a franchise tax. Unless otherwise noted, whenever direct tax or indirect tax is mentioned in the text, use the definitions given on page 206.

Checkpoint Solution

Sample answer:

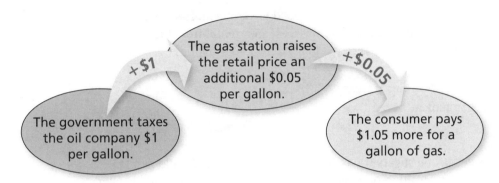

Example 6 Instructor Notes

A value-added tax (VAT) is an indirect tax on consumption (see Section 2.3). A VAT is levied against businesses whenever value is added to a product and when the product is sold. So, ultimately, the VAT is passed on to the consumer. For instance, consider a company that builds a tablet computer in a country with a VAT. The company pays a VAT on each part that it buys to produce the tablet computer. When the company sells the tablet computer to a retailer, the retailer pays a VAT on the tablet computer. Finally, when a consumer buys the tablet computer from the retailer, the price includes all VATs collected earlier.

Many European and other developed countries use a VAT. In Canada, the VAT is called the Goods and Services Tax. The tax is used to provide revenue for the federal government. Essential goods and services, such as groceries, prescriptions, and medical services, are exempt from the tax. Technically, exempt items are taxed at 0% and are referred to as "zero-rated supplies."

Checkpoint Solution

Here is a sample answer for each argument.

For the bill:

I would vote for an additional sales tax on sugary sodas and juice drinks. This tax could help reduce obesity while raising money for health programs. The tax should not apply to bottled water, diet sodas, coffee, tea, or milk.

Against the bill:

I would vote against an additional sales tax on soda. Taxing food does not change long-term behaviors with respect to appropriate food choices. It takes lifestyle changes and education. An additional tax could also jeopardize jobs in the beverage industry.

Section 5.2 Graduated Income Tax

Example 1 Instructor Notes

On page 212, the table showing the graduated income tax for the taxable income of a single person in 2010 has been simplified from the actual table used. For instance, the first row in the IRS 2010 tax tables essentially says, "If your taxable income is over $0 but not over $8375, then the tax is 10% of the amount over $0." What is the marginal tax rate for a taxable income of $8375.25? For the amount of $8375, it would be taxed at the 10% rate, and the remaining $0.25 would be taxed at the 15% rate.

To make a spreadsheet similar to the one in Example 1(a), have students use the steps below. (See *http://math.andyou.com/content/05/02/data/mthu_data_0502_212_01.xls*.)

1. Enter the titles "Taxable Income," "Marginal Tax Rate," and "Tax," into row 1.
2. Enter 8375 into cell A2, $= 34000 - 8375$ into cell A3, and $= 67850 - 34000$ into cell A4.
3. Enter the formula = SUM(A2:A4) into cell A5.
4. Enter 0.1 into cell B2, 0.15 into cell B3, and 0.25 into cell B4.
5. Enter the formula = A2*B2 into cell C2.
6. Select cell C2. From the **Edit** menu, choose **Copy.**
7. Select cells C3 and C4. From the **Edit** menu, choose **Paste.**
8. Enter the formula = SUM(C2:C4) into cell C5.

To format the cells, have students use the steps below.

1. Select cells A2 through A5.
2. From the **Format** menu, choose **Cells . . ..**
3. In the **Format Cells** dialog, select the **Number** tab.
4. From the **Category:** list, select **Currency.**
5. For **Decimal places:** enter 2. **For Symbol,** choose $ from the drop down list. Then click **OK.**
6. Select cells B2 through B4.
7. From the **Format** menu, choose **Cells . . ..**
8. In the **Format Cells** dialog, select the **Number** tab.
9. From the **Category:** list, select **Percentage.**
10. For **Decimal places:** enter 0. Then click OK.
11. Select cells B2 through B5. Repeat Steps 2 through 5.

Checkpoint Solution

Students can use a spreadsheet to calculate the income tax owed. (See *http://math.andyou.com/content/05/02/data/mthu_data_0502_212_01a.xls*.)

Example 2 Instructor Notes

Using a spreadsheet is an easy way to calculate a graduated income tax, as shown in Examples 1 and 2. (See *http://math.andyou.com/content/05/02/data/mthu_data_0502_213_02.xls*.)

Also notice that the tax tables on pages 212 and 213 are for single taxpayers. The tables below show the graduated income tax for the taxable income (after deductions) of a married couple filing jointly or separately in 2010. Ask students to compare the rates with the single taxpayer table shown on page 212. (See also Exercises 1–6.)

Married Filing Jointly in 2010	
Taxable Income	Marginal Tax Rate
$0–$16,750	10%
$16,751–$68,000	15%
$68,001–$137,300	25%
$137,301–$209,250	28%
$209,251–$373,650	33%
$373,651+	35%

Married Filing Separately in 2010	
Taxable Income	Marginal Tax Rate
$0–$8375	10%
$8376–$34,000	15%
$34,001–$68,650	25%
$68,651–$104,625	28%
$104,626–$186,825	33%
$186,826+	35%

Checkpoint Solution

Students can use a spreadsheet to calculate the income tax owed.
(See *http://math.andyou.com/content/05/02/data/mthu_data_0502_213_02a.xls*.)

The state income tax is $16,378.60.

The effective tax rate is

$$\frac{16,378.60}{200,000.00} \approx 0.082 = 8.2\%.$$

Example 3 Instructor Notes

Tax terms can be confusing, especially when considering gross income, adjusted gross income, and taxable income. Recall that gross income is all income from whatever source derived. (See Section 5.1 Example 2 Math Help.)

- Adjusted gross income is gross income less allowable adjustments, such as individual retirement account contributions, alimony payments, and unreimbursed business expenses.

- Taxable income is adjusted gross income less allowances for personal exemptions and itemized deductions.

Checkpoint Solution

The table shows the federal income tax to income earned ratio.

Income Group	Total Federal Income Tax Revenue	Adjusted Gross Income Earned	Federal Income Tax Revenue to Income Earned Ratio
Top 1%	38%	20%	$\frac{38}{20} = 1.90$
Next 4%	21%	15%	$\frac{21}{15} = 1.40$
Next 5%	11%	11%	$\frac{11}{11} = 1.00$
Next 15%	16%	22%	$\frac{16}{22} \approx 0.73$
Next 25%	11%	20%	$\frac{11}{20} = 0.55$
Bottom 50%	3%	12%	$\frac{3}{12} = 0.25$

The more money you make, the more you pay in federal income taxes. This is how a progressive system is supposed to work.

Example 4 Instructor Notes

To investigate U.S. federal revenue from individual income taxes (or other sources of federal revenue), use the historical tables at the Office of Management and Budget. (See *http://www.whitehouse.gov/omb/budget/Historicals.*)

Checkpoint Solution

Students can use a spreadsheet to draw both graphs. (See *http://math.andyou.com/content/05/02/data/mthu_data_0502_215_04a.xls.*)

a.

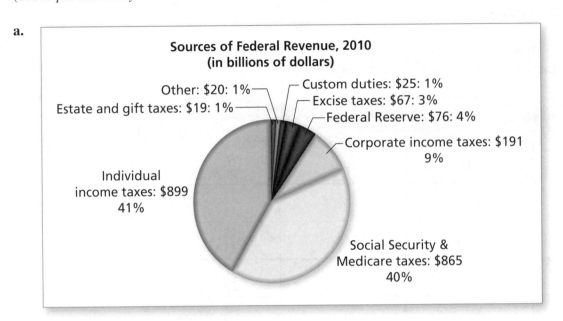

b. *Sample answer:*

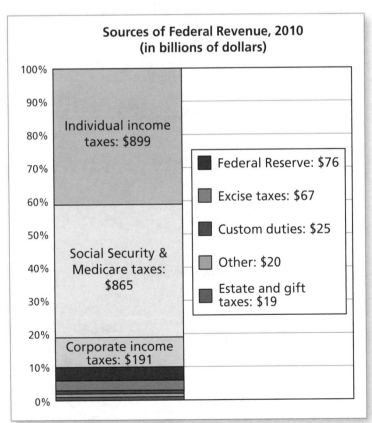

c. *Sample answer:* I prefer the circle graph. It shows more data and is more intuitive when considering parts of a whole.

Example 5 Instructor Notes

Explain that when dividing large numbers with one or more "trailing zeros" (the zeros after the last nonzero digit), you can simplify the division by "removing" the same number of trailing zeros from the numerator and denominator. For instance, to perform the division in Example 5(a), note that you can write

$$\overbrace{\frac{1,000,000,000,000}{\underbrace{13,000,000,000,000}_{\text{Trailing zeros}}}}^{\text{Trailing zeros}} = \frac{1 \times 1,000,000,000,000}{13 \times 1,000,000,000,000}.$$

Next, divide out the common factor 1,000,000,000,000 from both the numerator and the denominator of the fraction.

$$\frac{1 \times \cancel{1,000,000,000,000}}{13 \times \cancel{1,000,000,000,000}} = \frac{1}{13} \qquad \text{Remove 12 zeros from numerator and denominator.}$$

This fraction is easier to enter into a calculator (or to use in long division) than the original fraction. After dividing

$$\frac{1}{13} \approx 0.0769 = 7.69\%$$

you obtain the same answer shown in Example 5(a).

Checkpoint Solution

Sample answer:

Use a graduated tax on taxable income using the following table.

Taxable Income	Marginal Tax Rate
$0 – $10,000	10%
$10,001 – $35,000	10%
$35,001 – $90,000	10%
$90,001 – $500,000	10%
$500,001 – $2,000,000	10%
$2,000,001+	10%

Eliminate loopholes by removing all deductions except for the standard deduction, personal exemptions, child care, health and education costs, and retirement. The alternative minimum tax would be abolished because there would no longer be loopholes. Capital gains would be taxed as ordinary income, except up to $250,000 in profit on the sale of your primary residence. There would be little or no changing of the tax laws from year to year, other than rate and threshold adjustments due to inflation.

Example 6 Instructor Notes

Note: Students may want to review the Math Help for page 216 before continuing.

To perform the division in Example 6, note that you can write

$$\frac{1{,}280{,}000{,}000{,}000}{13{,}000{,}000{,}000{,}000} = \frac{128}{1300}.$$ Remove 10 zeros from numerator and denominator.

This fraction is easier to enter into a calculator (or to use in long division) than the original fraction. After dividing

$$\frac{128}{1300} \approx 0.09846 \approx 9.8\%$$

you obtain the same answer shown in Example 6.

Checkpoint Solution

Sample answer:

The first thing I would do is try to minimize Social Security, Medicare, and Medicaid fraud. The penalties for fraud need to be severe to prohibit these crimes, reduce expenditures, and increase revenue through fines. I would then cut the fat from other mandatory programs, and eliminate pet projects that fall into this category. Most non-defense spending programs would be put on hold for at least one year. Any remaining deficit would have to be settled by cutting defense spending.

Section 5.3   Property Tax

Example 1 Instructor Notes

Property tax rates are often expressed in mills. A mill is equal to $\frac{1}{10}$ of a cent, or $\frac{1}{1000}$ of a dollar.

To change the tax rates in Example 1 to decimal form, divide by 1000, as shown.

a. $38.7 \text{ mills} = \frac{38.7}{1000} = 0.0387$

b. $71 \text{ mills} = \frac{71}{1000} = 0.071$

Depending on where you live, property taxes may be used to fund public education, fire departments, snow removal, public libraries, debt, and many other services. Also, property taxes may be combined (see Example 3) or expressed in individual millages (see Exercises 9–13).

Checkpoint Solution

c. Property tax $= 0.0068(0.08)(400,000) = \$217.60$

d. Property tax $= 0.0174(1)(400,000) = \$6960.00$

Example 2 Instructor Notes

To change the tax rates in Example 2 to decimal form, divide by 1000, as shown.

a. $21.3 \text{ mills} = \dfrac{21.3}{1000} = 0.0213$

b. $80.2 \text{ mills} = \dfrac{80.2}{1000} = 0.0802$

Checkpoint Solution

c. Effective rate $= 0.0274(0.597) \approx 0.0164 = 1.64\%$

d. Effective rate $= 0.0034(1) \approx 0.0034 = 0.34\%$

e. Effective rate $= 0.167(0.037) \approx 0.0062 = 0.62\%$

Example 3 Instructor Notes

It should be noted that in the formula

$$
\boxed{\begin{array}{c}\text{Property}\\\text{tax}\end{array}} = \boxed{\begin{array}{c}\text{Tax rate}\\\text{(decimal form)}\end{array}} \times \underbrace{\boxed{\begin{array}{c}\text{Assessment level}\\\text{(decimal form)}\end{array}} \times \boxed{\text{Market value}}}_{\text{Assessed value}}
$$

from page 224, the market value used is the one determined by the assessor not the appraiser.

In Example 1, the property tax was calculated by multiplying the tax rate, the assessment level, and the market value. In Example 3, the assessed value is given. So, the property tax is calculated by multiplying the tax rate and the assessed value.

Be sure students understand that to change the tax rate in Example 3 to decimal form, divide by 1000, as shown.

$$185 \text{ mills} = \frac{185}{1000} = 0.185$$

Checkpoint Solution

Your monthly home insurance bill is

$$\frac{\$650}{12} = \$54.17.$$

Your annual property tax is

$$0.358(85,050) = \$30,447.90.$$

Your monthly property tax bill is

$$\frac{\$30,447.90}{12} = \$2537.33.$$

Your total monthly payment is

$$\$1073.64 + \$54.17 + 2537.33 = \$3665.14.$$

Example 4 Instructor Notes

To change the tax rate in Example 4 to decimal form, divide by 1000, as shown.

$$40 \text{ mills} = \frac{40}{1000} = 0.04$$

Checkpoint Solution

The graph shows that the homestead tax credit is about $255 for a property with an assessed value of $125,000. So, the property tax is

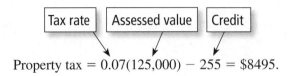

Property tax = 0.07(125,000) − 255 = $8495.

The homeowner pays $8495 for property tax.

Example 5 Instructor Notes

To find the estimate of $176 billion in Example 5, solve the equation

70% of (Total property tax) = $410 billion.   Original equation

Begin by writing 70% as 0.7, $410 billion as 410,000,000,000, and letting T be the total property tax. Then solve for T.

$0.7T = 410{,}000{,}000{,}000$ Rewrite original equation.

$T = \dfrac{410{,}000{,}000{,}000}{0.7}$ Divide each side by 0.7.

$T \approx \$586{,}000{,}000{,}000$ Use a calculator.

So, the lost revenue is about $586,000,000,000.

Checkpoint Solution

Sample answer:

I think that allowing religious organizations to be exempt from property tax is a violation of the first amendment. A church is just another type of club, but it gets special treatment due to its religious nature. Churches can be enormously profitable and the only benefits they provide are to their own members. In order for any other organization to gain tax-exempt status, they must adhere to rules and regulations, declare their income, and prove their worth to society as a whole.

It is wrong to offer benefits to religious institutions because it assumes that all religious institutions benefit society by merely existing. Churches do not need to perform any service at all in order to get these massive exemptions; they merely need to declare themselves religious to be tax-free, which puts a larger tax burden on non-members. (Source: *Should Churches Be Tax-Exempt?, http://uspolitics.about.com/b/2008/03/25/churches-non-profits-and-politics.htm*)

Example 6 Instructor Notes

Another way to determine the tax savings in Example 6 is to first calculate the property tax without the exemption.

$$\text{Property tax without exemption} = 0.065(75{,}000)$$
$$= \$4875$$

Next, subtract the property tax found in Example 6 to obtain

$$\$4875 - \$4550 = \$325.$$

This matches the tax savings found in Example 6.

Checkpoint Solution

The amount of the exemption is

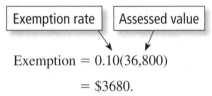

$$\text{Exemption} = 0.10(36{,}800)$$
$$= \$3680.$$

This is under the maximum, so the exemption is \$3680.

The property tax is

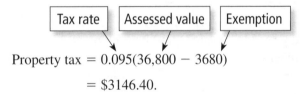

$$\text{Property tax} = 0.095(36{,}800 - 3680)$$
$$= \$3146.40.$$

The tax savings from the \$3680 reduction in the assessed value is

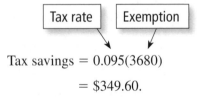

$$\text{Tax savings} = 0.095(3680)$$
$$= \$349.60.$$

The veteran pays \$3146.40 in property tax each year and saves \$349.60 from the exemption each year.

From age 26 to age 40, the veteran pays $\$3146.40 \times 15 = \$47{,}196.00$ in property taxes and saves $\$349.60 \times 15 = \$5244.00$ from the exemption.

Section 5.4   Social Security & Payroll Taxes

Example 1 Instructor Notes

It is highly unusual for employees to actually receive their full gross pay for a given pay period. (Gross pay is the amount of money before taking taxes or deductions.) This is true because state and federal laws require employers to make several payroll deductions. In Example 1, the payroll deductions were federal income tax, state income tax, Social Security tax, and Medicare tax. Additional payroll deductions include local income tax, medical insurance, life insurance, retirement plans, and union dues. The amount of money received after all payroll deductions have been made is called take-home pay or net pay. Normally, each paycheck is accompanied by a payroll statement that shows the gross pay, the deductions, and the net pay received by the employee. Using the general procedures demonstrated in Chapter 5, you can check your payroll statement for errors and report any errors to your employer. Many employers hire outside firms to do payroll, so your employer may be unaware of the errors.

Checkpoint Solution

a. Taxable income: $75,000

Federal income tax:	$14,931.25	(See page 212.)
California income tax:	$ 4,872.26	(See page 213.)
Social Security tax:	$ 9,300.00	(12.4% of $75,000)
Medicare tax:	$ 2,175.00	(2.9% of $75,000)
Total:	**$31,278.51**	

You pay 31,278.51/75,000 ≈ 41.7% of your taxable income to these four taxes.

b. Taxable income: $200,000

Federal income tax:	$51,116.75	(See page 212.)
California income tax:	$16,809.76	(See page 213.)
Social Security tax:	$13,243.20	(12.4% of $106,800)
Medicare tax:	$ 5,800.00	(2.9% of $200,000)
Total:	**$86,969.71**	

You pay 86,969.71/200,000 ≈ 43.5% of your taxable income to these four taxes.

The more you make (up to $106,800), the higher your percent toward these four taxes. The percent toward these four taxes will decrease above $106,800 due to the threshold on Social Security taxes.

Example 2 Instructor Notes

Explain that to calculate the employee's federal income tax in Example 2(b), first calculate the employee's taxable income. (This assumes the employee is single, does not have any other taxable income, and claims the standard deduction.)

$$\text{Taxable income} = \text{Salary} + \text{Holiday bonus} - \text{401(k) employee deferral} -$$
$$\text{Standard deduction} - \text{Exemption}$$
$$= 60{,}000 + 1000 - 3050 - 5700 - 3650$$
$$= \$48{,}600$$

So, the taxable income is $48,600. Using the table on page 212 and a spreadsheet, you can calculate the federal income tax owed by the employee as shown.
(See *http://math.andyou.com/content/05/04/data/mthu_data_0504_235_02.xls*.)

	A Taxable Income	B Marginal Rate	C Tax
1			
2	$8,375.00	10%	$837.50
3	$25,625.00	15%	$3,843.75
4	$14,600.00	25%	$3,650.00
5	$48,600.00		$8,331.25
6			

To calculate the employee's state income tax, first note that Massachusetts has a personal exemption of $4400 and does not tax employee 401(k) deferrals. So, with respect to state income taxes, the employee's taxable income is

$$\text{State taxable income} = \text{Salary} + \text{Holiday bonus} - \text{401(k) employee deferral} -$$
$$\text{Personal exemption}$$
$$= 60{,}000 + 1000 - 3050 - 4400$$
$$= \$53{,}550.$$

So, the employee in Example 2 owes $53{,}550 \times 0.053 = \$2838.15$ in state income taxes.

Checkpoint Solution

c. Divide the total compensation package by 12. The employer pays $80,759 ÷ 12 = $6729.92 each month.

d. The employee takes home $42,114.10 ÷ 12 = $3509.51 each month.

e. *Sample answer:*

Most employees do not understand the actual costs of their total compensation package. On the other hand, most employers do not adequately communicate to employees the cost of the benefits they provide. If both parties are fully aware of the actual costs and take-home pay, they may gain a mutual respect for each other's situation and use this knowledge to reach fair compensation levels in future negotiations.

Example 3 Instructor Notes

In Example 3, students can calculate the amount contributed to Social Security using a spreadsheet as shown. (See *http://math.andyou.com/content/05/04/data/mthu_data_0504_236_03.xls*.)

	A	B	C	D	E
1	Year	Employee Contribution	Years Compounded	Assumed Interest Rate	Value at end of 2010
2	2001	$5,000.00	10	4.0%	$7,401.22
3	2002	$5,200.00	9	4.0%	$7,401.22
4	2003	$5,300.00	8	4.0%	$7,253.42
5	2004	$5,400.00	7	4.0%	$7,106.03
6	2005	$5,600.00	6	4.0%	$7,085.79
7	2006	$5,800.00	5	4.0%	$7,056.59
8	2007	$6,100.00	4	4.0%	$7,136.14
9	2008	$6,300.00	3	4.0%	$7,086.64
10	2009	$6,600.00	2	4.0%	$7,138.56
11	2010	$6,600.00	1	4.0%	$6,864.00
12		$57,900.00			$71,529.60
13					

The calculations show the value of the employee contributions to the Social Security system assuming all payments had earned 4% interest each year. Including the matching contributions from the employer, the total value would be $71,529.60 × 2, or about $140,000.

Checkpoint Solution

Sample answer:

Overall, I think that privatization of Social Security would be worse for most workers. The system would change from a defined benefit plan to a defined contribution plan with no guarantees. Some workers might get lucky and hit the stock market lottery, but we shouldn't put most people's retirement at the whim of the stock market. Congress needs to stop raiding the Social Security trust fund and start looking for ways to strengthen the current system.

Example 4 Instructor Notes

Note that the spreadsheet in Example 4 rounds the dollar values to the nearest cent (see Steps 6, 7, 10, 11, 15, 19, and 20 in the Example 4 Math Help). Also, note that the Total Income is found by multiplying the monthly benefit in Column B by 12 and then adding the product to the benefit received so far. (See *http://math.andyou.com/content/05/04/data/mthu_data_0504_237_04.xls*.)

Checkpoint Solution

Suggest that students create a spreadsheet to help them make the graph.
(See *http://math.andyou.com/content/05/04/data/mthu_data_0504_237_04a.xls*.)

The graph shows how total income at full retirement age catches up to total income when retiring early.

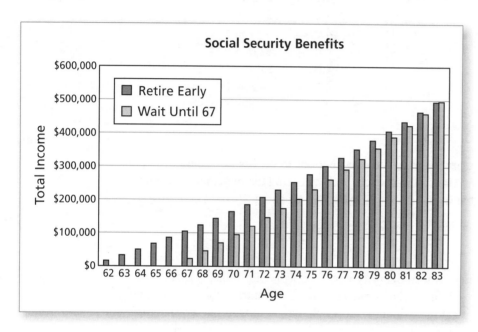

Example 5 Instructor Notes

Your class discussion of the viability of Social Security might raise the question, "How much will I need to retire?" You can suggest that students try using one of the many retirement calculators online. Most likely, they will see that Social Security will not provide nearly enough money to support them during retirement.

Estimate your Social Security benefits:

https://secure.ssa.gov/acu/ACU_KBA/main.jsp?URL=/apps8z/ARPI/main.jsp?locale=en&LVL=4

Retirement calculators:

- AARP
- Bankrate.com
- Bloomberg
- CNN
- MSN

Checkpoint Solution

Sample answer:

Republican view:

The general political philosophy of the Republican party is that citizens should take care of themselves. They believe that the answers do not lie with the government generally, but rather with the people. They want less government interference and tend to believe more strongly in property rights and less strongly in well-fare rights, holding economic equity above equality.

Democratic view:

The general political philosophy of the Democratic party is that the government should take care of people who cannot take care of themselves. They believe in a larger federal government, and often implement tax plans to try to help the less privileged. They tend to believe the government must look out for the greater good above the individual person in terms of well-fare and do what is necessary to make the populace more "equal."

I tend to agree with the Republican view. Our founding fathers stated that we could pursue happiness, not that we were entitled to happiness. If you make bad financial decisions, then you should be prepared to handle the consequences. To expect the government to fix your bad decisions is ludicrous and the type of thinking that will only lead to Socialism and/or Communism. However, matters such as Social Security and Medicare are not government handouts. We have all paid taxes specifically for these benefits.

Example 6 Instructor Notes

The Social Security Board of Trustees is composed of six trustees: the Secretary of the Treasury, the Secretary of Labor, the Secretary of Health and Human Services, the Commissioner of Social Security, and two Public Trustees. The two Public Trustees are nominated by the President, confirmed by the Senate, and serve four-year terms. These positions were established by the 1983 Social Security amendments so two people outside of the federal government could review the financial projections. The annual reports are required by law under Section 201 of the Social Security Act. (See *http://www.ssa.gov/OP_Home/ssact/title02/0201.htm.*) The primary purpose is to report to Congress on the financial status of the Social Security and Medicare Trust Funds. The Social Security report evaluates the finances of the Old-Age and Survivors Insurance (OASI) Trust Fund, the Disability Insurance (DI) Trust Fund, and the combined (OASDI) Trust Funds. The Medicare report covers the Hospital Insurance (HI) Trust Fund and the Supplementary Insurance (SMI) Trust Fund. Some of the conclusions from the 2011 Annual Report (See *http://www.ssa.gov/OACT/TR/2011/tr2011.pdf*):

- "Under current law, the cost of Social Security will generally increase faster than the program's income because of the aging of the baby-boom generation, continuing low fertility compared to the baby-boom period, and increasing life expectancy."

- "Based on the Trustees' best estimate, program cost will exceed non-interest income in 2011, as it did in 2010, and remain higher throughout the remainder of the 75-year projection period."

- ". . . the DI Trust Fund is projected to become exhausted in 2018."

- " The projected trust fund shortfalls should be addressed in a timely way so that necessary changes can be phased in gradually and workers and beneficiaries can be given time to adjust to them. "

If your students are interested in reading more about the Social Security Board of Trustees, visit *www.economics21.org.*

Checkpoint Solution

A 1% COLA costs the federal government

$$\$713 \text{ billion} \times 0.01 = \$7.13 \text{ billion}$$

in increased Social Security benefits.

Hopefully, the taxes paid by working people increased by at least 1% to cover this additional cost. Otherwise, this COLA will further erode the Social Security trust fund that is already in danger of default in the near future.

Chapter 6

Section 6.1   Introduction to Lending

Example 1 Instructor Notes

Not all loans involve a lending institution. People sometimes borrow money from relatives or friends when

- the purpose of the borrowed money is too risky for lending institutions.
- the borrower has a poor or nonexistent credit history.

Discuss with students some suggestions for wisely handling lending to or borrowing from relatives or friends.

- Make out a promissory note. If there is a default on the loan, the lender will need the note to take an income tax loss.
- Create a repayment schedule.

Following these suggestions will help keep the transaction more businesslike; it can be easy for the borrower to regard the loan as a "gift."

Checkpoint Solution

A negotiable contract requires a payment of money, describes or specifies who gets paid, and is capable of change through negotiation. The key feature is the third one, which means that status as payer or payee of the note is legally transferable from one person to another. The crucial phrase on the note itself is "to the order of." A document without these words is not negotiable.

Example 2 Instructor Notes

To help borrowers understand the contractual obligations of a particular loan, the federal government requires lending institutions to disclose to each borrower in writing several pertinent facts regarding the loan before the borrower is asked to sign a promissory note. This requirement is governed by the Truth in Lending Act.
(See *http://www.fdic.gov/regulations/laws/rules/6500-1400.html.*)
Some of the required disclosures include:

- the loan proceeds

- the total amount due

- the finance charge (see page 255)

- the annual percentage rate (see page 256)

Checkpoint Solution

The loan occurs on March 17 and is due 120 days from that date.

14 days	Days remaining in March
30 days	Days in April
31 days	Days in May
30 days	Days in June
+ 15 days	Days in July
120 days	

So the note is due on July 15.

The total amount due is as follows:

$5000.00	Loan proceeds
$250.00	Interest
+ $77.95	Other charges
$5327.95	Total amount due

Example 3 Instructor Notes

Lending institutions use many terms that borrowers may find confusing. For instance, in Example 3, the "cost of credit" is $141.06 and the "loan proceeds" are $1007.94. Explain that this means that you paid $141.06 to borrow $1007.94. So, loan proceeds are how much money you receive, and cost of credit is how much you pay to get that money.

Encourage students, as they encounter new terms, to write definitions in their own words to help them learn and better understand the terms.

Checkpoint Solution

a. The total amount due is

$$\text{Total amount due} = 24(\$74.20) \qquad \text{24 monthly payments}$$
$$= \$1780.80.$$

The loan proceeds are

$$\text{Loan proceeds} = \text{price of computer} + \text{sales tax}$$
$$= \$1599.99 + (0.07)(\$1599.90) \qquad \text{7\% sales tax}$$
$$= \$1711.99.$$

The cost of credit is

$$\text{Cost of credit} = \text{total amount due} - \text{loan proceeds}$$
$$= \$1780.80 - \$1711.99$$
$$= \$68.81.$$

b. The total amount due is

$$\text{Total amount due} = (30)(12)(\$1342.05) \qquad \text{30 years, 12 payments per year}$$
$$= \$483,138.$$

The loan proceeds are $250,000.

The cost of credit is

$$\text{Cost of credit} = \text{total amount due} - \text{loan proceeds}$$
$$= \$483,138 - \$250,000$$
$$= \$233,138.$$

Example 4 Instructor Notes

To calculate the finance charge in Example 1, first the monthly payment, $65.08, was calculated (see Section 6.2). The monthly payment M for an installment loan with a principal of P taken out for n months at an annual percentage rate of r (in decimal form) is

$$M = P\left[\frac{r/12}{1 - \left(\frac{1}{1 + (r/12)}\right)^n}\right].$$

Using $P = \$1438.95$, $r = 8\% = 0.08$, and $n = 24$, the monthly payment is

$$M = \$1438.95\left[\frac{0.08/12}{1 - \left(\frac{1}{1 + (0.08/12)}\right)^{24}}\right] = \$65.08.$$

Next, the monthly payment and the number of payments were used to find the total amount due.

$$\text{Total amount due} = (\text{number of payments})(\text{monthly payment})$$
$$= (24)(\$65.08)$$
$$= \$1561.92$$

Then the amount financed was subtracted from the total amount due to determine the finance charge.

$$\text{Finance charge} = \text{total amount due} - \text{amount financed}$$
$$= \$1561.92 - \$1438.95$$
$$= \$122.97$$

Checkpoint Solution

The completed disclosure is shown below.

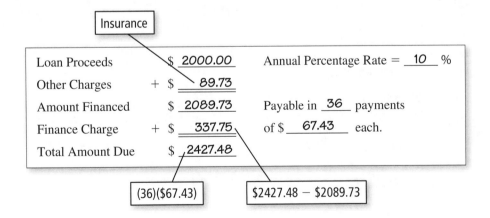

Example 5 Instructor Notes

To make a spreadsheet similar to the one in Example 5, have students use the steps below. (See *http://math.andyou.com/content/06/01/data/mthu_data_0601_256_05.xls*.)

1. Enter the title "Rate" in Row 1 and the titles "Days," "4%," "8%," "12%," "16%," "20%," and "24%" into Row 2.
2. Enter 60 into cell A3, 120 into cell A4, 180 into cell A5, 240 into cell A6, 300 into cell A7, and 365 into cell A8.
3. Enter the formula = ROUND(1000*0.04*A3/365, 2) into cell B3.
4. Select cell B3. From the **Edit** menu, choose **Copy.**
5. Select cells B4 through B8. From the **Edit** menu, choose **Paste.**
6. Enter the formula = ROUND(1000*0.08*A3/365, 2) into cell C3.
7. Select cell C3. From the **Edit** menu, choose **Copy.**
8. Select cells C4 through C8. From the **Edit** menu, choose **Paste.**
9. Enter the formula = ROUND(1000*0.12*A3/365, 2) into cell D3.
10. Select cell D3. From the **Edit** menu, choose **Copy.**
11. Select cells D4 through D8. From the **Edit** menu, choose **Paste.**
12. Enter the formula = ROUND(1000*0.16*A3/365, 2) into cell E3.
13. Select cell E3. From the **Edit** menu, choose **Copy.**
14. Select cells E4 through E8. From the **Edit** menu, choose **Paste.**
15. Enter the formula = ROUND(1000*0.2*A3/365, 2) into cell F3.
16. Select cell F3. From the **Edit** menu, choose **Copy.**
17. Select cells F4 through F8. From the **Edit** menu, choose **Paste.**
18. Enter the formula = ROUND(1000*0.24*A3/365, 2) into cell G3.
19. Select cell G3. From the **Edit** menu, choose **Copy.**
20. Select cells G4 through G8. From the **Edit** menu, choose **Paste.**

To format the cells, from the Format menu, choose Cells, select the Number tab, and from the Category list, select Currency. Select 2 decimal places and the $ symbol.

Checkpoint Solution

Use a spreadsheet to complete the calculations.
(See *http://math.andyou.com/content/06/01/data/mthu_data_0601_256_05a.xls*.)

$$I = Prt$$
$$= (\$1000)(0.04)\left(\frac{90}{365}\right)$$
$$= \$9.86$$

	A	B	C	D	E	F	G
1					Rate		
2	**Days**	**4%**	**8%**	**12%**	**16%**	**20%**	**24%**
3	60	$6.58	$13.15	$19.73	$26.30	$32.88	$39.45
4	90	**$9.86**	**$19.73**	**$29.59**	**$39.45**	**$49.32**	**$59.18**
5	120	$13.15	$26.30	$39.45	$52.60	$65.75	$78.90
6	180	$19.73	$39.45	$59.18	$78.90	$98.63	$118.36
7	240	$26.30	$52.60	$78.90	$105.21	$131.51	$157.81
8	300	$32.88	$65.75	$98.63	$131.51	$164.38	$197.26
9	365	$40.00	$80.00	$120.00	$160.00	$200.00	$240.00

Example 6 Instructor Notes

Recall from page 256 that interest calculated only on the principal is simple interest. Also, the rate at which this interest is calculated is the annual percentage rate (APR), or nominal APR. The term effective APR is an APR that, depending on the particular legal definition, can include fees or other charges, and compound interest (see Section 6.2). Note that the APR in Example 6(b) is an effective APR because the calculation includes a service charge.

Checkpoint Solution

The annual percentage rate for this loan is

$$r = \frac{I}{Pt}$$

$$= \frac{\$10}{(\$100)\left(\frac{21}{365}\right)} \qquad I = \$10, P = \$100, t = \frac{21}{365}$$

$$\approx 1.738$$

$$= 173.8\%.$$

Section 6.2 Buying Now, Paying Later

Example 1 Instructor Notes

A spreadsheet of the data in Example 1 is available for download at
http://math.andyou.com/content/06/02/data/mthu_data_0602_262_01.xls. Students may also
access a Monthly Payment Calculator at *http://math.andyou.com/tools/mp_calculator.html*.

Depending on whether students calculate by hand or use a calculator, a spreadsheet, or a monthly
payment calculator, their numbers may differ by a few pennies from what is shown in the
examples and answers.

It should be noted that when computing monthly payments and amortization schedules, some
lending institutions round to the nearest cent. Other institutions give themselves a slight advantage
by always rounding up to the next highest cent when calculating interest due to them. In most
transactions, the total difference in these two rounding procedures should amount to only a
few pennies.

Sometimes, the final payment will need to be adjusted due to round-off error in calculating the
monthly payment. To find the final payment in an amortization schedule, add the balance before
the final payment to the final interest payment.

Checkpoint Solution

The loan proceeds are $1200 and the total amount due is $6 \times \$203.51 = \$1221.06$. So, the cost of
credit is $\$1221.06 - \$1200.00 = \$21.06$.

If the loan term doubles, the monthly payment becomes

$$M = P\left[\frac{r/12}{1 - \left(\frac{1}{1 + (r/12)}\right)^n}\right] = \$1200\left[\frac{0.06/12}{1 - \left(\frac{1}{1 + (0.06/12)}\right)^{12}}\right] = \$103.28.$$

The cost of credit for this loan is

Cost of credit $= 12(\$103.28) - \$1200 = \$39.36.$

No, the cost of credit does not double when the loan term doubles. The relationship between cost
of credit and term is more complicated than that. As term increases, cost of credit may increase at
a slower or faster rate depending on the interest rate and the initial term length.

Example 2 Instructor Notes

The spreadsheet shown in Example 2 is available at
http://math.andyou.com/content/06/02/data/mthu_data_0602_263_02.xls. Emphasize that
while the numbers in the spreadsheet are shown to two decimal places, the actual numbers in
the calculations may be carried out to more than two decimal places.

Checkpoint Solution

a. You pay 60($506.91) = $30,414.60. So, the interest paid is $30,414.60 − $25,000 = $5414.60.

b. If the annual percentage rate is 9%, then your monthly payment is

$$M = P\left[\frac{r/12}{1 - \left(\frac{1}{1 + (r/12)}\right)^n}\right]$$

$$= \$25,000\left[\frac{0.09/12}{1 - \left(\frac{1}{1 + (0.09/12)}\right)^{60}}\right] \qquad P = \$25,000, r = 0.09, n = 60$$

$$= \$518.96.$$

So, the interest paid is 60($518.96) − $25,000 = $6137.60.

If the annual percentage rate is 10%, then your monthly payment is

$$M = P\left[\frac{r/12}{1 - \left(\frac{1}{1 + (r/12)}\right)^n}\right]$$

$$= \$25,000\left[\frac{0.10/12}{1 - \left(\frac{1}{1 + (0.10/12)}\right)^{60}}\right] \qquad P = \$25,000, r = 0.10, n = 60$$

$$= \$531.18.$$

So, the interest paid is 60($531.18) − $25,000 = $6870.80.

Example 3 Instructor Notes

Note that Example 3 has been simplified for illustrative purposes. The point of the example is to demonstrate how long it takes to pay off a credit card when making only minimum payments. Refer to Exercises 19–24 for more about credit.

Checkpoint Solution

a. Using a spreadsheet, you can see that it would take 66 months to pay off the debt if you paid $75 each month.
(See *http://math.andyou.com/content/06/02/data/mthu_data_0602_264_03a.xls*.)

	A	B	C	D	E
1	Payment Number	Balance before Payment	Monthly Payment	Interest	Balance after Payment
2	1	$2,500.00	$75.00	$58.33	$2,483.33
3	2	$2,483.33	$75.00	$57.94	$2,466.28
4	3	$2,466.28	$75.00	$57.55	$2,448.82
5	4	$2,448.82	$75.00	$57.14	$2,430.96
6	5	$2,430.96	$75.00	$56.72	$2,412.69
63	62	$297.42	$75.00	$6.94	$229.36
64	63	$229.36	$75.00	$5.35	$159.71
65	64	$159.71	$75.00	$3.73	$88.44
66	65	$88.44	$75.00	$2.06	$15.50
67	66	$15.50	$15.86	$0.36	$0.00
68	Total			$2,390.86	

b. Sum the interest column to see that the total interest paid is $2390.86.

Example 4 Instructor Notes

To find the interest in Example 4, note that the loan is for $30,000.

6% for 72 months

$$\text{Interest} = \text{amount paid} - \text{loan proceeds}$$
$$= \$35{,}797.68 - \$30{,}000.00$$
$$= \$5797.68$$

8% for 72 months

$$\text{Interest} = \text{amount paid} - \text{loan proceeds}$$
$$= \$37{,}872.00 - \$30{,}000.00$$
$$= \$7872.00$$

Checkpoint Solution

If the annual percentage rate is 5%, then your monthly payment is

$$M = \$40{,}000\left[\frac{0.05/12}{1 - \left(\dfrac{1}{1 + (0.05/12)}\right)^{60}}\right] \qquad P = \$40{,}000, \, r = 0.05, \, n = 60$$

$$= \$754.85.$$

If the annual percentage rate is 8%, then your monthly payment is

$$M = \$40{,}000\left[\frac{0.08/12}{1 - \left(\dfrac{1}{1 + (0.08/12)}\right)^{60}}\right] \qquad P = \$40{,}000, \, r = 0.08, \, n = 60$$

$$= \$811.06.$$

The amount you can save on the 5-year loan by having a credit score of 760 or above is

$$60(\$811.06) - 60(\$754.85) = \$3372.60.$$

Example 5 Instructor Notes

According to the publication "The Federal Reserve System in Brief," the Federal Reserve System is the central bank of the United States. The Federal Reserve

- manages our nation's supply of money and credit and operates at the center of the nation's financial system.
- keeps the wheels of business rolling with currency, coin, and payments services, such as electronic funds transfer and check-clearing.
- serves as the banker for the federal government by providing financial services for the U.S. Department of the Treasury.
- supervises and regulates a large share of the nation's banking and financial system.
- administers banking and finance-related consumer protection laws.

(See *http://www.frbsf.org/publications/federalreserve/fedinbrief/index.html.*)

Checkpoint Solution

Sample answer:

Out of these three factors, inflation rate appears to have had the highest impact on the prime interest rate. Although it fluctuates during this period, the prime interest rate had its greatest overall increase starting in the 1960s and peaking in 1981. This is also the period that the CPI was increasing the most rapidly. From 1981 through 2010, the CPI has followed a linear pattern, meaning the rate of inflation was slowly decreasing. During this same period, the prime interest rate showed a large overall decline.

There is also a noticeable correlation between the political party of the president and prime interest rate. The parties look close to even for the years 1961–76 and 1993–2008, but the prime interest rate increased dramatically during the Democratic presidency from 1977–80 and then went back down during the Republican presidencies of 1981–92.

There doesn't seem to be much relation between recent wars and the prime interest rate. But the rate did increase from approximately 4% to 8%, and then go back down during both the Vietnam and Iraq wars.

Example 6 Instructor Notes

In Example 6, it should be noted that the graph showing total consumer credit in the United States excludes home mortgages. (See Exercise 18.)

In the solution to Example 6, the average indebtedness per household in 1952 was

$$\frac{\$30,000,000,000}{46,000,000} \approx \$652$$

or about \$700. The average indebtedness per household in 2008 was

$$\frac{\$2,561,000,000,000}{117,000,000} \approx \$21,889$$

or about \$21,900. So, the average indebtedness per household increased by a factor of

$$\frac{\$21,900}{700} \approx 31.29.$$

During the same time, the CPI increased by a factor of

$$\frac{\$21,900}{700} \approx 8.12.$$

Checkpoint Solution

Sample answer:

Lendol Calder may be right that the "now and then" comparison is not as straightforward as it seems, but I think that consumer debt is indeed a national problem. People unable to pay their mortgage debt contributed to the subprime mortgage crisis of the 2000s, which had a hand in causing the 2008 recession. Consumers need to spend money for the economy to pick up, but for the millions who are in debt, spending more money would be personally irresponsible.

Section 6.3   Home Mortgages

Example 1 Instructor Notes

In Example 1, the monthly payment formula from Section 6.2 is used. Remind students that the monthly payment M for an installment loan with a principal of P taken out for n months at an annual percentage rate of r (in decimal form) is

$$M = P\left[\frac{r/12}{1 - \left(\frac{1}{1 + (r/12)}\right)^n}\right].$$

To find the interest in Example 1, subtract the loan proceeds (in this case, $250,000) from the total amount paid.

Checkpoint Solution

c.   When the annual percentage rate is 8%, your monthly payment will be

$$M = \$250,000\left[\frac{0.08/12}{1 - \left(\frac{1}{1 + (0.08/12)}\right)^{360}}\right] = \$1834.41.$$

That means you pay $360(\$1834.41) - \$250,000 = \$410,387.60$ in interest. So, the increase in interest paid when the APR goes from 6% to 8% is $\$410,387.60 - \$289,596.80 = \$120,790.80$.

d.   No, if the interest you pay doubled when APR doubled in general, then it would have done so in the last example.

e.   Yes, if the principal changes from $250,000 to $500,000, and the APR is still 4%, then your monthly payment will be

$$M = \$500,000\left[\frac{0.04/12}{1 - \left(\frac{1}{1 + (0.04/12)}\right)^{360}}\right] = \$2387.08.$$

That means you pay $360(\$2387.08) - \$500,000 = \$359,348.80$ in interest. This is twice what you paid in interest when the principal was $250,000.

f.   Yes. The monthly payment formula is $M = P\left[\dfrac{r/12}{1 - \left(\frac{1}{1 + (r/12)}\right)^n}\right].$

If the principal doubles, the P in the monthly payment formula will double, causing the monthly payment itself to double. Because you will be paying that monthly payment for the same term length, the total amount of money paid will double. Total interest paid is the difference between the total amount paid and the principal. Because the total amount of money paid and principal both double and the total interest paid is the difference between those two, the total interest paid also doubles.

Example 2 Instructor Notes

To find the interest in Example 2, subtract the loan proceeds (in this case, $250,000) from the total amount paid.

Checkpoint Solution

d. The monthly payment is

$$M = \$250{,}000 \left[\frac{0.12/12}{1 - \left(\dfrac{1}{1 + (0.12/12)} \right)^{240}} \right] \quad \text{20 years}$$

$$= \$2752.72.$$

So, the total interest paid is $240(\$2752.72) - \$250{,}000 = \$410{,}652.80$.

e. The monthly payment is

$$M = \$250{,}000 \left[\frac{0.12/12}{1 - \left(\dfrac{1}{1 + (0.12/12)} \right)^{360}} \right] \quad \text{30 years}$$

$$= \$2571.53.$$

So, the total interest paid is $360(\$2571.53) - \$250{,}000 = \$675{,}750.80$.

f. The monthly payment is

$$M = \$250{,}000 \left[\frac{0.12/12}{1 - \left(\dfrac{1}{1 + (0.12/12)} \right)^{480}} \right] \quad \text{40 years}$$

$$= \$2521.25.$$

So, the total interest paid is $480(\$2521.25) - \$250{,}000 = \$960{,}200.00$.

g. No. It can be concluded that as the annual percentage rate increases, total interest paid over the term of the loan does not increase at the same rate. In all examples so far, the total interest paid has increased by a greater factor than the APR.

Example 3 Instructor Notes

A spreadsheet was used in Example 3 to make an amortization table. (See *http://math.andyou.com/content/06/03/data/mthu_data_0603_276_03.xls.*) This is a useful method for homeowners who are trying to keep up with their mortgage balance, as well as their home's equity.

To access a home's equity, a homeowner can obtain a second mortgage. A second mortgage is a loan that uses the home as collateral to guarantee repayment and allows the homeowner to receive the full amount at once and to repay it over a fixed period of time. A homeowner can also obtain a home equity line of credit (HELOC). A HELOC is a loan that uses the home as collateral to guarantee repayment and is structured as a revolving line of credit, similar to a credit card: the lender agrees to lend a maximum amount of money within an agreed period of time, and the borrower can use the entire credit line, or borrow specific amounts from time to time. The interest rate on a HELOC is generally variable, although some lenders offer fixed rate HELOCs. For more information, read "What you should know about home equity lines of credit" at *http://www.federalreserve.gov/pubs/equity/equity_english.htm.*

Checkpoint Solution

c. An amortization schedule showing the effect of the additional $100 monthly payment is shown at *http://math.andyou.com/content/06/03/data/mthu_data_0603_276_03a.xls.*

	A	B	C	D	E	F
1	Payment Number	Balance before Payment	Interest on Balance	Monthly Payment	Extra Payment	Balance after Payment
2	1	$250,000.00	$1,250.00	$1,498.88	$100.00	$249,651.12
3	2	$249,651.12	$1,248.26	$1,498.88	$100.00	$249,300.50
4	3	$249,300.50	$1,246.50	$1,498.88	$100.00	$248,948.12
5	4	$248,948.12	$1,244.74	$1,498.88	$100.00	$248,593.98
6	5	$248,593.98	$1,242.97	$1,498.88	$100.00	$248,238.07
303	302	$6,670.53	$33.35	$1,498.88	$100.00	$5,105.00
304	303	$5,105.00	$25.53	$1,498.88	$100.00	$3,531.65
305	304	$3,531.65	$17.66	$1,498.88	$100.00	$1,950.42
306	305	$1,950.42	$9.75	$1,498.88	$100.00	$361.30
307	306	$361.30	$1.81	$363.10	$0.00	$0.00
308	Total			$457,521.50	$30,500.00	

You pay off the mortgage after 306 months, which is 4.5 years sooner.

d. By making the additional payments, you paid a total of $457,521.50 + $30,500.00 = $488.021.50. This is a savings of $539,596.80 − $488,021.50 = $51,575.30.

Example 4 Instructor Notes

The spreadsheet in Example 4 is available at
http://math.andyou.com/content/06/03/data/mthu_data_0603_277_04.xls.

Examples 2, 3, and 4 show several different ways to pay for a $250,000 mortgage. The table below compares the different ways.

Example	Term	Monthly Payment	Extra Payment or Balloon Payment	Total Payment	Total Interest
2(a)	20 years	$1791.08	None	$429,859.20	$179,859.20
2(b)	30 years	$1498.88	None	$539,596.80	$289,596.80
2(c)	40 years	$1375.53	None	$660,254.40	$410,254.40
3	30 years	$1548.88	$50.00 per month	$510,932.87	$260,932.87
4	10 years	$1498.88	$209,214.31 balloon payment	$389,079.91	$139,079.47

120($1498.88) + $209,214.31

Checkpoint Solution

Your monthly payment is

$$ M = \$200,000 \left[\frac{0.065/12}{1 - \left(\dfrac{1}{1 + (0.065/12)} \right)^{240}} \right] = \$1491.15. $$

You could also use Excel's built-in payment function, pmt(), to find the monthly payment. A spreadsheet showing the amortization schedule is shown below.
(See *http://math.andyou.com/content/06/03/data/mthu_data_0603_277_04a.xls.*)

	A	B	C	D	E
1	Payment Number	Balance before Payment	Interest on Balance	Monthly Payment	Balance after Payment
2	1	$200,000.00	$1,083.33	$1,491.15	$199,592.19
3	2	$199,592.19	$1,081.12	$1,491.15	$199,182.17
4	3	$199,182.17	$1,078.90	$1,491.15	$198,769.92
5	4	$198,769.92	$1,076.67	$1,491.15	$198,355.45
6	5	$198,355.45	$1,074.43	$1,491.15	$197,938.73
57	56	$173,952.65	$942.24	$1,491.15	$173,403.75
58	57	$173,403.75	$939.27	$1,491.15	$172,851.87
59	58	$172,851.87	$936.28	$1,491.15	$172,297.01
60	59	$172,297.01	$933.28	$1,491.15	$171,739.13
61	60	$171,739.13	$930.25	$1,491.15	$171,178.24
62	Total		$60,647.02		

The balloon payment is $171,178.24. The total interest paid is $60,647.02.

Example 5 Instructor Notes

Ask students if they conclude from Example 5 that it costs more to buy than to rent. In some cases, it does. Of course, there are many situations when buying is less expensive than renting. The point is that either buying or renting is expensive, and the advantages of one over the other demand careful consideration. In general, the longer a person plans to live in a home, the more advantageous buying becomes.

You can compare the costs of buying and renting using the calculator at *http://www.ginniemae.gov/rent_vs_buy/rent_vs_buy_calc.asp?Section=YPTH.*

Checkpoint Solution

Sample answer:

a. An important thing to consider when choosing to buy or rent is your own lifestyle and personal preferences. Some benefits of renting are not worrying about property values rising or falling and the convenience of not having to fix it yourself when the roof leaks or the plumbing malfunctions. Benefits of buying include being able to make whatever modifications you want, have pets, make more noise, and not having to worry about getting kicked out when your lease ends.

    You should also consider that you may not be able to find similar homes available to rent and buy in the same area. If you do, even small distances apart can have a big effect on the amount you spend on transportation during your years there.

b. I think that the home mortgage interest tax deduction unfairly favors those wealthy enough to afford buying homes. People with high incomes are likely to buy homes and those with low incomes are more likely to rent. Even middle class people with mortgages are likely to take the standard tax deduction and not even benefit from the mortgage interest deduction. Although the income tax system of the U.S. is supposed to be progressive, this tax deduction disproportionally helps the wealthy. The typical defense is that the tax deduction gives incentive for home ownership, and high rates of home ownership are good in general. But there is little evidence that shows it actually gives this incentive.

Example 6 Instructor Notes

Section 6.3 illustrates some of the complexities of home mortgages. After the housing bubble of the 1990s and 2000s, new federal rules went into effect in 2010 to help consumers. One of the new rules requires mortgage lenders to provide consumers a good faith estimate. (See *http://portal.hud.gov/hudportal/documents/huddoc?id=gfestimate.pdf*.) The good faith estimate encourages consumers to shop for the best loan and aids them in comparing loans. There are also online tools, such as this mortgage comparison calculator at *https://www.federalreserve.gov/apps/mortcalc/*, to help consumers.

Checkpoint Solution

Foreclosures are bad for banks since they lose money if they can't get enough by selling the house to pay off the mortgage balance. They also lose resources plus even more money dealing with the legal mess that results from foreclosing a home.

Section 6.4   Savings & Retirement Plans

Example 1 Instructor Notes

The interest rates used in Chapter 6 are mainly for illustrative purposes and do not necessarily reflect what is currently available in the U.S. marketplace. You can use an online resource, such as *bankrate.com*, to investigate current rates.

To find a balance compounded monthly using a calculator, have students apply formula

$$A = P\left(1 + \frac{r}{12}\right)^n.$$

On page 284, the formula for the account balance is for interest compounded monthly. The formula for quarterly compounding is

$$A = P\left(1 + \frac{r}{4}\right)^n \qquad \text{Interest compounded quarterly}$$

where n is the number of quarters the interest is compounded. (Note that 3 months = 1 quarter.) The formula for daily compounding is

$$A = P\left(1 + \frac{r}{365}\right)^n \qquad \text{Interest compounded daily}$$

where n is the number of days the interest is compounded. The formula for annual compounding is given in the Math Help for page 285.

Checkpoint Solution

c. The balance on her 18th birthday is

$$A = P\left(1 + \frac{r}{12}\right)^n \qquad \boxed{12(18)}$$

$$= \$5000\left(1 + \frac{0.10}{12}\right)^{216}$$

$$= \$30.023.47.$$

d. The balance on her 26th birthday is

$$A = P\left(1 + \frac{r}{12}\right)^n \qquad \boxed{12(26)}$$

$$= \$5000\left(1 + \frac{0.10}{12}\right)^{312}$$

$$= \$66,597.32.$$

Example 2 Instructor Notes

In Example 1, the formula for the account balance is for interest compounded monthly. In Example 2, however, the balances are calculated for interest compounded annually. The balance A in a savings account with a principal of P, for n years at an annual percentage rate of r (in decimal form), compounded annually, is

$$A = P(1 + r)^n. \quad \text{Interest compounded annually}$$

This formula is used to find the account balances in Example 2.

a. Let $P = \$4444.44$, $r = 0.05$, and $n = 100$.

$$A = \$4444.44(1 + 0.05)^{100} = \$4444.44(1.05)^{100} = \$584{,}449.45$$

After 100 years, Benjamin Franklin expected each account balance to have about $584,449.

b. Let $P = \$100{,}000$, $r = 0.041$, and $n = 100$.

$$A = \$100{,}000(1 + 0.041)^{100} = \$100{,}000(1.041)^{100} = \$5{,}559{,}976.44$$

In 1991, the account balance for Boston was about $5,559,976.

c. Let $P = \$40{,}000$, $r = 0.041$, and $n = 100$.

$$A = \$40{,}000(1 + 0.041)^{100} = \$40{,}000(1.041)^{100} = \$2{,}223{,}990.57$$

In 1991, the account balance for Philadelphia was about $2,223,991.

To obtain the estimate of what Franklin intended for both cities to have in 1991, first find 25% of the result of part (a). He expected each city to have $0.25 \times \$584{,}449 = \$146{,}112.25$ in 1891.

Then, using the formula $A = P(1 + r)^n$, where $P = \$146{,}112.25$, $r = 0.05$, and $n = 100$, the amount Franklin expected for one city in 1991 was $A = \$146{,}112.25(1 + 0.05)^{100} = \$19{,}213{,}944.66$. So, Franklin expected the account balance for both cities to be about $38,427,890 in 1991.

Students can read Benjamin Franklin's last will and testament by visiting The Franklin Institute. (See *http://sln.fi.edu/franklin/family/lastwill.html*.)

Checkpoint Solution

Using the graph on page 165, the CPI in 1790 appears to be about 10 and the CPI in 1991 appears to be about 140. So, the approximate value of $5.6 million (1991) in 1790 dollars is

$$\$5{,}600{,}000\left(\frac{10}{140}\right) = \$400{,}000.$$

Example 3 Instructor Notes

Have students find a balance in an increasing annuity using their calculators, applying the following steps for the formula

$$A = M\left[\frac{[1 + (r/12)]^n - 1}{r/12}\right].$$

1. Divide r by 12 and add 1.
2. Raise to the nth power.
3. Subtract 1.
4. Divide by $(r/12)$.
5. Multiply by M.
6. Round to the nearest cent.

Checkpoint Solution

d. The balance after 45 years at 4%, compounded monthly, is

$$A = M\left[\frac{(1 + r/12)^n - 1}{r/12}\right]$$

$$= \$100\left[\frac{(1 + 0.04/12)^{540} - 1}{0.04/12}\right]$$

$$= \$150,946.97.$$

e. The balance after 45 years at 6%, compounded monthly, is

$$A = M\left[\frac{(1 + r/12)^n - 1}{r/12}\right]$$

$$= \$100\left[\frac{(1 + 0.06/12)^{540} - 1}{0.06/12}\right]$$

$$= \$275,599.26.$$

f. The balance after 45 years at 8%, compounded monthly, is

$$A = M\left[\frac{(1 + r/12)^n - 1}{r/12}\right]$$

$$= \$100\left[\frac{(1 + 0.08/12)^{540} - 1}{0.08/12}\right]$$

$$= \$527,453.99.$$

Example 4 Instructor Notes

In Example 4, a spreadsheet was used to estimate the balance in the 401(k) plan.
(See *http://math.andyou.com/content/06/04/data/mthu_data_0604_287_04.xls*.) There
are also many websites that offer retirement calculators like those shown below.

- 401(k) Planning: *http://www.401kplanning.org/calculators-tools/401k-savings-calculator/*

- AARP: *http://www.aarp.org/work/retirement-planning/401k_calculator/*

- Bankrate.com: *http://www.bankrate.com/calculators/retirement/*
  401-k-retirement-calculator.aspx

Checkpoint Solution

You will be 59 at the end of 37 years.

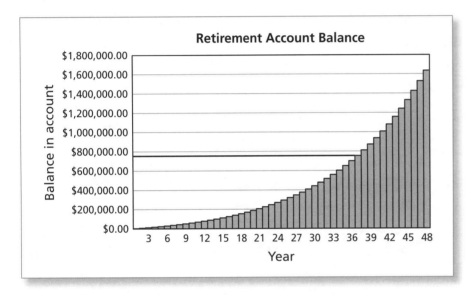

The account balance appears to be about $750,000 after 37 years. So with interest the total balance
at the end of the year will be about $750,000 + $750,000(0.06) = $795,000.

Example 5 Instructor Notes

In Example 5, a spreadsheet was used to estimate how much you can withdraw. (See *http://math.andyou.com/content/06/04/data/mthu_data_0604_288_05.xls*.) There are also many websites that offer retirement income calculators like those shown below.

- Ameriprise Financial: *http://budgeting-investing.ameriprise.com/ budgeting-and-forecasting/calculators/RetirementIncome.asp*

- EstimatePension.com: *http://www.estimatepension.com/ Retirement-Withdrawal-Calculator.aspx*

- Money-Zine.com: *http://www.money-zine.com/Calculators/ Retirement-Calculators/Retirement-Withdrawal-Calculator/*

Checkpoint Solution

For parts (a)–(c), students can use the following spreadsheet to answer the questions. *http://math.andyou.com/content/06/04/data/mthu_data_0604_288_05a.xls*

a. Using the spreadsheet with a beginning balance of $1,000,000, 5% interest, monthly withdrawals of $5833.33, and duration 25 years, you find that the balance will run out during the 299th month. This plan would last you almost 25 years, or until you are 93 years old.

b. Using the spreadsheet with a beginning balance of $1,000,000, 4% interest, monthly withdrawals of $5000, and duration 30 years, you find that the balance will run out during the 329th month. This plan will last you about $27\frac{1}{2}$ years, or until you are 95 years old.

c. Using the spreadsheet with a beginning balance of $1,000,000, 6% interest, monthly withdrawals of $8333.33, and duration 16 years, you find that the balance will run out during the 183rd month. This plan will last you a little over 15 years, or until you are 83 years old.

Sample answer:

I would choose option A. It pays a sufficient amount and would allow me to live to be 93 which is about 10 years longer than my life expectancy would be. If I was getting pretty old and was still in good health I would consider reducing my withdrawals so the account would last longer. If I had the option, instead of one of these retirement plans I would choose one that allowed for increasing withdrawals to account for inflation.

Example 6 Instructor Notes

There are many assumptions used to create the spreadsheet in Example 6. (See *http://math.andyou.com/content/06/04/data/mthu_data_0604_289_06.xls*.) One important assumption is how long you can expect to live. According to data compiled by the Social Security Administration (SSA) at *http://www.ssa.gov/planners/lifeexpectancy.htm*:

- A man reaching age 65 today can expect to live, on average, until age 83.

- A woman turning age 65 today can expect to live, on average, until age 85.

Also, about one out of every four 65-year-olds today will live past age 90, and one out of 10 will live past age 95. You can use the SSA's life expectancy calculator (*http://www.ssa.gov/OACT/population/longevity.html*) to estimate how long you might live. You can also estimate your Social Security benefits (*http://www.ssa.gov/estimator/*). To estimate how much you need to save to fund your retirement, make a spreadsheet or try using an online calculator (*http://www.choosetosave.org/ballpark/*).

Checkpoint Solution

Sample answer:

Defined contribution plans are subject to market risk. If someone has a defined contribution plan and their investments do poorly, it will negatively affect their retirement income. A defined benefit plan, on the other hand, pays the same amount to the retiree no matter what. If the market doesn't do well, the employer will be the only one hurt since they still have to pay out the promised amount. This risk is the reason many companies have defined contribution plans instead. The government has much more money to work with than the average company and people will always be paying taxes, so market risk isn't as big of a problem for them. For this reason, government jobs are much more likely to have defined benefit plans than private sector jobs.

Chapter 7

Section 7.1   Linear Patterns

Example 1 Instructor Notes

Point out to students that in mathematics, the term "line" means "straight line." In Example 1(a), discuss how a scatter plot can be useful in detecting patterns in data. To use a spreadsheet to create a scatter plot similar to the one in Example 1(a), use the steps below. (See *http://math.andyou.com/content/07/01/data/mthu_data_0701_302_01.xls.*)

1. Create a spreadsheet like the one shown.
2. Select cells A2 through A12 and B2 through B12.
3. From the **Insert** menu, choose **Chart . . ..**
4. Select the **Standard Types** tab. **Under Chart** type:, select **XY (Scatter).** Click **Next.**
5. Click **Next** again.
6. Select the **Titles** tab. Enter "Men's Height" for **Chart title:,** "Femur length (in.)" for **Value (X) axis:,** and "Height (in.)" for **Value (Y) axis:.**
7. Select the **Legend** tab. Uncheck **Show legend.** Click **Finish.**

Checkpoint Solution

c. The spreadsheet shows the relationship between femur length and height in women. (See *http://math.andyou.com/content/07/01/data/mthu_data_0701_302_01a.xls.*)

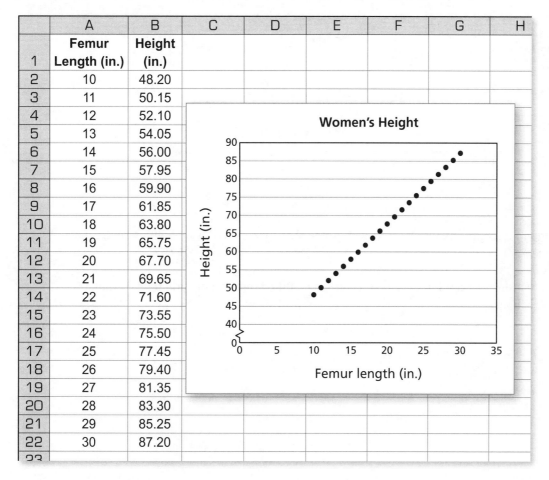

d. From the graph, you can see that all the data points lie on a line.

Example 2 Instructor Notes

To use a spreadsheet to create a scatter plot similar to the one in Example 2(a), have students use the steps given in the Math Help at *Math.andYou.com*.
(See *http://math.andyou.com/content/07/01/data/mthu_data_0701_303_02.xls*.)

Checkpoint Solution

A table showing the relationship between foot length and women's shoe size is shown in the spreadsheet below.
(See *http://math.andyou.com/content/07/01/data/mthu_data_0701_303_02a.xls*.)

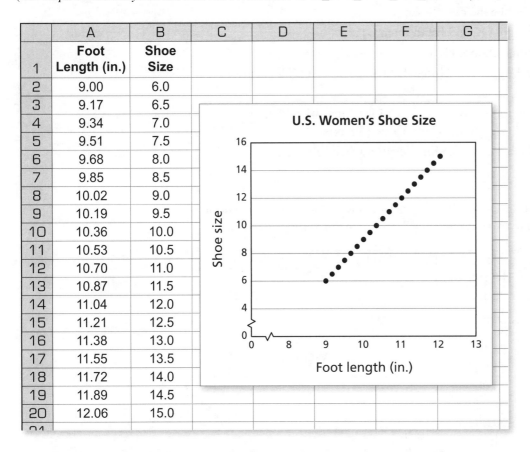

	A	B	C	D	E	F	G
	Foot Length (in.)	**Shoe Size**					
1							
2	9.00	6.0					
3	9.17	6.5					
4	9.34	7.0					
5	9.51	7.5					
6	9.68	8.0					
7	9.85	8.5					
8	10.02	9.0					
9	10.19	9.5					
10	10.36	10.0					
11	10.53	10.5					
12	10.70	11.0					
13	10.87	11.5					
14	11.04	12.0					
15	11.21	12.5					
16	11.38	13.0					
17	11.55	13.5					
18	11.72	14.0					
19	11.89	14.5					
20	12.06	15.0					

c. Each time the foot length changes by 0.17 inches, the shoe size increases by half a size. So the pattern is linear.

d. Using the spreadsheet to graph the data, you can see that the points on the graph lie on a line. So the graph is linear.

Example 3 Instructor Notes

Have students use a spreadsheet to draw a "best-fitting line" similar to the one in Example 3 using the steps below.
(See *http://math.andyou.com/content/07/01/data/mthu_data_0701_304_03.xls*.)

1. Create a spreadsheet like the one shown.
2. Select cells A2 through A20 and B2 through B20.
3. From the **Insert** menu, choose **Chart . . ..**
4. Select the **Standard Types** tab. Under **Chart type:**, select **XY (Scatter).** Then click **Next.**
5. Click **Next** again.
6. Select the **Titles** tab. Enter "Ages of Women at First Marriage (U.S.)" for **Chart title:**, "Year" for **Value (X) axis:**, and "Age" for **Value (Y) axis:**.
7. Select the **Legend** tab. **Uncheck Show** legend. Click **Finish.**
8. Select the scatter plot. From the **Chart** menu, choose **Add Trendline . . ..**
9. Select the **Type** tab. Under **Trend/Regression** type, choose **Linear.**
10. Select the **Options** tab. Under **Forecast,** enter 10 for **Forward.** Click **OK.**

	A	B
1	Year	Age
2	1960	20.3
3	1965	20.6
4	1970	20.8
5	1975	21.1
6	1980	22.0
7	1985	23.3
8	1990	23.9
9	1995	24.5
10	2000	25.1
11	2005	25.3
12	2010	26.1

Checkpoint Solution

From the approximate best fit line, it looks like the marriage rate will be about 23 marriages per 1000 unmarried women in 2020.

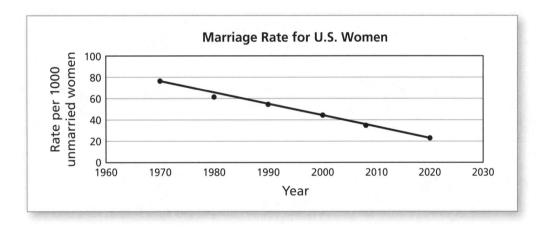

Example 3 shows that women have been getting married at later ages over the past few decades. The data in this checkpoint show that the percentage of women getting married at all has been declining. It makes sense that with more women waiting until they're older to get married, fewer total women would get married.

Example 4 Instructor Notes

Review the table in Example 4. Point out that it shows the distance (in miles) the Canada Geese have traveled since February 10th. For example, on April 30th, the Canada Geese have traveled 1200 miles since February 10th.

For more information about Canada Geese, students can visit The Cornell Lab of Ornithology website, All About Birds. (See *http://www.allaboutbirds.org/guide/Canada_Goose/id/ac*.)

Checkpoint Solution

Use the Chapter 1 (page 6) formula, $t = \dfrac{d}{r}$, where t is time, d is distance, and r is rate.

$$t = \frac{6000 \text{ miles}}{4 \text{ miles/hour}}$$

$$= 1500 \text{ hours}$$

It takes the gray whale 1500 hours, or about 2 months to journey from Baja California, Mexico to the Bering Sea.

Example 5 Instructor Notes

Review the concept of proportional patterns. Make sure students understand that when one variable is a constant multiple of another variable, the pattern with the two variables is proportional. Tell students that if they take a more advanced course in mathematics, they may see different words used, such as the two variables are "directly proportional" or "show direct variation." They might also see an equation, such as

$$y = kx$$

where k is a nonzero number called the constant of proportionality, and the equation can be read as "y is directly proportional to x."

While this text does not require students to write this equation, you may want to point out that writing the equation can help students to make a table of values. For instance, in Example 5, the pattern is "the distance the spring stretches is 3/2 times the weight in pounds." So, the constant of proportionality is $k = 3/2$ and

$$\text{Distance} = \frac{3}{2} \times \text{weight} \quad \text{or} \quad y = \frac{3}{2}x.$$

Using this equation, students can create the table below.

x	0	$\frac{1}{2}$	1	$\frac{3}{2}$	2	$\frac{5}{2}$	3	$\frac{7}{2}$	4
y	0	$\frac{3}{4}$	$\frac{3}{2}$	$\frac{9}{4}$	3	$\frac{15}{4}$	$\frac{9}{2}$	$\frac{21}{4}$	6

Checkpoint Solution

c. Elasticity is the tendency of a material to return to its original shape. This spring is more elastic since the same weight causes it to stretch less.

d. You can see that the distance in inches the spring stretches is $\frac{3}{4}$ times the weight in pounds.

So if the weight is 7 pounds, the distance stretched is $\frac{3}{4} \times 7 = \frac{21}{4}$ inches.

Example 6 Instructor Notes

Another way of analyzing the statement in Example 6 is to calculate the proportion

$$\frac{\text{Skull height}}{\text{Total height}}$$

for the various ages in the chart.

One year: $\dfrac{6}{4 \times 6} = \dfrac{1}{4}$

3 years: $\dfrac{6.5}{5 \times 6.5} = \dfrac{1}{5}$

5 years: $\dfrac{7}{6 \times 7} = \dfrac{1}{6}$

10 years: $\dfrac{7.5}{7 \times 7.5} = \dfrac{1}{7}$

15 years: $\dfrac{9}{7.5 \times 9} = \dfrac{1}{7.5}$

Adult: $\dfrac{9}{8 \times 9} = \dfrac{1}{8}$

The ratios are not the same. So, the total height is not a constant multiple of the skull height.

Checkpoint Solution

The length of the lizard's head appears to be about an eighth of the length of its body. So the ratio of skull length to total length is approximately $\dfrac{1}{8}$.

Section 7.2   Exponential Patterns

Example 1 Instructor Notes

In Example 1, the differences of consecutive volumes are not the same.

$$0.889 - 0.836 = 0.053 \quad 0.945 - 0.889 = 0.056 \quad 1.005 - 0.945 = 0.060$$

$$1.068 - 1.005 = 0.063 \quad 1.135 - 1.068 = 0.067 \quad 1.207 - 1.135 = 0.072$$

Also, each difference is greater than the preceding difference, which means the rate of increase is increasing. So, you can conclude that the pattern is not linear. [Review from Section 7.1 that a sequence of numbers has a linear pattern when each successive number increases (or decreases) by the same amount.]

Checkpoint Solution

A spreadsheet showing the volume for shells with up to 24 chambers is shown below. (See *http://math.andyou.com/content/07/02/data/mthu_data_0702_312_01a.xls*.)

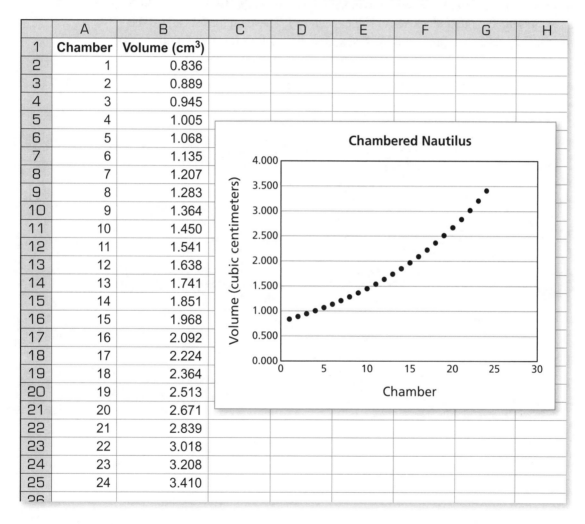

	A	B	C	D	E	F	G	H
1	Chamber	Volume (cm³)						
2	1	0.836						
3	2	0.889						
4	3	0.945						
5	4	1.005						
6	5	1.068						
7	6	1.135						
8	7	1.207						
9	8	1.283						
10	9	1.364						
11	10	1.450						
12	11	1.541						
13	12	1.638						
14	13	1.741						
15	14	1.851						
16	15	1.968						
17	16	2.092						
18	17	2.224						
19	18	2.364						
20	19	2.513						
21	20	2.671						
22	21	2.839						
23	22	3.018						
24	23	3.208						
25	24	3.410						
26								

The graph curves upward. The vertical difference between consecutive data points increases as the number of chambers increases. This is consistent with the definition of exponential growth; if each successive number increases by the same percent, they will increase by greater and greater amounts.

Example 2 Instructor Notes

In Example 2, explain that the populations shown in the graph are estimates and may differ slightly from populations listed by other sources.

In the solution to Example 2, note that the ratios are all approximately equal to 1.40. Review from Section 1.3 that you can use a percent to represent change. Work through some examples from page 313 with students. For instance, you can write 1.40 as 140% and say that the 4500 B.C. world population was 140% of the 5000 B.C. world population. Or, you can say that the world population increased by 40%. In general, you can say that the world population was increasing by about 40% every 500 years from 5000 B.C. through 1500 A.D.

Checkpoint Solution

No, if the population had followed the pattern, there would have been about $423(1.40^7) \approx 595$ million people in the world. Instead the population increased by over 1300% to about 6.07 billion. The agricultural and industrial revolutions of the 17th, 18th, and 19th centuries caused life expectancy to increase dramatically. Improvements in health care from the 19th century through modern times have caused continued increases in life expectancy. These increases caused the population to grow much faster than predicted by the exponential pattern it followed up to 1500.

Example 3 Instructor Notes

In the solution to Example 3, note that the average of the ratios is about 1.50.

$$\frac{1.58 + 1.81 + 1.50 + 1.34 + 1.43}{5} \approx 1.5 \qquad \text{Round to the nearest tenth.}$$

Assuming this ratio was true for 2011 and 2006 you can estimate the 2011 population by multiplying the 2006 population by 1.5.

$$\begin{aligned} \text{2011 population} &= \text{2006 population} \times 1.5 \\ &= 9789 \times 1.5 \\ &\approx 14{,}700 \qquad \text{Round to the nearest hundred.} \end{aligned}$$

So, you can estimate that the population increased to about 14,700 nesting pairs.

Note the rounding used in the calculations above. Students can review rounding of numbers in a real-life context in Section 1.2.

Checkpoint Solution

If the population continued to increase by 50% every 5 years, there would be about $(1.5)(1.5)(9789) \approx 22{,}000$ nesting pairs in 2016.

Example 4 Instructor Notes

In the solution to Example 4, note that the average of the ratios is about 0.7.

$$\frac{0.568 + 0.480 + 0.833 + 0.760}{4} \approx 0.7 \qquad \text{Round to the nearest tenth.}$$

So, it appears that, every 5 years, the tiger population is about 70% what is was 5 years ago.

Checkpoint Solution

Estimating the bar heights from the graph in Example 4, the estimated percents of remaining tiger habitat from 1985 through 2010 are:

Year	Estimated Percent of Remaining Tiger Habitat
1985	23%
1990	16%
1995	12%
2000	10%
2005	8%
2010	7%

$$\frac{16\%}{23\%} \approx 0.696 \qquad \frac{12\%}{16\%} = 0.750$$

$$\frac{10\%}{12\%} \approx 0.833 \qquad \frac{8\%}{10\%} = 0.800$$

$$\frac{7\%}{8\%} = 0.875$$

Although the rate of decrease varies, it appears that the percent of remaining tiger habitat decreases to about 80% of what it was 5 years ago. This means that the rate of decrease is about 20% every 5 years.

Example 5 Instructor Notes

Here are some general observations about the graph in Example 5.

- The graph is increasing from left to right.

- The point of maximum growth occurs at one-half of the maximum sustainable population.

- Before reaching the point of maximum growth, the growth rate is increasing.

- After reaching the point of maximum growth, the growth rate is decreasing.

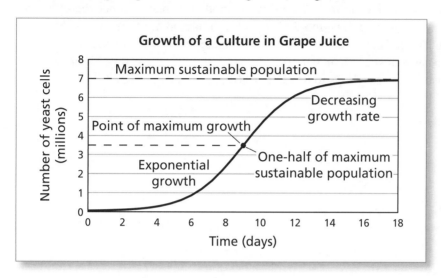

Checkpoint Solution

Sample answer:

I think it's possible that Malthus' prediction will come true, that population will grow exponentially until a permanent poor class is created due to lack of resources, but I don't think it's inevitable. Many developed countries have declining fertility rates and the percentage of people living in poverty has decreased throughout the world recently. Many predict the world population will level off around the year 2050. It's also possible that Malthus underestimated the ability of science to create new means of subsistence. Great advancements in agricultural efficiency have been made since his time and scientists are currently working on lab-grown meat. I also think that through improved awareness of the population problem and better education and access to birth control, even areas where population growth is the highest and poverty is the worst, like Sub-Saharan Africa, could improve before a Malthusian catastrophe happens.

Example 6 Instructor Notes

Example 6 introduces a very common mathematical term: probability. In the context of Example 6, probability is a number that represents the likelihood that the mother and baby fur seals locate each other. Note that the probabilities are between 0 and 1, including 0 and 1. Point out that probabilities can be written as fractions, decimals, or percents. Probability is presented in greater detail in Chapter 8.

Checkpoint Solution

The pup's chance of survival decreases as the number of trips by the mother increases. Since there is a chance of failure on any given trip, there will be more chances for failure on multiple trips. For example, if the pup does nothing and the mother calls 17 times per minute, there will be about a 95% chance of success, but the chance of success on two trips drops to $(0.95)(0.95) = 0.9025$, or 90.25%. On three trips, the chance of success drops to $(0.95)(0.95)(0.95) \approx 0.857$, or 85.7%, and so on.

Section 7.3   Quadratic Patterns

Example 1 Instructor Notes

In Example 1, discuss with students how to tell that the pattern is not linear. Because the first differences are not the same, the pattern cannot be linear. Also, notice that each difference is greater than the preceding difference, which means the rate of increase is increasing. This also supports the conclusion that the pattern is not linear. [Review from Section 7.1 that a sequence of numbers has a linear pattern when each successive number increases (or decreases) by the same amount.]

Explain that the "speed" listed in the table is the velocity of the bat when it makes contact with the ball. Also, the situation in Example 1 has been simplified by not considering several factors, such as air resistance and air density.

Checkpoint Solution

Continue the pattern from when speed is 115 mph. The second difference is a constant 1, so the first difference between 115 mph and 120 mph increases to 33, and the first difference between 120 mph and 125 mph increases to 34, making the distance equal to $397 + 33 + 34 = 464$ when speed is 125 mph.

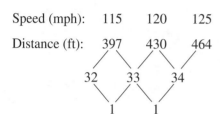

Speed (mph):   115   120   125

Distance (ft):   397   430   464

Instructor Notes and Checkpoint Solutions   **167**

Example 2 Instructor Notes

Tell students that the graph of the curve in Example 2(b) is parabolic and is called a *parabola*. Students can view some sample graphs of parabolas in the Math Help at *Math.andYou.com* to see that parabolas are U-shaped graphs. When graphing a model based on real-life data, point out that you might only see part of the "U."

Checkpoint Solution

Use a spreadsheet to make a scatter plot and column graph.
(See *http://math.andyou.com/content/07/03/data/mthu_data_0703_325_02a.xls*.)

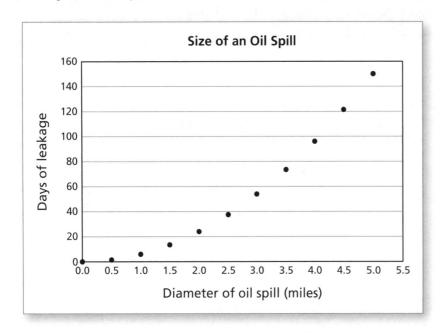

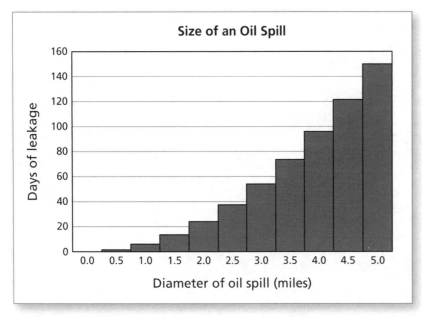

Sample answer:

I think the scatter plot shows the data the best because it makes it easier to visualize the relationship between the size of the oil spill and the number of days. Also it is easier to imagine a curve fitting those data points and using it to predict future data.

Example 3 Instructor Notes

Students can use a spreadsheet to draw a "best-fitting line" and a "best-fitting quadratic" similar to the graph in Example 3 using the steps below.
(See *http://math.andyou.com/content/07/03/data/mthu_data_0703_326_03.xls.*)

1. Create a spreadsheet like the one at the link above.
2. Select cells A2 through A53 and B2 through B53.
3. From the **Insert** menu, choose **Chart . . ..**
4. Select the **Standard Types** tab. Under **Chart type:**, select **XY (Scatter).** Then click **Next.**
5. Click **Next** again.
6. Select the **Titles** tab. Enter "Carbon Dioxide Levels in Earth's Atmosphere" for **Chart title:,** "Year" for **Value (X) axis:,** and " CO_2 parts per million " for **Value (Y) axis:.**
7. Select the **Legend** tab. Uncheck **Show legend.** Click **Finish.**
8. Select the scatter plot. From the **Chart** menu, choose Add **Trendline . . ..**
9. Select the **Type** tab. Under **Trend/Regression type,** choose **Linear.**
10. Select the **Options** tab. Under **Forecast,** enter 40 for **Forward.** Click **OK.**
11. Select the scatter plot. From the **Chart** menu, choose **Add Trendline . . ..**
12. Select the **Type** tab. Under **Trend/Regression type,** choose **Polynomial.** Enter 2 for **Order:.**
13. Select the **Options** tab. Under **Forecast,** enter 40 for **Forward.** Click **OK.**

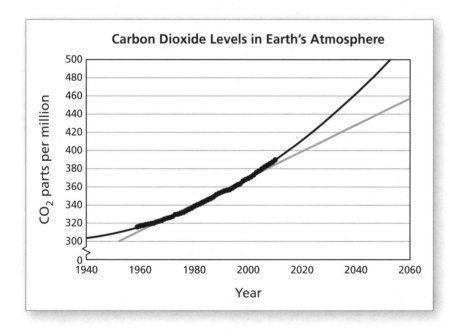

Checkpoint Solution

The patterns in both harvests appear to be quadratic. The number of blades of grass increases as the nitrogen level increases at first, but eventually starts to decrease. This means that initially more nitrogen is good for growing grass, but there is a point where it doesn't help anymore. After that point, increased nitrogen hurts grass growth.

Example 4 Instructor Notes

Looking at the graph in Example 4, students might think that the pattern is exponential. Have them consider the ratios of consecutive terms.

$$\frac{100}{25} = 4 \qquad \frac{225}{100} = 2.25 \qquad \frac{400}{225} \approx 1.78 \qquad \frac{625}{400} \approx 1.56$$

$$\frac{900}{625} = 1.44 \qquad \frac{1225}{900} \approx 1.36 \qquad \frac{1600}{1225} \approx 1.31$$

The ratios of consecutive terms are not equal. So, the pattern is *not* exponential.

Checkpoint Solution

c. The table in Example 4 says that the speed needed to get 100,000 pounds of lift is 150 mph.

d. The quadratic pattern in Example 4 shows that it takes higher speeds to lift heavier planes. It also takes a longer time to reach a higher speed, so bigger planes need longer runways so they'll have enough time to accelerate to the necessary speed.

Example 5 Instructor Notes

In Example 5, the ratios of consecutive terms are not equal.

$$\frac{16}{4} = 4 \qquad \frac{36}{16} = 2.25 \qquad \frac{64}{36} \approx 1.78 \qquad \frac{100}{64} \approx 1.56$$

$$\frac{144}{100} = 1.44 \qquad \frac{196}{144} \approx 1.36 \qquad \frac{256}{196} \approx 1.31$$

So, the pattern is *not* exponential.

Checkpoint Solution

Rewrite the table using 1-second intervals. Each first difference tells you how much the distance increased during 1 second, or the speed of the shot put ball. Each second difference tells you how much the speed of the shot put ball increased during 1 second.

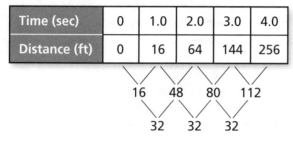

Time (sec)	0	1.0	2.0	3.0	4.0
Distance (ft)	0	16	64	144	256

First differences: 16   48   80   112   changes in distance

Second differences: 32   32   32   changes in speed

As you can see, the speed is increasing by 32 feet per second each second. You can summarize this information in a table. (Note that at 0 seconds, the speed is 0 feet per second because you have not dropped the ball yet.)

	Time (sec)	Change in Speed (ft/sec)	Speed (ft/sec)
a.	0	--	0
b.	1	32	0 + 32 = 32
c.	2	32	32 + 32 = 64
d.	3	32	64 + 32 = 96
e.	4	32	96 + 32 = 128

Example 6 Instructor Notes

In Example 6, the ratios of consecutive terms are not equal.

$$\frac{8.61}{2.16} \approx 3.99 \qquad \frac{19.35}{8.61} \approx 2.25 \qquad \frac{34.38}{19.35} \approx 1.78$$

$$\frac{53.70}{34.38} \approx 1.56 \qquad \frac{77.31}{53.70} \approx 1.44 \qquad \frac{105.21}{77.31} \approx 1.36$$

So, the pattern is *not* exponential.

Checkpoint Solution

a. False, a linear increase in diameter causes a linear increase in circumference. From Example 6, a linear increase in circumference causes a quadratic increase in muscle strength. So, a linear increase in diameter causes a quadratic increase in muscle strength.

b. True, a quadratic increase in diameter causes a quadratic increase in circumference. From Example 6, a quadratic increase in circumference causes a linear increase in muscle strength. So, a quadratic increase in diameter causes a linear increase in muscle strength.

c. True, a linear increase in cross sectional area causes a quadratic increase in diameter. From part (b), a quadratic increase in diameter causes a linear increase in cross sectional area. So, a linear increase in cross sectional area causes a linear increase in muscle strength.

Section 7.4   Fibonacci & Other Patterns

Example 1 Instructor Notes

Although the Fibonacci sequence starts with 0 and 1, explain to your students that a general Fibonacci sequence can start with other numbers. For instance, in Example 1, the number of breeding pairs for each month starts with 1 and 1. So, the number of pairs follows the Fibonacci pattern

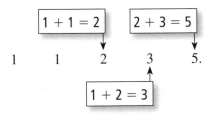

In the solution to Example 1, note that the table lists the number of breeding pairs for each month. To determine the total number of rabbits for each month, multiply the number of pairs by 2.

Checkpoint Solution

Begin by entering the data into a spreadsheet. Then create a scatter plot showing the two growth patterns. (See *http://math.andyou.com/content/07/04/data/mthu_data_0704_334_01a.xls*.)

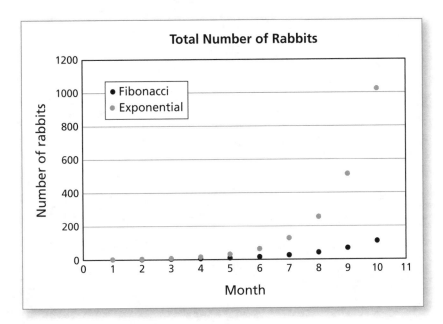

The number of rabbits with the exponential pattern is greater than or equal to that of the Fibonacci pattern at every point. With the exponential pattern, the number doubles each month while the Fibonacci sequence of rabbits increases at a slower rate.

Example 2 Instructor Notes

In Example 2, the first two bone lengths are 2 and 3. If the lengths follow a Fibonacci pattern, then the lengths should be

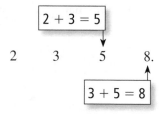

These numbers match the lengths of the bones in the x-ray, so the lengths follow a Fibonacci pattern.

Checkpoint Solution

a. The top number of the triangle is a 1. Every other number is a sum of the two numbers above it. If there is only one number above a certain number, the missing number is implied to be zero.

b. The sum of the "diagonals" shown by the red lines forms the Fibonacci sequence. The sums of the first 6 diagonals shown are 1, 1, 2, 3, 5, and 8.

Example 3 Instructor Notes

In Example 3, the drawing begins with two 1-unit squares. So, the first two numbers in the sequence are 1 and 1. You can then generate more numbers in this sequence as shown.

$1 + 1 = 2$ $\quad$ $2 + 3 = 5$ $\quad$ $5 + 8 = 13$ $\quad$ $13 + 21 = 34$

1 $\quad$ 1 $\quad$ 2 $\quad$ 3 $\quad$ 5 $\quad$ 8 $\quad$ 13 $\quad$ 21 $\quad$ 34 $\quad$ 55

$1 + 2 = 3$ $\quad$ $3 + 5 = 8$ $\quad$ $8 + 13 = 21$ $\quad$ $21 + 34 = 55$

These numbers match the ones shown in the figure in Example 3.

Checkpoint Solution

Sample answers:

a. Sunflower

b. Romanesque broccoli

c. Aloe polyphylla, or Spiral Aloe

For general information on Fibonacci spirals found in plant life, visit *world-mysteries.com* at *http://www.world-mysteries.com/sci_17.htm*.

Example 4 Instructor Notes

To make a spreadsheet similar to the one in Example 4, have students use the steps below. (See *http://math.andyou.com/content/07/04/data/mthu_data_0704_337_04.xls*.)

1. Enter the titles "Term" and "Ratio" in Row 1.
2. Enter 0 into cell A2 and 1 into cell A3.
3. Enter the formula = A2 + A3 into cell A4.
4. Select cell A4. From the **Edit** menu, choose **Copy.**
5. Select cells A5 through A21. From the **Edit** menu, choose **Paste.**
6. Enter the formula = A4/A3 into cell B4.
7. Select cell B4. From the **Edit** menu, choose **Copy.**
8. Select cells B5 through B21. From the **Edit** menu, choose **Paste.**

Checkpoint Solution

Sample answer:

Some structures that show golden ratios are the United Nations Headquarters, the Mosque of Uqba, and the Great Pyramid at Giza. Artworks showing the golden ratio include The Sacrament of the Last Supper by Salvador Dali and some of Leonardo Da Vinci's works in De Divina Proportione.

U.N. Headquarter in New York City designed by Oscar Niemeyer

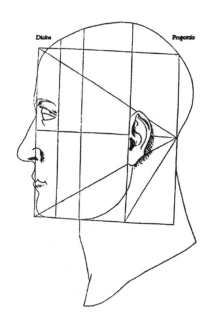

Illustration of a human head by Leonardo Da Vinci from De Divina Proportione

Example 5 Instructor Notes

In Example 5, an astronomical unit is defined as the mean distance between Earth and the Sun, or about 93 million miles.

Johannes Kepler published the laws of planetary motion based on observation. After they were published, the laws were validated by Isaac Newton (1642–1727). Further, Newton showed that each law can be deduced from a set of universal laws of motion and gravitation that govern the movement of all objects in space, including comets and satellites. For instance, consider the comet named after Edmund Halley (1656–1742), as shown in the figure. The orbit of Halley's comet is an ellipse.

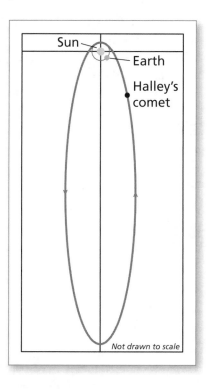

Checkpoint Solution

The completed table is below.

Planet	Mercury	Venus	Earth	Mars	Jupiter	Saturn
(Period)^2	0.058	0.378	1.000	3.538	140.707	867.715
(Mean Distance)^3	0.058	0.378	1.000	3.540	140.852	867.432

The square of the period is approximately equal to the cube of the mean distance for each planet listed, which verifies Kepler's Third Law. There are some differences, but these are most likely due to rounding or inaccuracy in measurement. Notice that the error increases as the planets' periods and distances increase.

Example 6 Instructor Notes

The 41st parallel is a circle of latitude. A circle of latitude is an imaginary east-west circle on Earth. Circles of latitude are often called parallels because they are parallel to each other.

It should be noted that during either equinox, every location in the world receives equal amounts of daylight and darkness, not just the northern hemisphere.

Checkpoint Solution

Sample answer:

The tides of the ocean can be modeled by sine waves since they come up and go down in a repeating pattern. The motion of water, light, sound, and seismic waves from an earthquake can be modeled by sine waves because they travel in waves. Oscillation such as a spring bouncing back and forth or something swinging on a rope is periodic and can be modeled by sine waves. Sunrise and sunset times are related to the hours of daylight discussed in Example 6 and can also be modeled by sine waves.

Chapter 8

Section 8.1 Assigning a Measure to Likelihood

Example 1 Instructor Notes

In Example 1, note the different ways that the probabilities can be written.

- The probability of a meteoroid hitting Earth, 0.75, can also be written as $\frac{3}{4}$ or 75%.

- The probability of Apophis hitting Earth, 0, can also be written as 0%.

- The probability of 2000 SG344 hitting Earth, $\frac{1}{435}$, can also be written as 0.0023 or 0.23%.

- The probability of 2008 TC3 hitting Earth, 1, can also be written as 100%.

Checkpoint Solution

a. Equally likely to happen or not happen; it is generally considered that there is a 50–50 chance that a given person will be male or female. So, there is a 50% chance that a family's oldest child is a girl.

b. Unlikely; Assuming there is a 50% chance that a child is a girl, there is a $(0.50)(0.50) = 0.25$ or 25% chance that both children are girls.

Example 2 Instructor Notes

According to the National Hurricane Center at *http://www.nhc.noaa.gov/*, the terms hurricane and typhoon are regionally specific names for a strong tropical cyclone. Cyclones with maximum sustained surface winds of less than 39 miles per hour are usually called tropical depressions. If the cyclone reaches winds of at least 39 miles per hour, then it is called a tropical storm (or in Australia a Category 1 cyclone with an assigned name). If winds reach 74 miles per hour, then the cyclone is called

- a hurricane in the North Atlantic Ocean region and in parts of the Northeast Pacific Ocean and the South Pacific Ocean regions.

- a typhoon in parts of the Northwest Pacific Ocean region.

- a Category 3 cyclone in parts of the Southwest Pacific Ocean and the Southeast Indian Ocean regions.

- a very severe cyclonic storm in the North Indian Ocean region.

- a tropical cyclone in the Southwest Indian Ocean region.

Checkpoint Solution

a. This voting pattern is very unlikely. There is almost no chance that every state above the given dividing line in the continental United States would vote Democratic (blue) and every state below the line would vote Republican (red). It is very unlikely even that Idaho would vote Democratic or California would vote Republican. If this scenario actually happened, the Republican Party would win with 291 electoral votes. (270 votes are needed to win the election.)

b. This voting pattern is also very unlikely. There is almost no chance that every state west of the Mississippi in the continental United States would vote Democratic and every state to the east would vote Republican. It's very unlikely even that New York would vote Republican or Texas would vote Democratic. If this scenario actually happened, the Republican Party would win with 311 electoral votes.

Example 3 Instructor Notes

You may want to explain how the probabilities are given in Example 3. Instead of using a fraction, decimal, or percent, the annual risk of being killed in a plane crash is given as "about 1 in 11 million." This is a convenient way of writing a probability that some may find easier to understand than the other ways. For instance, discuss these other ways of writing the probability 1 in 11 million.

- Fraction: $\dfrac{1}{11,000,000}$

- Decimal: 0.000000091

- Percent: 0.0000091%

Checkpoint Solution

Per 100 million passenger miles, there are about 31 motorcycle deaths, 2 plane deaths, 1.5 train deaths, and 1.5 automobile deaths. So, for the same number of miles traveled, the risk of death while riding a motorcycle is about $\dfrac{31}{2} = 15.5$ times worse than the risk while flying in a plane and about $\dfrac{31}{1.5} \approx 20.7$ times worse than the risk while riding in a train or automobile. For the same number of miles traveled, the risk of death while flying is about $\dfrac{2}{1.5} \approx 1.3$ times worse than the risk while riding in a train or automobile. Travel by train and automobile have the same risk of death.

There are 2 deaths for every 100 million airplane miles flown. So, the risk of death from taking a 2000-mile plane flight is

$$\dfrac{2}{100,000,000}(2000) = 0.00004,$$

or 0.004%. It is true that the more you fly, the more you increase the likelihood of an accident. Flying carries a certain risk of an accident. So, by flying multiple times, you take that risk over and over, increasing your overall likelihood of an accident.

Example 4 Instructor Notes

Here are some observations about the risk map shown in Example 4.

- The vertical axis represents the significance of a risk. Be sure students understand that the vertical axis displays rankings, not probabilities, where 1 is "most significant" and 0 is "least significant."

- The horizontal axis represents a risk's likelihood of occurrence.

- The risk map is divided into four quadrants, labeled I, II, III, and IV.

- Risks in Quadrant I are called primary risks because they are likely to occur and are significant in consequence.

- Risks in Quadrant II are significant in consequence. However, these risks are less likely to occur than those in Quadrant I. So, the risks in Quadrant II are second in priority after the primary risks.

- Risks in Quadrant III are unlikely to occur and are less significant. In general, these risks have the least priority compared to the others.

- Risks in Quadrant IV are less significant than those in Quadrants I and II. However, the risks in Quadrant IV are more likely to occur than those in Quadrants II and III. So, these risks have a higher priority than those in Quadrant III.

Checkpoint Solution

Sample answers:

a. Examples of prevent-at-source risks are a company's sales decreasing or its stock price falling. These are likely because sales and stock prices can change every day. They are significant because if sales decrease enough, the company may not have enough money to pay its operating expenses and if stock prices fall, investors may stop investing in the company. These events fall in quadrant I: high likelihood, high significance.

b. Examples of detect-and-monitor risks are a company's server crashing or building burning down. These events are unlikely because there are usually many safeguards in place to prevent them. They are very significant because they would prevent the company from doing its day-to-day work. These events fall in quadrant II: low likelihood, high significance.

c. An example of a monitor risk is employees missing work due to sickness and vacation. This is likely because people miss work almost everyday. It has low significance because most companies are designed to run smoothly even when some employees are missing. Employees missing work should be monitored because if too many missed work all at once, it could cause a problem. This falls in quadrant IV: high likelihood, low significance.

d. An example of a low-control risk is running out of pens or a similar office supply. This is unlikely because there are always extra pens lying around at most companies. It is insignificant because more pens could be quickly purchased at a supply store. This falls in quadrant III: low likelihood, low significance.

Example 5 Instructor Notes

There is a lot of information that an actuary may use to create a life insurance questionnaire or to set rates. For instance, consider the information below from the American Cancer Society. (See *http://www.cancer.org/Cancer/CancerBasics/lifetime-probability-of-developing-or-dying-from-cancer.*)

Cancer	Males		Females	
	Risk of developing	Risk of dying	Risk of developing	Risk of dying
Bladder	3.80%	0.85%	1.16%	0.33%
Breast	0.13%	0.03%	12.15%	2.81%
Colon and rectum	5.30%	2.17%	4.97%	2.01%
Leukemia	1.52%	1.00%	1.10%	0.71%
Lung and bronchus	7.67%	6.95%	6.35%	5.05%
Melanoma of the skin	2.36%	0.40%	1.56%	0.21%

After reviewing the above information, students may better understand why a life insurance questionnaire may ask, "Have you ever had cancer?"

Checkpoint Solution

Sample answer:

As long as your answers are kept confidential, I think it is reasonable that you are asked to supply this information. The insurance comes with your employment package. So, the actuaries do not need your information to set an insurance premium. They do need it to estimate how much money to reserve for insurance benefits if an employee dies.

Example 6 Instructor Notes

Here are some observations about the world life expectancies shown in the map on page 357 and countries with populations of 13 million or more.

- Australia, Canada, France, Italy, and Spain have life expectancies over 80 years.

- Afghanistan, Angola, Mozambique, Nigeria, and South Africa have life expectancies under 50 years.

- Of the three most populous countries in North America, Canada has the highest life expectancy (81.3), followed by the United States (78.2), and Mexico (76.3).

Checkpoint Solution

a. The graph shows that as age increases, the years of life remaining decreases. The decrease appears to be almost linear until the age of 60 or 70 when it flattens out and approaches zero. The graph also shows that males have fewer years of life remaining than females at every age.

b. Given the age and gender of a person applying for insurance, an actuary would use this graph to find the number of years of life remaining for the person. Then the actuary would calculate an annual or monthly premium so that the amount the person pays into the policy would accumulate to at least enough to pay the benefit at the time the person is expected to die.

c. Yes, the graph seems reasonable. It makes sense that as a person gets older, the number of years of life remaining decreases. When the graph is approximately linear, the slope is about -1. This is reasonable because after living one more year, you should expect to have one less year remaining. It is also reasonable that the graph flattens out eventually. If it continued to decrease linearly, it would become negative.

Section 8.2   Estimating Likelihood

Example 1 Instructor Notes

You may want to review some of the terms used in theoretical probability.

Experiment An activity with an uncertain result

Outcome The possible results of an experiment

Event A collection of one or more outcomes

Favorable outcome The outcomes of a specific event

Here is how these terms apply to Example 1(a).

Experiment The Daily Number is drawn.

Outcome All 3-digit numbers, 000 to 999; 1000 possible numbers

Event You pick one 3-digit number.

Favorable outcome The number you pick is the Daily Number.

Checkpoint Solution

You have a $\dfrac{1}{1000}$ chance to win each time you play. You play 10 times each day for 100 days.

So, you expect to win

$$\left(\frac{1}{1000}\right)\left(\frac{10 \text{ times}}{\text{day}}\right)(100 \text{ days}) = 1 \text{ time.}$$

You spend

$$\left(\frac{\$1}{\text{ticket}}\right)\left(\frac{10 \text{ tickets}}{\text{day}}\right)(100 \text{ days}) = \$1000.$$

If you win once, you will win \$500, making your net earnings \$500 − \$1000 = −\$500.

Example 2 Instructor Notes

The bar graph in the Math Help at *Math.andYou.com* shows the number of combinations assigned to each of the 14 teams in the NBA Draft Lottery. In Example 2, you determined the probability that the team with the worst record wins the first pick is 25%. The bar graph supports this conclusion because the height of the bar for the team with the worst record is greater than the heights of all the other bars.

Is it more likely that the team with the worst record will *not* win the first pick? Using the bar graph, imagine stacking all of the bars for the other 13 teams, as shown in the figure at the right. The height of this stack is greater than the height of the bar for the worst team. So, it is more likely that the team with the worst record will *not* win the first pick.

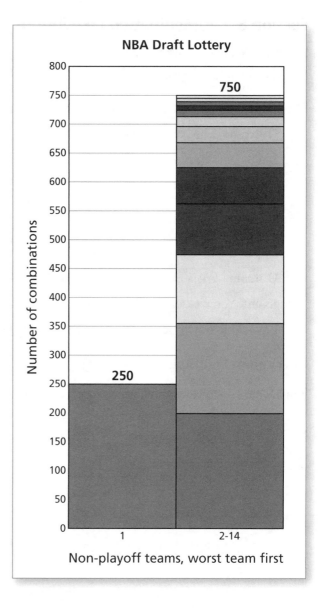

NBA Draft Lottery

Number of combinations

Non-playoff teams, worst team first

Checkpoint Solution

c. Students can use a spreadsheet to calculate the probability for each team.
   (See *http://math.andyou.com/content/08/02/data/mthu_data_0802_363_02a.xls*.)

d. The total of the probabilities column is 100%. The sum of the probabilities of any comprehensive list of events will be 100%.

Example 3 Instructor Notes

Here are some observations about the sample shown in Example 3.

- If neither of the parents have brown eyes, then there is no chance of their children having brown eyes. (Look at the last three rows of the table.)

- If both parents have blue eyes, there is an extremely high probability (99%) that their children will have blue eyes.

- If one parent has blue eyes and the other has brown eyes, then there is no chance of their children having green eyes.

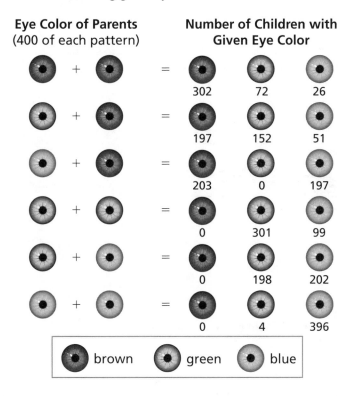

Eye Color of Parents
(400 of each pattern)

**Number of Children with
Given Eye Color**

302	72	26
197	152	51
203	0	197
0	301	99
0	198	202
0	4	396

brown   green   blue

Checkpoint Solution

Of the 400 children with two, brown-eyed parents, 302 have brown eyes, 72 have green eyes, and 26 have blue eyes. So the probability is

$$\text{Probability} = \frac{n}{T} = \frac{72 + 26}{400} = 24.5\%.$$

Example 4 Instructor Notes

Here is another way to represent the responses in Example 4. The graph below is a Pareto chart, a bar graph with the bars ordered in decreasing height with the tallest bar at the left. This helps highlight important data and is used frequently in business. A Pareto chart is a common type of information design. (More about information design is presented in Section 9.1.)

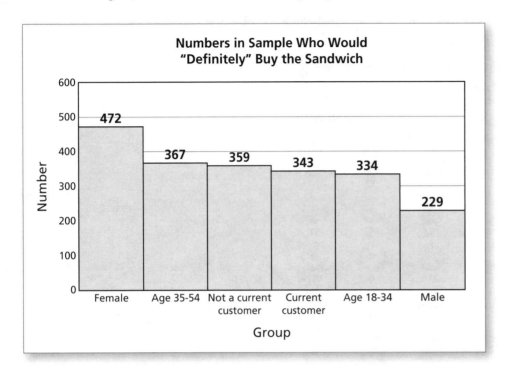

Checkpoint Solution

a. 334 of the 418 people in the 18–34 age group said they would buy the sandwich.

$$\text{Probability} = \frac{334}{418} \approx 0.80 = 80\%$$

So, a person between the ages of 18 and 34 is likely to buy the sandwich.

b. 359 of the 418 non-customers said they would buy the sandwich.

$$\text{Probability} = \frac{359}{418} \approx 0.86 = 86\%$$

So, someone who is not a current customer is very likely to buy the sandwich.

Example 5 Instructor Notes

To determine how many times more likely it is to die in a bicycling accident than by a bee sting, divide the probability of a fatal bicycle accident by the probability of a fatal bee sting.

$$\frac{0.0002}{0.00001} = 20$$

Checkpoint Solution

The probabilities that a person dies from heart disease, cancer, and stroke are 1/6, 1/7 and 1/28, respectively. The probability that a person dies from one of these is equal to the sum of the probabilities of dying from each of them.

$$\text{Probability} = \frac{1}{6} + \frac{1}{7} + \frac{1}{28} \approx 0.345 = 34.5\%$$

Example 6 Instructor Notes

In Example 6, a spreadsheet was used to create a scatter plot by entering the probability and latitude of each location.
(*See http://math.andyou.com/content/08/02/data/mthu_data_0802_367_06.xls*.) The latitude of a location on Earth is the angular distance of that location north or south of the Equator. The latitude is usually measured in degrees. The latitude of the equator is 0°. The latitude of the North Pole is 90° north, which can be written as 90° N. The latitude of the South Pole is 90° south, which can be written as 90° S. These latitudes are shown in the figure below. The locations in Example 6 are north of the Equator. So, the latitudes on the scatter plot in the solution are 30° N, 35° N, 40° N, 45° N (shown in the figure below), and 50° N.

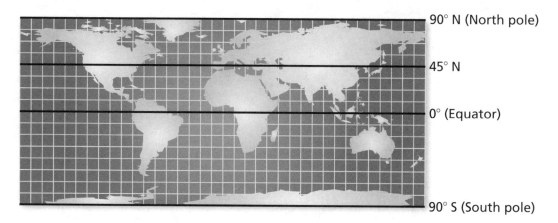

Checkpoint Solution

Sample answer:

Other possible factors include the city's altitude, average temperature on December 25, whether the city lies in a lake effect snowbelt, and the landscape of the area.

Section 8.3   Expected Value

Example 1 Instructor Notes

In Example 1, because you pay $1 for a ticket, the payoff if you win $5000 is

$$5000 - 1 = \$4999.$$

Here are some additional steps for finding the expected value in Example 1.

$$\text{Expected value} = \left(\frac{1}{10,000}\right)(4999) + \left(\frac{9999}{10,000}\right)(-1)$$

$$= \frac{4999}{10,000} + \left(\frac{-9999}{10,000}\right)$$

$$= \frac{4999 - 9999}{10,000}$$

$$= \frac{-5000}{10,000}$$

$$= -\$0.50$$

Checkpoint Solution

Sample answers:

Using the *Lottery Simulator* at *http://math.andyou.com/tools/lottery_simulator.html*, I won 13 times and lost 99,987 times. My total profit was

$$13(5000) - 100,000(1) = -\$35,000.$$

Because the expected profit per game is −$0.50, the expected profit for 100,000 games is $100,000(-\$0.50) = -\$50,000$. So, even though I did better than expected, I still lost $35,000. It is clear that playing the Big Four Lottery 100,000 times is not a good way to spend $100,000.

I do not think there is anything wrong with state lotteries as long as they are honest and not intentionally deceptive. No knowledge of statistics or probability is needed to know that your chances of winning are very small. I do not think state lotteries are a form of regressive tax for the poor because not all poor people play the lottery and not all financially secure people abstain from it.

Example 2 Instructor Notes

In Example 2(c), if the company sells 100,000 policies that have an annual premium of $300, then the company can expect to gross

$$(100,000)(\$300) = \$30,000,000.$$

If the probability of a house fire is 0.0002, then the company can expect that the number of fires among the 100,000 policies will be

$$(0.0002)(100,000) = 20 \text{ fires.}$$

Because each policy is for $200,000, the company can expect that the total amount of the payouts will be

$$(20)(\$200,000) = \$4,000,000.$$

This leaves a gross profit of

$$\$30,000,000 - \$4,000,000 = \$26,000,000.$$

Checkpoint Solution

Some properties may not be completely insured. For instance, in Example 2, the policy pays $200,000 if there is a house fire, but the value of the house could be more than $200,000. Also, some properties may not be insured at all.

Example 3 Instructor Notes

To make a spreadsheet similar to the one in Example 3, have students use the steps below. (See *http://math.andyou.com/content/08/03/data/mthu_data_0803_376_03.xls.*)

1. Enter the titles "Number," "Payoff," "Probability," and "Expected Value" into row 1.
2. Enter 1 into cell A2.
3. Enter the formula = A2 + 1 into cell A3.
4. Select cell A3. From the **Edit** menu, choose **Copy.**
5. Select cells A4 through A7. From the **Edit** menu, choose **Paste.**
6. Enter the title "Total" into cell A8.
7. Enter the formula = 3*A2 into cell B2.
8. Select cell B2. From the **Edit** menu, choose **Copy.**
9. Select cells B3 through B7. From the **Edit** menu, choose **Paste.**
10. Enter 0.1667 into cell C2.
11. Select cell C2. From the **Edit** menu, choose **Copy.**
12. Select cells C3 through C7. From the **Edit** menu, choose **Paste.**
13. Enter the formula = B2*C2 into cell D2.
14. Select cell D2. From the **Edit** menu, choose **Copy.**
15. Select cells D3 through D7. From the **Edit** menu, choose **Paste.**
16. Enter the formula =SUM(D2:D7) into cell D8.

To format the cells, use the steps below.

1. Select cells B2 through B7.
2. From the **Format** menu, choose **Cells . . ..**
3. In the **Format Cells** dialog, select the **Number** tab.
4. From the **Category:** list, select **Currency.**
5. For **Decimal places:,** enter 2. For **Symbol,** choose $ from the drop down list. Then click OK.
6. Repeat Steps 1–5 for cells D2 through D8.
7. Select cells C2 through C7.
8. From the **Format menu,** choose **Cells . . ..**
9. In the **Format Cells** dialog, select the **Number** tab.
10. From the **Category:** list, select **Percentage.**
11. For **Decimal places:,** enter 2. Then click **OK.**

Checkpoint Solution

Students can use a spreadsheet to find the expected value for each possible roll of the die. (See *http://math.andyou.com/content/08/03/data/mthu_data_0803_376_03a.xls.*)

The probability of rolling each number of dots is $\frac{1}{12} \approx 8.33\%$. The expected value for each number of dots is the payoff multiplied by the probability of that roll happening. The expected value of the offer is the sum of the individual expected values. I would take the uncle's offer. It has the highest expected value, $13, compared to $10 and $10.50, and the highest potential payout, $24, compared to $20 and $18.

Example 4 Instructor Notes

You may want to explain to your students that profit is calculated as (net sales) − (cost of development).

Cell phone A:

Net Sales	Profit = Net Sales − Cost
$5,000,000	$5,000,000 − $2,500,000 = $2,500,000
$3,000,000	$3,000,000 − $2,500,000 = $500,000
$1,500,000	$1,500,000 − $2,500,000 = −$1,000,000

Cell phone B:

Net Sales	Profit = Net Sales − Cost
$4,000,000	$4,000,000 − $1,500,000 = $2,500,000
$2,000,000	$2,000,000 − $1,500,000 = $500,000
$500,000	$500,000 − $1,500,000 = −$1,000,000

Checkpoint Solution

For cell phone C, the company's profit is found by subtracting $2 million from the net sales. For cell phone D, the company's profit is found by subtracting $1.5 million from the net sales. A decision tree is shown below.

I would develop cell phone C because it has a much higher expected value, $1.5 million, compared to $0.65 million. It also has the greatest profit, $3 million, in the best case scenario and the least loss, $0.5 million, in the worst case scenario.

Example 5 Instructor Notes

According to Daniel Kahneman and Amos Tversky's "Prospect Theory: An Analysis of Decision Under Risk," people give less weight to outcomes that are merely probable in comparison with outcomes that are obtained with certainty (see Example 5). They called this tendency the certainty effect and concluded that it contributes to risk aversion in choices involving sure gains and to risk seeking in choices involving sure losses. This is depicted in the figure below using the scenario described in Example 5.

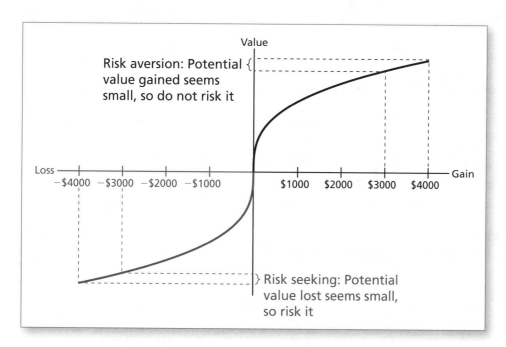

Checkpoint Solution

Sample Answers:

Insurance on anything of value (house, car, jewelry, etc.) is an example of people fearing losses more than they value gains. They would rather pay to eliminate the chance of loss than keep the money or invest it.

If a student expects a certain score on a test, his or her disappointment from scoring lower than expected would likely be greater than the pleasure gained from scoring higher than expected.

Example 6 Instructor Notes

Students can make a spreadsheet similar to the one in Example 6(a) using the steps listed in the Math Help at *Math.andYou.com*.
(See *http://math.andyou.com/content/08/03/data/mthu_data_0803_379_06.xls*.)

Checkpoint Solution

Assume that you invest $1000. A spreadsheet showing the expected value of each investment is shown below. (See *http://math.andyou.com/content/08/03/data/mthu_data_0803_379_06a.xls*.)

	A	B	C	D
1	**Speculative Investment**			
2	**Result**	**Payoff**	**Probability**	**Expected Value**
3	Complete loss	−$1,000	20%	−$200
4	No gain	$0	35%	$0
5	100% gain	$1,000	35%	$350
6	400% gain	$4,000	5%	$200
7	2000% gain	$20,000	5%	$1,000
8	**Total**		**100%**	**$1,350**
9				
10	**Conservative Investment**			
11	**Result**	**Payoff**	**Probability**	**Expected Value**
12	Complete loss	−$1,000	2%	−$20
13	No gain	$0	38%	$0
14	20% gain	$200	55%	$110
15	30% gain	$300	5%	$15
16	**Total**		**100%**	**$105**

If you have to pick only one investment, I think that the conservative investment is the best choice because it has only a slight chance of loss and is still expected to have a decent return. The expected value of the payoff is $105. This is a return of

$$\frac{\$105}{1000} = 0.105 = 10.5\%.$$

On the other hand, if you could make a great number of speculative investments, the average payoff would approach the expected value, $1350. This is a very high return of

$$\frac{\$1350}{1000} = 1.35 = 135\%.$$

Section 8.4 Expecting the Unexpected

Example 1 Instructor Notes

In Example 1, explain that the repeated multiplication of 1/6 is written in what is called exponential form. This is shorthand notation used by mathematicians to represent repeated multiplication.

Repeated multiplication   Exponential form

$$\underbrace{\left(\frac{1}{6}\right)\left(\frac{1}{6}\right)\left(\frac{1}{6}\right)\left(\frac{1}{6}\right)\left(\frac{1}{6}\right)}_{\text{Multiply same factor 5 times.}} = \qquad \left(\frac{1}{6}\right)^{5}$$

Checkpoint Solution

Sample answer:

Using the Zee Dice game, I rolled a YAHTZEE on my 16th try. If you have a 1/22 chance of rolling a YAHTZEE on any roll, the average number of rolls it should take to roll a YAHTZEE is 22. So I rolled a YAHTZEE a little quicker than expected. Note: Students will need Java to run the Zee Dice simulator. (See *http://www.zeedice.com/game1/*.)

Example 2 Instructor Notes

Benford's Law is named after physicist Frank Benford (1883–1948), who stated it in 1938. It should be noted that the law had been previously stated by astronomer and mathematician Simon Newcomb (1835–1909) in 1881. Benford's Law is also called the first digit law.

In Benford's Law, note that the probability that a leading digit is 1 is 30.1%. This is almost 3 times greater than the expected probability of $\frac{1}{9} \approx 11.1\%$. In fact, you would expect the probability of each of the 9 digits to be about 11.1%. According to Benford's Law, however, this is not the case, as shown in the table.

Leading digit	Probability
1	30.1%
2	17.6%
3	12.5%
4	9.7%
5	7.9%
6	6.7%
7	5.8%
8	5.1%
9	4.6%

Checkpoint Solution

A computer program can be used to analyze the first digits of the various numbers on a tax form. The frequency of each first digit in the tax return can be compared to the expected frequency according to Benford's Law. If there are any unusual results, the filer can be investigated further.

Example 3 Instructor Notes

Students can use a spreadsheet to find the probabilities in Example 3.
(See *http://math.andyou.com/content/08/04/data/mthu_data_0804_386_03.xls*.)

First, note that $\frac{366}{366} = 1$ and that each factor is $\frac{1}{366}$ less than the previous factor.

1. Enter 1 into cell A1.
2. Enter the formula = A1 - 1/366 into cell A2.
3. Select cell A2. From the **Edit** menu, choose **Copy.**
4. Select cells A3 through A35. From the **Edit** menu, choose **Paste.**
5. Enter the formula = PRODUCT(A1:A35) into cell A36.
6. Enter the formula = 1 - A36 into cell A37.

Checkpoint Solution

The spreadsheet below shows the probability that all 40 students have different birthdays.
(See *http://math.andyou.com/content/08/04/data/mthu_data_0804_386_03a.xls*.)

	A	B	C	
1	Number of Students	Unused Birthdays	Probability of Different Birthdays	
2	1	366	100.00%	
3	2	365	99.73%	
4	3	364	99.18%	
5	4	363	98.37%	
36	35	332	18.65%	
37	36	331	16.87%	
38	37	330	15.21%	
39	38	329	13.67%	
40	39	328	12.25%	
41	40	327	10.95%	

The probability that all 40 students have different birthdays is 10.95%. So, the probability that at least 2 students have the same birthday is

$$1 - 0.1095 = 0.8905 = 89.05\%.$$

Example 4 Instructor Notes

Here are some additional steps for the solution to Example 4.

a. The probability that the 65-year-old man lives to age 80 is 59% = 0.59. So, the probability that he does not live to age 80 is 1 − 0.59 = 0.41. The probability that the 65-year-old female lives to age 80 is 70% = 0.70. So, the probability that she does not live to age 80 is 1 − 0.70 = 0.30.

b. The probability that the 65-year-old man lives to age 90 is 19% = 0.19. So, the probability that he does not live to age 90 is 1 − 0.19 = 0.81. The probability that the 65-year-old female lives to age 90 is 30% = 0.30. So, the probability that she does not live to age 90 is 1 − 0.30 = 0.70.

Checkpoint Solution

c. The probability that both women do not survive to age 80 is (1 − 0.70)(1 − 0.70) = 0.09. The probability that at least 1 woman survives to age 80 is 1 − 0.09 = 0.91. So, there is a 91% chance that at least 1 woman will survive to age 80.

   The probability that both women do not survive to age 90 is (1 − 0.30)(1 − 0.30) = 0.49. The probability that at least 1 woman survives to age 90 is 1 − 0.49 = 0.51. So, there is a 51% chance that at least 1 woman will survive to age 90.

d. The probability that both men do not survive to age 80 is (1 − 0.59)(1 − 0.59) = 0.1681. The probability that at least 1 man survives to age 80 is 1 − 0.1681 = 0.8319. So, there is an 83.19% chance that at least 1 man will survive to age 80.

   The probability that both men do not survive to age 90 is (1 − 0.19)(1 − 0.19) = 0.6561. The probability that at least 1 man survives to age 90 is 1 − 0.6561 = 0.3439. So, there is a 34.39% chance that at least 1 man will survive to age 90.

Example 5 Instructor Notes

In the solution to Example 1, after the contestant chooses a door, the host reveals the goat behind one of the remaining doors. At this point, the contestant has only two doors to consider. Assuming the contestant chooses door 1, here are the situations.

1. In this situation, the host can reveal the goat behind either door 2 or door 3. The contestant can only win by staying with door 1.

2. In this situation, the host only has one choice and must reveal the goat behind door 3 (the other goat is behind door 1, the door the contestant picked). The contestant can only win by switching.

3. In this situation, the host only has one choice and must reveal the goat behind door 2 (the other goat is behind door 1, the door the contestant picked). The contestant can only win by switching.

Checkpoint Solution

Note: The Monty Hall Game at *Math.andYou.com* requires Internet Explorer.
(See *http://math.andyou.com/tools/montyhallsimulator/montysim.htm*.)

Sample answer:

When I played the Monty Hall Game 20 times, by staying, I won 5 times and lost 15 times. This is a winning percentage of $\frac{1}{4}$ or 25%. The expected winning percentage is $\frac{1}{3}$ or about 33.3%, which is 8.3% greater than my winning percentage. Although my winning percentage was a little less than expected, it still supports the claim that staying is not the best strategy.

When I played the Monty Hall Game 20 times, by switching, I won 14 times and lost 6 times. This is a winning percentage of $\frac{7}{10}$ or 70%. The expected winning percentage is $\frac{2}{3}$ or about 66.7%, which is 3.3% less than my winning percentage. Although my winning percentage was a little greater than expected, it still supports the claim that switching is the best strategy.

Example 6 Instructor Notes

Students can use a spreadsheet to find the probabilities in Example 6. First, note

that $\dfrac{1,000,000}{1,000,000} = 1$ and that each factor is $\dfrac{1}{1,000,000}$ less than the previous factor.

(See *http://math.andyou.com/content/08/04/data/mthu_data_0804_389_06.xls.*)

1. Enter 1 into cell A1.
2. Enter the formula = A1 - 1/1000000 into cell A2.
3. Select cell A2. From the **Edit** menu, choose **Copy.**
4. Select cells A3 through A365. From the **Edit** menu, choose **Paste.**
5. Enter the formula = PRODUCT(A1:A365) into cell A366.
6. Enter the formula = 1 - A366 into cell A367.

Checkpoint Solution

As shown in Section 5.2, you can use a spreadsheet to find the amounts of state and federal taxes you owe. (See *http://math.andyou.com/content/08/04/data/mthu_data_0804_389_06a.xls.*)

a. Federal Tax:

	A Taxable Income	B Marginal Rate	C Tax
1			
2	$8,375.00	10%	$837.50
3	$25,625.00	15%	$3,843.75
4	$48,400.00	25%	$12,100.00
5	$89,450.00	28%	$25,046.00
6	$201,800.00	33%	$66,594.00
7	$126,350.00	35%	$44,222.50
8	**$500,000.00**		**$152,643.75**

The federal income tax on $500,000 is $152,643.75.

State Tax:

	A Taxable Income	B Marginal Rate	C Tax
1			
2	$7,124.00	1.25%	$89.05
3	$9,766.00	2.25%	$219.74
4	$9,767.00	4.25%	$415.10
5	$10,348.00	6.25%	$646.75
6	$9,761.00	8.25%	$805.28
7	$453,234.00	9.55%	$43,283.85
8	**$500,000.00**		**$45,459.77**

The state income tax on $500,000 is $45,459.77.

The total income tax is 152,643.75 + 45,459.77 = $198,103.52, making your lump-sum payment equal to 500,000.00 − 198,103.52 = $301,896.48.

Sample answer:

b. Yes, I agree that Americans should pay state income tax on lottery winnings. Lottery winnings are income and should be taxed as such. They are not even earned like regular income, so I think a lottery winner should be happy with what they get.

Chapter 9   Information Design

Section 9.1

Example 1 Instructor Notes

Explain that in a stacked area graph, the amount is represented by the difference between two line graphs. For instance, in the stacked area graph in Example 1, you can estimate that there were about 10,000 truck fatalities in 1995.

Checkpoint Solution

Students can access the data in the spreadsheet available at *Math.andYou.com*. (See *http://math.andyou.com/content/09/01/data/mthu_data_0901_402_01.xls*.) You can compare motorcycle accident fatalities in 1994 and 2009 as numbers and percents.

Numbers:

In 1994, there were 2320 motorcycle accident fatalities. In 2009, there were 4462 motorcycle accident fatalities. There were about twice as many motorcycle accident fatalities in 2009 than in 1994.

Percents:

To compare motorcycle accident fatalities as percents, divide the number of motorcycle fatalities for the year by the total number of motor vehicle accident fatalities for the year.

$$\textbf{1994:} \quad \frac{2320}{34{,}318} \approx 0.07$$

$$\textbf{2009:} \quad \frac{4462}{28{,}936} \approx 0.15$$

In 1994, motorcycle accident fatalities accounted for about 7% of motor vehicle accident fatalities. In 2009, motorcycle accident fatalities accounted for about 15% of motor vehicle accident fatalities.

Example 2 Instructor Notes

The vertical axis on the left of the figure shown in Example 2 (also shown below) lists the proportion of total Internet traffic for a household in 1995. In 1995, 75% of the traffic was Web, 5% was Email, and 20% was Other. The vertical axis on the right lists the proportion of the total Internet traffic in 2010. In 2010, 20% of the traffic was Web, 15% was Peer-to-peer, 50% was Video, 2% was Email, 10% was Gaming, and 4% was Other. (Note that the sum of these values is not 100% due to rounding.)

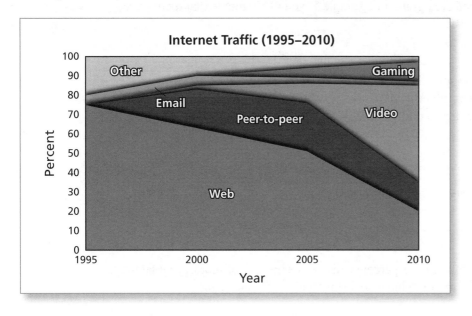

Checkpoint Solution

Sample answer:

The stacked area graph shows that Web traffic has decreased as a proportion of total Internet traffic for a household since 1995, but it does not show whether the actual volume of Web traffic has increased or decreased since 1995. So, you cannot conclude that the household's Web usage has declined.

Example 3 Instructor Notes

Students can use a spreadsheet to create a radar graph similar to the one in Example 3 using the steps below. (See *http://math.andyou.com/content/09/01/data/mthu_data_0901_404_03.xls*.)

1. Create a spreadsheet like the one shown.
2. Select cells A1 through A19, B1 through B19, and C1 through C19.
3. From the **Insert** menu, choose **Chart . . ..**
4. Select the **Standard Types** tab. Under **Chart type:**, select **Radar.** Click **Next.**
5. Click **Next** again.
6. Select the **Titles** tab. Enter "Percent of 18-Year-Olds in School" for **Chart title:**. Click **Finish.**

	A	B	C
1		**1998**	**2007**
2	Czech Republic	63.8	87.0
3	Denmark	74.6	80.0
4	Estonia	65.5	82.7
5	Ireland	73.1	93.9
6	Greece	69.3	65.9
7	Spain	64.8	70.0
8	France	82.6	76.7
9	Latvia	61.1	85.3
10	Lithuania	67.0	91.4
11	Hungary	61.7	83.0
12	Netherlands	78.6	82.3
13	Austria	67.5	72.8
14	Poland	73.0	93.9
15	Portugal	65.8	64.8
16	Romania	37.4	69.9
17	Finland	84.5	93.8
18	Sweden	96.0	94.8
19	United States	61.8	65.5

Checkpoint Solution

Sample answer:

Here are some other observations that you can make about the radar graph.

- Eight of the countries experienced a large increase in the percent of 18-year-olds in school (more than an additional 10% in school). Those countries are the Czech Republic, Estonia, Hungary, Ireland, Latvia, Lithuania, Poland, and Romania.

- Sweden had the greatest percent of students enrolled in school in both 1998 and 2007.

- By drawing a circle at 90%, you can see that in 2007, Finland, Lithuania, Poland, and Sweden had more than 90% of 18-year-olds enrolled in school.

Example 4 Instructor Notes

To watch a video about information design, including the graph shown in Example 4 (at about the 6:20 mark), watch the David McCandless video on "Information Is Beautiful." (See *http://www.youtube.com/watch?v=pLqjQ55tz-U*.)

Checkpoint Solution

Sample answer:

Here are some other observations that you can make about the area graph.

- The three largest peaks occur around the Fourth of July, Thanksgiving, and Christmas.

- The three small peaks at the beginning of the year occur around Martin Luther King, Jr. Day, Valentine's Day, and Easter.

- Overall, box office revenue is higher during the summer than the rest of the year (except for the two peaks at the end of the year).

The most important observation that you can make from the area graph is that there is a strong correlation between box office revenue and holidays.

Example 5 Instructor Notes

You can watch the "Wealth and Health of Nations" change at Gapminder.org.
(See *http://www.gapminder.org/world/*.) Here are some observations about the animation.

- The countries on the graph are color-coded by continent.

- You can hover the mouse pointer over a bubble to reveal the name of the country. When you do this, the life expectancy, income per person, and population will be highlighted.

- You can follow a particular country by clicking its bubble, or by selecting it from the list. (You can also select multiple countries to follow.)

For more information, read the Gapminder world guide.
(See *http://www.gapminder.org/GapminderMedia/wp-uploads/tutorial/Gapminder_World_Guide.pdf*.)

Checkpoint Solution

The four most eye-catching periods in the animation are 1949–1958, 1959–1961, 1962–1978, and 1979–present. The following table summarizes the behavior of China's dot during those pivotal time periods and the reasons why China's dot behaved as it did.

Time Period	China's Dot	Explanation
1949-1958	A large vertical increase indicates a large gain in life expectancy.	In 1949, the Chinese Civil War ended and Mao Zedong established the People's Republic of China.
1959-1961	A large vertical decrease indicates a large loss in life expectancy.	A great famine struck China at the same time the government was trying to shift the nation's focus from agriculture to industry.
1962-1978	A large vertical increase indicates a large gain in life expectancy.	China rebounded after the great famine.
1979-present	A large shift to the right indicates an increase in income per person and a vertical increase indicates a gain in life expectancy.	Economic reforms begun under Deng Xiaoping spurred tremendous economic growth.

Example 6 Instructor Notes

Here are some observations about the stream graph shown in Example 6.

- The height of the color shows the revenue in millions of dollars. This is indicated by the scale at the left side of the graph.

- The opening weekend of a movie tends to have the greatest revenue, while the remaining weekends of the movie's release tend to be less and less.

You may want to point out that the total height of each vertical "bar" represents the total revenue of all movies in a weekend. So, from the graph you can deduce that *Toy Story 3* was responsible for almost 50% of the revenue that was earned on its opening weekend.

Checkpoint Solution

When a movie has a particularly long run at the box office, its color will begin to stand out against the colors of other movies around it as you follow the graph from left to right. For instance, in the full graph for 2010, *Avatar*'s long run is noticeable because the red color used to represent *Avatar* stands out against the shades of green used to represent movies released a month or two after *Avatar*.

To check out the complete 2010 movie stream graph, visit *xach.com*. (See *http://www.xach.com/moviecharts/.*)

Section 9.2   Describing Average

Example 1 Instructor Notes

Make sure students see that in a data set, there are the same number of values above the median as there are below. For instance, the median of the data set below is 3, with four values below and four values above the median.

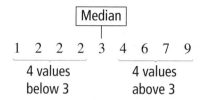

It should be noted that if no entry in a data set is repeated, then the data set has no mode. Also, if two entries occur with the same greatest frequency, then each entry is a mode and the data set is called *bimodal*. (See also Section 9.3, Example 6.)

Point out that while the mean, median, and mode each describe the "average" of a data set, there are advantages and disadvantages of using each. The mean takes into account every value, while the median and mode do not, perhaps making the mean more reliable. When there are *outliers*, however, the mean can be greatly affected while the median and mode will be unaffected. (Students will learn more about outliers on pages 416 and 417.)

Remind students they can use a spreadsheet to help determine the mean, median, and mode of a data set. (See *http://math.andyou.com/content/09/02/data/mthu_data_0902_412_01.xls*.)

Checkpoint Solution

Brazil's population pyramid is more bottom heavy than the United States pyramid. In Brazil, a relatively large percent of the population is between 0 and 15. Comparing the two pyramids, it appears that Brazil's mean, median, and mode ages are less than those of the United States.

Example 2 Instructor Notes

In Example 2, note that in each graph the vertical scale represents age groups. So, 0 represents the 0 to 4 age group, 5 represents the 5 to 9 age group, 10 represents the 10 to 14 age group, and so on.

In the solution to Example 2, young age group refers to ages 0 to 14, working age group refers to ages 15 to 59, and old age group refers to ages 60 and over.

Checkpoint Solution

a. This is the population pyramid of Mexico. Mexico is a newly industrialized country, which is the transition stage between a developing country and a developed country. Mexico's population pyramid is beginning to change from an expansive pyramid to a constrictive pyramid. The life expectancy in a newly industrialized country like Mexico is higher than the life expectancy in a developing country like Afghanistan, so the pyramid is not as bottom heavy as Afghanistan's.

b. This is the population pyramid of Canada. Canada is a developed country and has a population pyramid similar to the population pyramid of the United States. Canada has a higher life expectancy than Mexico and Afghanistan, so a larger percent of its population is in the older age groups.

c. This is the population pyramid of Afghanistan. Afghanistan is a developing country with a lower life expectancy than countries like the United States and Canada and newly industrialized countries like Mexico. Because Afghanistan is a very poor developing country, it has a high birth rate and a high death rate. This results in Afghanistan's population pyramid being the most bottom heavy of the three shown. Afghanistan's population pyramid is a classic example of an expansive population pyramid.

Example 3 Instructor Notes

Show students how a box-and-whisker plot highlights some of the important features of a data set. To graph a box-and-whisker plot, you must know the following values.

- The minimum value
- The lower (or first) quartile
- The median (or second quartile)
- The upper (or third) quartile
- The maximum value

The three quartiles divide an ordered data set into approximately four equal parts. About one quarter of the data fall on or below the first quartile. About one half of the data fall on or below the second quartile (the median). About three quarters of the data fall on or below the third quartile. Here is an example of three quartiles dividing an ordered data set into approximately four equal parts.

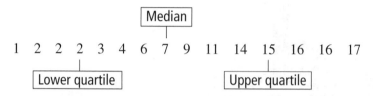

You can also use the *Box-and-Whisker Plot Generator* located in Tools to make box-and-whisker plots. (See *http://math.andyou.com/tools/boxandwhisker.html*.)

Checkpoint Solution

Sample answer:

Here are some other observations that you can make about the weights of the players.

- About 10 of the players weigh between 170 and 188.75 pounds.
- About 10 of the players weigh between 188.75 and 200 pounds.
- About 10 of the players weigh between 200 and 215 pounds.
- About 10 of the players weigh between 215 and 240 pounds.
- There is not a very large difference between the ranges of weights for the quartiles. The greatest range is 25 pounds and the smallest range is 10 pounds. The weights are clustered much closer to the mean for the Los Angeles Angels than they are for the Chicago Bears.

Example 4 Instructor Notes

Note that students can use the *Histogram Generator* located in Tools to make histograms. (See *http://math.andyou.com/tools/hggenerator.html*.)

As in Example 3, the median weight of the Chicago Bears is about 233 pounds, as shown in the figure in Example 4. In the United States, the median weight of males ages 20–29 is about 175 to 180 pounds. The median weight of males ages 30–39 is about 190 pounds.

Checkpoint Solution

Sample answer:

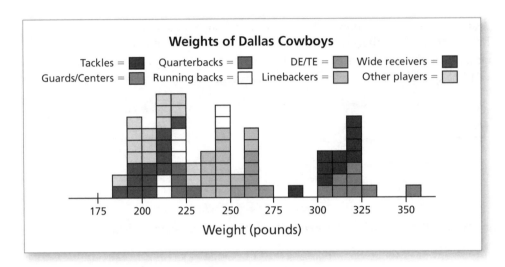

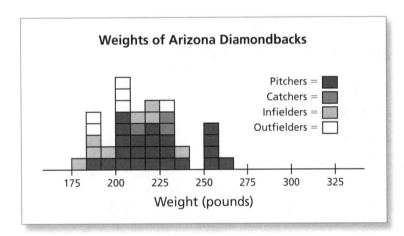

The histograms are similar to the two in Example 4.

- The weights of the Dallas Cowboys are distributed similar to the weights of the Chicago Bears. For instance, wide receivers are on the far left, linebackers are in the middle, and tackles, guards, and centers are on the far right.

- The weights of the Arizona Diamondbacks are distributed similar to the weights of the Los Angeles Angels. For instance, there is a wide range of pitcher weights.

Example 5 Instructor Notes

Explain to students that an outlier in a data set is a value that is much smaller or larger than the other values in the data set. For instance, consider the data in the table that shows the ages of everyone in a classroom.

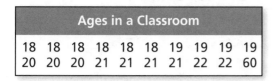

Ages in a Classroom									
18	18	18	18	18	18	19	19	19	19
20	20	20	21	21	21	21	22	22	60

The age of 60 is an outlier because 60 is much larger than the other values. This is easy to see in a histogram.

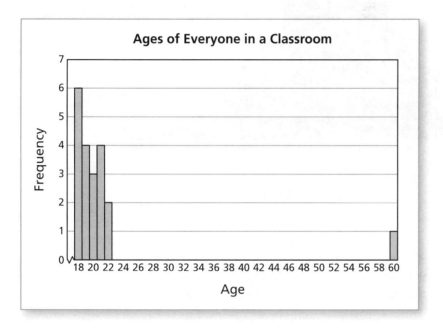

Checkpoint Solution

Sample answer:

The median is often used instead of the mean to represent the average home price. This is because the mean is sensitive to houses that have very high prices.

Example 6 Instructor Notes

Explain to students that an IQ, or intelligence quotient, is a score from one of the standardized IQ tests used to measure intelligence. The graph below shows the typical range of scores. Note that about 95% of IQ scores lie between 70 and 130, while about 99.7% of the scores lie between 55 and 145. Also, about 16% of the scores are above 115. In Example 6, each estimated IQ is greater than 115.

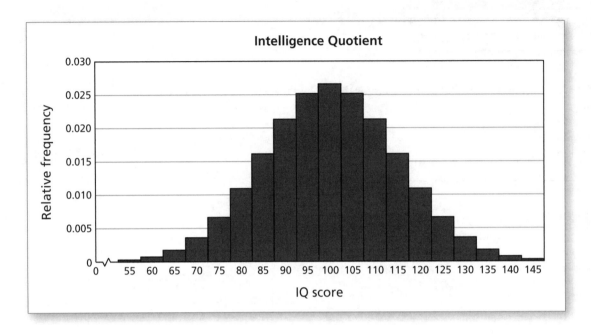

Checkpoint Solution

Adding an IQ score of 200 to the data set will increase the mean from 135 to about 140. Anytime you add numbers to a data set that are larger than the current data, the mean will increase. Likewise, if you add numbers to a data set that are smaller than the current data, the mean will decrease.

Adding an IQ score of 200 to the data set will change the median from 130.5 to 131. Because the data values are not extremely spread out, adding one number to the set will not greatly affect the median.

Section 9.3   Describing Dispersion

Example 1 Instructor Notes

To confirm the claim in the "Standard Deviation and Dispersion" box that says in any data set, at least 75% of the values lie within 2 standard deviations, at least 89% lie within 3 standard deviations, and at least 94% lie within 4 standard deviations, students can enter the data for Example 1 into a spreadsheet. (See *http://math.andyou.com/content/09/03/data/mthu_data_0903_424_01.xls*.)

Data within 2 standard deviations is between $22 - 2(1) = 20$ and $22 + 2(1) = 24$.

Data within 3 standard deviations is between $22 - 3(1) = 19$ and $22 + 3(1) = 25$.

Data within 4 standard deviations is between $22 - 4(1) = 18$ and $22 + 4(1) = 26$.

In the spreadsheet, students can see that 41 of the values or about 91% lie within 2 standard deviations of the mean, 45 of the values or 100% lie within 3 standard deviations of the mean, and 45 of the values or 100% lie within 4 standard deviations of the mean. This is illustrated in the Math Help notes for Example 1 at *Math.andYou.com*.

Checkpoint Solution

Use the data given in the spreadsheet to create a histogram.
(See *http://math.andyou.com/content/09/03/data/mthu_data_0903_424_01.xls*.)

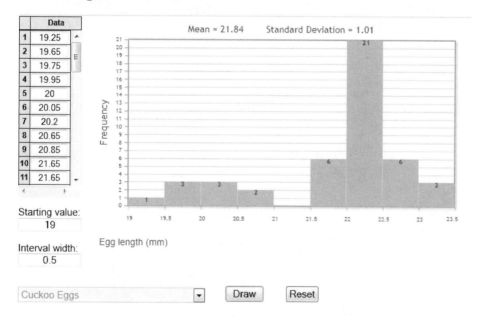

Example 2 Instructor Notes

A moving average is another way to analyze a set of data. Depending on the length of time, it can show short-term or long-term changes. For a 101-day moving average, as shown in the Checkpoint, the first point plotted is the average temperature of the first 101 days of 1955 (from January 1 to April 11). For the second 101 days, you subtract the first day and add another day to the end. So, the second plotted point is the average temperature from January 2 to April 12. Following this pattern, the third plotted point is the average temperature from January 3 to April 13, and so on.

Checkpoint Solution

You may need to help students understand the concept of moving average, as defined above. The line graph would be more helpful than the histogram because the line graph shows how the temperature has changed over time and the histogram does not.

Example 3 Instructor Notes

In the histogram in Example 3, "SD" stands for standard deviation. Tell your students that this notation will be used in graphs in the rest of this chapter.

Here are some observations about normal distributions and the normal distribution graph from page 426.

- Because the graph is symmetrical about the mean, you can draw a vertical line through the mean and both halves are mirror images.

- 50% of the data lies below the mean and 50% of the data lies above the mean.

- The mean, median, and mode are equal.

- Data values that are farther than 2 standard deviations from the mean are considered unusual. Notice that 4.6% of the data values are farther than 2 standard deviations from the mean.

- Data values that are farther than 3 standard deviations from the mean are considered very unusual. Notice that 0.2% of the data values are farther than 3 standard deviations from the mean.

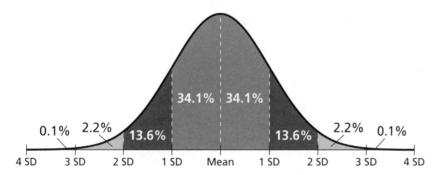

Checkpoint Solution

The number of chest sizes within 2 standard deviations of the mean is

$$185 + 420 + 749 + 1073 + 1079 + 934 + 658 + 370 + 92 = 5560.$$

This is $\frac{5560}{5738} \approx 0.968$ or about 96.8% of the total. This is close to the 95.4% predicted by a normal distribution.

Example 4 Instructor Notes

The histograms in Example 4 have normal distributions drawn on them because they can be approximated by normal distributions. This can be shown by comparing the percents found using the normal distribution and the actual data for several heights. Use 61 inches and 67 inches. A height of 61 inches is 3 standard deviations below the mean for males and about 1 standard deviation below the mean for females (notice that for females, 61.5 inches is exactly 1 standard deviation below the mean). A height of 67 inches is 1 standard deviation below the mean for males and about 1 standard deviation above the mean for females (notice that for females, 66.5 inches is exactly 1 standard deviation above the mean).

At most 61 inches tall

	Male	Female
Using normal distribution	0.2%	15.9%
Using actual data	0 or 0%	36 or 14.4%

At least 67 inches tall

	Male	Female
Using normal distribution	84.1%	15.9%
Using actual data	218 or 87.2%	35 or 14%

You can see from these tables that the percents using the normal distribution are close to the percents using the actual data for males and females.

Checkpoint Solution

Sample answer:

While Judge and Cable's study indicates a positive correlation between height and salary, this does not guarantee that a taller person will always be more successful than a shorter person. Many things matter for career success such as experience, who you know, personality, and intelligence. Each of these traits is weighted differently for different types of careers. It is not so much a question of whether height matters but a question of how much height matters. If you are a basketball player, height certainly matters for career success. If you run an online business from home, height probably does not matter at all.

Example 5 Instructor Notes

Bimodal distributions

- These can occur when two separate normal distributions are combined.

- Example: the time of day people go to a restaurant; it would be high around lunch and then again around dinner.

Flat distributions

- The frequencies are almost the same. When the frequencies are exactly the same, it is called a uniform distribution.

- Example: rolling a die; the frequency for each number should be almost the same.

Right-skewed distributions

- Named for the direction the "tail" of the graph is located. So, a right-skewed distribution has a "tail" to the right.

- Example: salaries at a company where a few executives have much higher salaries

Left-skewed distributions

- Named for the direction the "tail" of the graph is located. So, a left-skewed distribution has a "tail" to the left.

- Example: scores on a test where a few students have low scores

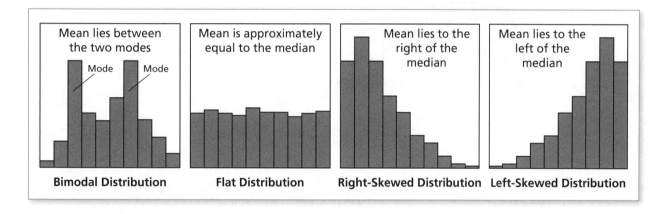

Checkpoint Solution

Sample answer:

Because Chutes and Ladders and Cootie tend to take fewer turns to finish than Candyland, those two games should be marketed to a slightly younger age group than Candyland because the younger age group may be less patient and less willing to play a game that takes too many turns.

Example 6 Instructor Notes

Here are some more findings from the National Association for Law Placement report. (See *http://www.nalp.org/marketfornewlawgraduatesup*.)

- 14% of salaries were between $135,000 and $145,000.

- 42% of salaries were $55,000 or less.

- Here are the median salaries for several of the job categories.

    - Private practice: $95,000

    - Judicial clerks: $46,500

    - Public interest: $40,000

- About 14% are looking for another job.

Checkpoint Solution

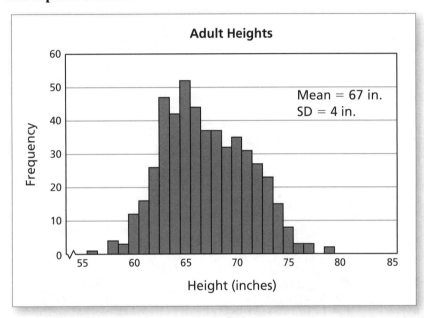

The histogram would display a greater dispersion than either of the two individual histograms. If you notice multiple peaks in a histogram, the peaks may represent several subpopulations with values that cluster around a certain value.

Section 9.4   Describing by Sampling

Example 1 Instructor Notes

Point out that in the "Inferring from a Sample" box on page 434, the margin of error in the estimated population mean refers only to the amount of error that occurs because of chance. When discussing Example 1 with your students, note the following.

- The mean and standard deviation are given in the histogram.

- The *Confidence Interval Calculator* is located in Tools.
  (See *http://math.andyou.com/tools/con_int_calculator.html*.)

- In the solution, the symbol "$\pm$" is read as "plus or minus." So, the phrase "80 cm $\pm$ 3.1 cm" is read as "80 centimeters plus or minus 3.1 centimeters."

A confidence interval is a range of values used to estimate the value of an unknown population mean. (Note that a confidence interval can also be constructed for other parameters, such as standard deviation.) A confidence level is the probability that the interval contains the population mean. Suppose a large number of different samples of the same size are collected and a 90% confidence interval is created for each sample. It should be expected that 90% of the intervals will contain the population mean. This is illustrated in the figure below.

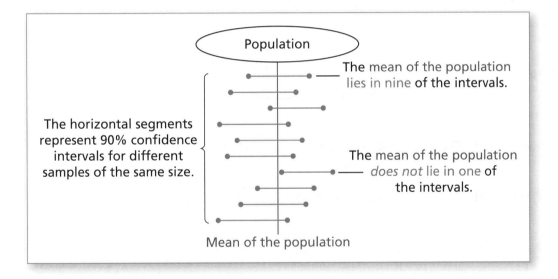

For instance, consider the 90% confidence interval found in Example 1, 80 cm $\pm$ 3.1 cm. This means you can be 90% confident that the population mean shoulder height of male black bears lies between 76.9 centimeters and 83.1 centimeters.

Checkpoint Solution

Using the *Confidence Interval Calculator* located in Tools, at a 99% confidence level you can estimate the population mean to be 80 cm $\pm$ 4.9 cm.
(See *http://math.andyou.com/tools/con_int_calculator.html*.)

Example 2 Instructor Notes

In some texts, you might see statistical inference referred to as inferential statistics. Either term refers to the use of a sample to draw conclusions about a population. Note that infer means "to conclude by reasoning from something known or assumed." In the context of statistics, you infer information about the population from what you know about the sample.

When determining the confidence level, students might think that it is always best to choose 99%; however, 99% may not always be the best choice. As the confidence level increases, the confidence interval widens. As the confidence interval widens, the precision of the estimate decreases. So, a 99% confidence level may produce an interval that is too wide and as a result conveys less information. For instance, it is better to be 95% confident that the average life of an automobile part is 6 to 8 years than to be 99% confident that the average life is 4 to 10 years (see figure below). As you construct confidence intervals, note that the goal is to obtain a narrow interval with a high level of confidence.

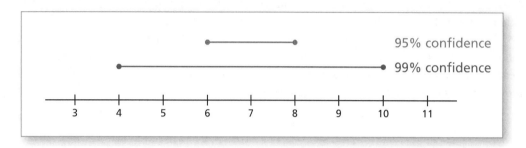

Checkpoint Solution

Using the *Confidence Interval Calculator* located in Tools, you can obtain the following. (See *http://math.andyou.com/tools/con_int_calculator.html*.)

- **90% Confidence Level:** The population mean is 98.25°F ± 0.11°F, or between 98.14°F and 98.36°F.

- **95% Confidence Level:** The population mean is 98.25°F ± 0.13°F, or between 98.12°F and 98.38°F.

- **99% Confidence Level:** The population mean is 98.25°F ± 0.16°F, or between 98.09°F and 98.41°F.

The accepted human body temperature of 98.6°F does not lie within any of those confidence intervals. You cannot say with 100% confidence that the study does not allow for the accepted human body temperature of 98.6°F. However, you can say with 99% confidence that the population mean body temperature lies between 98.09°F and 98.41°F.

Example 3 Instructor Notes

Here are some other reasons that a sample may not be representative of a population.

- **Underrepresentation:** Underrepresentation occurs when some parts of the population are left out of the process of choosing the sample.

- **Lack of response:** This occurs when people who are contacted for a survey cannot be reached or refuse to respond.

- **Misrepresentation:** This occurs when survey participants give dishonest replies. For instance, many people will say they voted in the last election, even though they did not.

Checkpoint Solution

Sample answer:

Here are some other reasons that a poll may go wrong.

- A significant number of people being polled may intentionally lie to the pollster.

- An Internet survey will not reach anyone who does not use a computer. For instance, an online survey that asks "Have you ever used the Internet?" should have a 100% response rate of "yes," but it is not true that 100% of the population has used the Internet.

- If a poll is being done by mail-in survey, a subpopulation that feels more strongly about an issue may be more likely to respond and may overrepresent itself. For instance, consider a local election for mayor in which a fervent grassroots minority responds strongly to a mail-in poll from the newspaper asking who the people are going to vote for. Even though the poll shows that the grassroots candidate will win by 58%, he only gets 40% of the vote and loses because the other candidate's supporters did not feel as strongly about mailing in their surveys.

Example 4 Instructor Notes

Here are two sampling techniques that often lead to biased samples.

- **Convenience sample:** A convenience sample is only made up of easily available members of a population. For instance, standing outside a grocery store and asking everyone going into the store, "What is your favorite grocery store?" Obviously, people who do not like this grocery store will be underrepresented in this sample, and those that do like this store will be overrepresented. So, the sample is not truly representative of the population.

- **Self-selected sample:** A self-selected sample is made up only of people who choose themselves by responding to an appeal. For instance, a television station might ask its viewers to go to a website and select the candidate for whom they are going to vote in an upcoming election. Usually only people who have a strong opinion will take the time to respond, which will result in a sample that is not truly representative of the population.

Checkpoint Solution

Sample answer:

In 1993, presidential candidate Ross Perot asked Americans to complete a survey in TV Guide and mail it in. The sample was biased for two reasons. First, response to the survey was voluntary so it could not guarantee a representative sample. Second, the questions on the survey were biased.

To read more about this infamous 1993 survey, you can visit
http://www.hillsdalesites.org/personal/dmurphy/Kclasses/math105/PerotPollStory.pdf.

Example 5 Instructor Notes

Here are some other sampling techniques.

- **Experiments:** An experiment is performed where a treatment is given to a sample and reactions are recorded. The sample may be split up into groups, with one group receiving the treatment, and the other group receiving nothing or a placebo (an unmedicated treatment that looks like the real one). This second group is called the control group.

- **Simulations:** A simulation is the use of a physical or mathematical model to reproduce certain conditions. For instance, the use of dummies to study the effects of automobile crashes on humans.

Note that the *Sample Size Calculator* is located in Tools.
(See *http://math.andyou.com/tools/sample_size_calculator.html.*)
Here are some observations about sample size.

- To decrease the width of the confidence interval, increase the sample size.

- When the population is spread out more (the standard deviation is large), you will need a larger sample size than for a population that is spread out less.

- When the confidence level increases, the sample size increases.

Checkpoint Solution

Sample answer:

To conduct the survey, you could call men and ask their opinions about men's health care products. It is important to survey enough people so that you can identify which subpopulations are most likely to use men's personal care products and what type of personal care products those subpopulations are most likely to use. Only surveying the minimum sample size may not give you enough information about the opinions of all the subpopulations, so you may want to increase the number of people you survey. Information about demographics and trends can be very valuable from a marketing standpoint. If you want to advertise your products in commercials and magazines, you need to know your target audience.

Example 6 Instructor Notes

A survey is used to gather information about a population without causing a change in the population. For instance, a survey might ask for a person's political party preference and annual income. In an experiment, a treatment is applied to part of a population and the responses are observed. Another part of the population may be used as the control group, which receives no treatment. A factor that can affect an experiment's results is the **placebo effect.** A placebo is a "fake" treatment that appears to be the real treatment. The placebo effect occurs when a subject reacts favorably to a placebo, even though the placebo has no benefit. For instance, to test a drug, here is one way the experiment could be set up.

- Patients are assigned to different treatment groups through random selection.

- The treatment group receives the drug.

- The control group receives a placebo.

- Both groups are "blind," meaning the patients in each group do not know whether they are receiving the drug or the placebo.

- In some cases, the doctors do not know if the patients are receiving the drug or the placebo. When this is done, the experiment is said to be double blind.

Checkpoint Solution

The question that is most likely to produce more people saying they believe Australians are more sports-minded than Americans is question (a). This is because question (a) is a loaded question. The question expresses the opinion that Australians are more sports-minded than Americans and then asks whether you agree with it. The other two questions are impartial and do not offer an opinion. For a survey, question (c) would be the best question to ask because it offers more choices and does not phrase the question in a yes/no format.

Chapter 10

Section 10.1   Health & Fitness

Example 1 Instructor Notes

Note that the MetLife tables are available at *Math.andYou.com. Ideal Body Weight Calculators* using the formulas by Halls, Hamwi, and Robinson are located in Tools. (Students will encounter the Robinson formula in Exercises 1–6.)
(See *http://math.andyou.com/tools/bodyweight_calculator.html*.)

According to the National Center for Health Statistics, the median height and weight for males ages 20–29 years are 5 feet 10 inches and 180 pounds, and for females ages 20–29 years are 5 feet 5 inches and 160 pounds. Substitute these median heights into the formulas by Halls and Hamwi. Substitute 10 for the male because the median height is 10 inches above 5 feet and substitute 5 for the female because the median height is 5 inches above 5 feet.

A male who is 5 feet 10 inches tall	**A female who is 5 feet 5 inches tall**
Halls: Weight $= 125 + 5(10) = 175$	Halls: Weight $= 145 + 5(5) = 170$
Hamwi: Weight $= 106 + 6(10) = 166$	Hamwi: Weight $= 100 + 5(5) = 125$

Notice that the formulas by Steven B. Halls give weights that are closer to the median weight for both males and females.

Checkpoint Solution

Students can use the graphs on page 452 to approximate the graphs of the average weights of men and women.

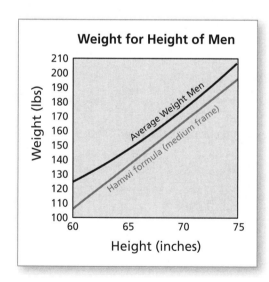

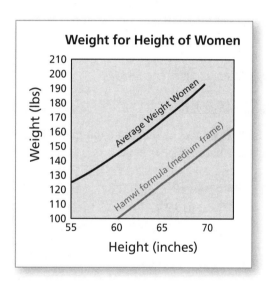

The graphs show that the Hamwi weights are consistently below the average weights of men and women. The Hamwi weights for men are fairly close to average, but the Hamwi weights for women are considerably lower than the average weights of women.

Example 2 Instructor Notes

To make a spreadsheet similar to the one in Example 2, have students use the steps given in the Math help at *Math.andYou.com*.
(See *http://math.andyou.com/content/10/01/data/mthu_data_1001_453_02.xls*.)

Checkpoint Solution

Body Mass Index of Woman:

In the formula for body mass index, substitute the body fat percentage that you calculated in Example 2 for BF, the woman's age for age, and 0 for gender because she is female.

$$BMI = (0.83 \times BF) - (0.19 \times age) + (9 \times gender) + 4.5$$
$$= (0.83 \times 25.4) - (0.19 \times 24) + (9 \times 0) + 4.5 \qquad \text{Substitute.}$$
$$\approx 21.0$$

The woman has a body mass index of about 21.0.

Body Mass Index of Man:

Part 1: Calculate Body Fat Percentage

First, calculate the man's body fat percentage.

Factor 1: (total body weight $\times$ 1.082) + 94.42 = (210 $\times$ 1.082) + 94.42 = 321.64
Factor 2: waist circumference $\times$ 4.15 = 36 $\times$ 4.15 = 149.4
Lean body mass = factor 1 − factor 2 = 321.64 − 149.4 = 172.24
Body fat weight = total body weight − lean body mass = 210 − 172.24 = 37.76
Body fat percentage = (body fat weight $\times$ 100)/total body weight
$$= (37.76 \times 100)/210 \approx 18.0$$

The man's body fat percentage is about 18.0%.

Part 2: Calculate Body Mass Index

In the formula for body mass index, substitute the man's body fat percentage for BF, the man's age for age, and 1 for gender because he is male.

$$BMI = (0.83 \times BF) - (0.19 \times age) + (9 \times gender) + 4.5$$
$$\approx (0.83 \times 18.0) - (0.19 \times 26) + (9 \times 1) + 4.5 \qquad \text{Substitute.}$$
$$= 23.5$$

The man has a body mass index of about 23.5.

Example 3 Instructor Notes

Using a spreadsheet is helpful when finding the target heart rate zone for different ages. (See *http://math.andyou.com/content/10/01/data/mthu_data_1001_454_03.xls.*)

The Cleveland Clinic gives the following steps to find your heart rate. (See *http://www.cchs.net/health/health-info/docs/0900/0984.asp?index=5508.*)

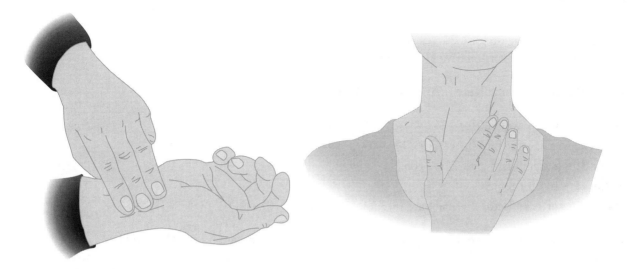

1. Place the tips of your index, second, and third fingers on the palm side of your other wrist, below the base of the thumb. Or, place the tips of your index and second fingers on your lower neck, on either side of your windpipe. (See illustrations.)

2. Press lightly with your fingers until you feel the blood pulsing beneath your fingers. You might need to move your fingers around slightly up or down until you feel the pulsing.

3. Use a watch with a second hand, or look at a clock with a second hand.

4. Count the beats you feel for 10 seconds. Multiply this number by six to get your heart rate per minute.

$$\text{Heart rate} = (\text{beats in 10 seconds}) \times 6$$

Checkpoint Solution

Instead of comparing fat calories burned per minute at the two rates, compare fat calories burned per minute as a percent of total calories burned per minute.

60–65% MHR: $\dfrac{\text{Fat calories burned per minute}}{\text{Total calories burned per minute}} = \dfrac{2.43}{4.86} = 0.5$

80–85% MHR: $\dfrac{\text{Fat calories burned per minute}}{\text{Total calories burned per minute}} = \dfrac{2.70}{6.86} \approx 0.39$

In the 60–65% zone, 50% of the total calories burned per minute are fat calories. In the 80–85% zone, only about 39% of the total calories burned per minute are fat calories. Because a greater percent of the total calories burned per minute are fat calories in the 60–65% zone than in the 80–85% zone, the 60–65% zone is called the "fat burning zone."

Example 4 Instructor Notes

Students can use the spreadsheet at *Math.andYou.com* to determine their daily caloric needs (or outgoing calories). In the spreadsheet, the basal metabolic rate (BMR) is multiplied by the activity level. So, the outgoing calories are $1888 \times 1.725 \approx 3257$. (See *http://math.andyou.com/content/10/01/data/mthu_data_1001_455_04.xls*.)

Checkpoint Solution

Sample answer:

The following calculations are for a 21-year-old woman who weighs 125 pounds, is 64 inches tall, and is extra active. The woman's daily caloric intake is 2000 calories.

Formula for Basal Metabolic Rate (BMR) in calories per day

> **Factor 1:** $4.545 \times$ weight (lb) $= 4.545 \times 125 \approx 568$
> **Factor 2:** $15.875 \times$ height (in.) $= 15.875 \times 64 = 1016$
> **Factor 3:** $5 \times$ age (yr) $= 5 \times 21 = 105$
> **Factor 4:** -161 for females
> **BMR** $=$ Factor 1 $+$ Factor 2 $-$ Factor 3 $+$ Factor 4 $\approx 568 + 1016 - 105 + (-161) = 1318$

Because the woman is extra active, multiply the woman's basal metabolic rate by 1.900 to find her outgoing calories.

> Outgoing calories $=$ BMR $\times$ activity level multiplier $\approx 1318 \times 1.900 \approx 2504$

To find the woman's daily calorie balance, subtract outgoing calories from incoming calories.

> Daily calorie balance $=$ incoming calories $-$ outgoing calories
> $$\approx 2000 - 2504$$
> $$= -504 \text{ calories}$$

Because the woman has a negative daily calorie balance, she should be losing weight.

Alternative solution:

Students can also use a spreadsheet to solve this problem.
(See *http://math.andyou.com/content/10/01/data/mthu_data_1001_455_04a.xls*.)

Example 5 Instructor Notes

In Example 5, the third statement is represented in the solution. About 28% of females are physically active, so a little bit more than one quarter of the graph should be for physically active. About 46% of males are physically active, so a little bit less than one half of the graph should be for physically active.

Checkpoint Solution

Sample answer:

The following circle graph represents the claim that reads, "Cardiovascular disease accounts for about 34% of all deaths in America."

Deaths in America

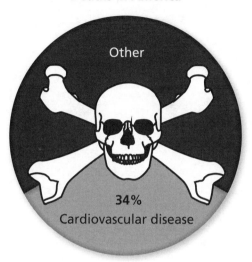

Example 6 Instructor Notes

In Example 6, the units for glucose and insulin may not be familiar and could be confusing. Encourage students not to be distracted by these units. All that is important for the example is to use the graph to describe the interaction between glucose and insulin.

Checkpoint Solution

Sample answer:

Both high cholesterol and high blood glucose levels increase your risk for cardiovascular disease. High blood glucose levels can damage your heart over time and increase your risk for cardiovascular disease. High blood glucose levels can also increase your LDL cholesterol and decrease your HDL cholesterol, which increases your risk for cardiovascular disease.

Section 10.2 The Olympics

Example 1 Instructor Notes

A look at records set in various sports over the past century shows that humans continue to run faster, jump higher, and throw farther than ever before. What is causing this?

One factor is training. Physiologists work to identify which systems in the human body limit performance, and then training techniques are used to improve those systems. Also, sports psychologists work with athletes to help them develop their minds to allow them to reach their peak performances. Also, physical trainers use devices to monitor athletes' bodies, providing more feedback than was available 20 years ago.

Equipment has also improved. For instance, bicycles are lighter and more aerodynamic than ever before. Even sports with no obvious technology, such as swimming, have benefited from technology, like new swimsuits that reduce drag.

Checkpoint Solution

Students can enter the data into a spreadsheet and make a scatter plot.
(See *http://math.andyou.com/content/10/02/data/mthu_data_1002_462_01a.xls*.)

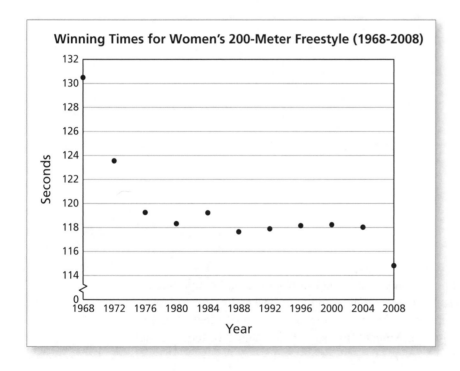

The winning time decreased dramatically between 1968 and 1976. From 1980 to 2004, the winning time stayed close to 118 seconds. The Olympic record set in 1988 was not broken until 2008. Italian swimmer Federica Pellegrini's winning time in 2008 was not only an Olympic record, but a world record. In response to the large number of swimmers who broke world records in 2008, FINA banned rubberized swimsuits from competition in 2010. You can read more about FINA's ban on the controversial swimsuits at *http://abcnews.go.com/Politics/full-body-swimsuit-now-banned-professional-swimmers/ story?id=9437780*.

Example 2 Instructor Notes

In Example 2, the graph shows the winning heights in meters. Remind students that they can use the *Length (Distance) Converter* located in Tools to convert units of measure. (See *http://math.andyou.com/tools/length_converter.html*.) For instance, 6 meters is about 20 feet. Also, note the gap in the graph from 1936 to 1948. The Olympics were not held during this time due to World War II.

The graph below shows the men's pole vault world record progression. Note the gap in the graph from the early 1940s to the late 1950s. Pole vault technology improved in the 1950s, and the world record heights started rising again.

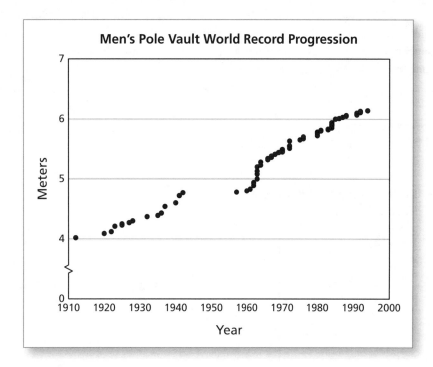

Checkpoint Solution

Sample answer:

Improvements in technology, including changes in the material from which the poles are made, allow high school students to pole vault at heights that would have broken Olympic records in 1950. For instance, in 1952, the Olympic record was 4.55 meters, or about 15 feet. At a 2007 Illinois state competition, high school junior Mitchell Erickson pole vaulted 16 feet 9 inches.

Example 3 Instructor Notes

In Example 3, note that the 1932 winning time is an outlier. You may want to review from Section 9.2 that an outlier in a data set is a value that is much larger (or smaller) than most of the other values in the data set. Also, note the gap in the graph from 1936 to 1948. The Olympics were not held during this time due to World War II.

Here are some other reasons for the improved times.

- More aerodynamic skating suits were developed.

- The use of "artificial" ice. Machines were invented to make ice for the tracks, which provided a consistent surface for the skaters to use.

- Skating on indoor tracks. With outdoor tracks, the skaters had no protection form the wind (and other weather conditions), which could adversely affect their times.

Checkpoint Solution

Students can enter the data into a spreadsheet and make a scatter plot.
(See *http://math.andyou.com/content/10/02/data/mthu_data_1002_464_03a.xls*.)

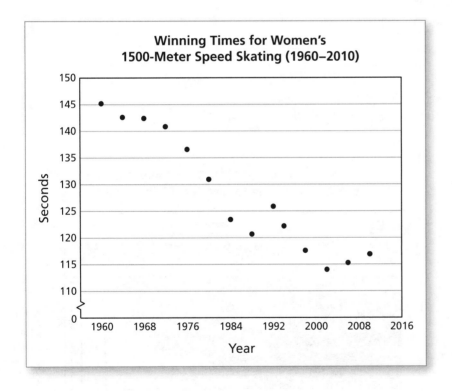

In general, the winning times for women's 1500-meter speed skating have decreased over the years.

Example 4 Instructor Notes

In Example 4, students can use the techniques from Section 1.4. To determine the average speed in miles per hour, you need to multiply 2 miles in 100 seconds by two carefully chosen forms of the number 1. Because there are 60 seconds in 1 minute and 60 minutes in 1 hour, you can multiply as shown.

$$\frac{2 \text{ mi}}{100 \text{ sec}} = \frac{2 \text{ mi}}{100 \text{ sec}} \times \frac{60 \text{ sec}}{1 \text{ min}} \times \frac{60 \text{ min}}{1 \text{ hr}}$$

$$= \frac{2 \text{ mi}}{100 \text{ sec}} \times \frac{60 \text{ sec}}{1 \text{ min}} \times \frac{60 \text{ min}}{1 \text{ hr}}$$

$$= \frac{7200 \text{ mi}}{100 \text{ hr}}$$

$$= 72 \text{ mi/hr}$$

Another way to determine the average speed in miles per hour is to write 2 miles in 100 seconds as 0.02 mi/sec. Then use the *Velocity Converter* located in Tools to convert from miles per second (mile/second) to miles per hour (mile/hour).
(See *http://math.andyou.com/tools/velocity_converter.html*.)

Checkpoint Solution

Sample answer:

You can use a spreadsheet to make a bar graph of the top 15 times.
(See *http://math.andyou.com/content/10/02/data/mthu_data_1002_465_04a.xls*.)

Another way to represent the data is by showing each skier in terms of time behind the winner. The stacked bar graph at the right illustrates the closeness of the top 15 times in the men's downhill at the 2010 Winter Olympics. Notice that all 15 skiers were within 1 second of winning.

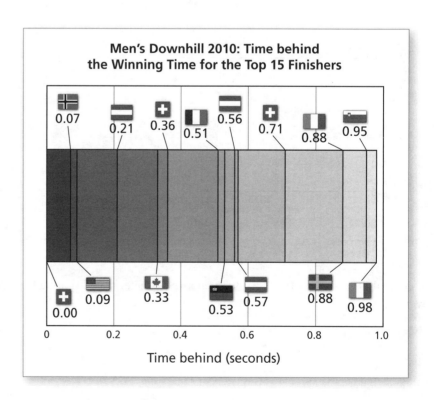

Example 5 Instructor Notes

In the Math Help at *Math.andYou.com*, students can read a collection of rules governing the panel of judges for a diving competition. Or they can check out the rules at the International Swimming Federation. (See *http://www.fina.org/H2O/*.)

Checkpoint Solution

Links to the dive videos are available at *Math.andYou.com*.

Sample answer:

Dive 1: I awarded this dive an 8.5 because it was well-executed. The diver's toes were pointed and feet were touching. The diver reached a sufficient height above the board when diving. There was very little splashing on entry. The diver was straight up and down on entry to the water.

Dive 2: I awarded this dive a 9.0 because it was well-executed. The diver's toes were pointed and feet were touching and the diver reached a decent height above the board when diving. There was some splashing. The diver was straight up and down on entry to the water.

Dive 3: I awarded this dive a 9.5 because it was very well-executed. The diver's toes were pointed and feet were touching. The diver was very composed throughout the motion of the dive and the dive was very acrobatic. Splashing was minimal and the diver's entry was in a straight up and down position.

Dive 4: I awarded this dive a 10.0 because it was incredibly well-executed. The diver's toes were pointed and feet were touching. The diver's acrobatics were incredibly well done and there was minimal splashing. The diver entered the water in a straight up and down position. What was particularly striking about this dive was how half-way through it changes from a tucked-in position to a flawless straight up and down position right before hitting the water.

Dive 5: I awarded this dive an 8.5 because it was well-executed. The diver's toes were pointed and feet were touching. The dive did not seem as composed as some of the others. The height from the board when jumping was not extremely high. There was some splashing. The acrobatics were well done but not as high-level as some of the others. The diving form looked a little loose.

Example 6 Instructor Notes

Before calculating the distance points in the solution to Example 6, note that

- 60 points are awarded for reaching the K-point.

- 1.8 points are awarded for each meter beyond the K-point (or deducted when the jump is short of the K-point).

The distance of the jump is 125 meters. Because the K-point is at 120 meters, the distance points are calculated as shown.

$$60 + 1.8(125 - 120) = 60 + 1.8(5) = 60 + 9 = 69 \text{ points}$$

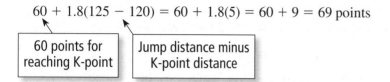

60 points for reaching K-point

Jump distance minus K-point distance

In the Math Help at *Math.andYou.com*, students can read a few rules governing the panel of judges for a ski jumping competition. Or they can check out the rules at the International Ski Federation. (See *http://www.fis-ski.com/uk/disciplines/skijumping/.*)

Checkpoint Solution

Students can enter the data into a spreadsheet and make a scatter plot. (See *http://math.andyou.com/content/10/02/data/mthu_data_1002_467_06a.xls.*)

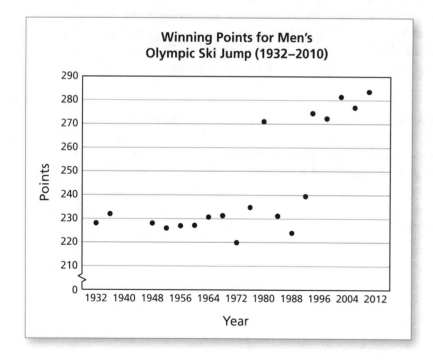

From 1932 through 1992, the scores were mostly between 220 and 240. From 1994 onward, the scores were higher than 270.

Section 10.3 Professional Sports

Example 1 Instructor Notes

Here is how the batting averages and earned run averages were found for the American League and the National League in 2010. Complete versions of these tables are provided at *Math.andYou.com*, including links to the original data at *mlb.com*.

American League		
Team	Hits	At Bats
Baltimore Orioles	1440	5554
~~Boston Red S~~	~~1516~~	~~5646~~
~~Texas Rangers~~	~~1556~~	~~5655~~
Toronto Blue Jays	1364	5495
Total	**20,131**	**77,467**

National League		
Team	Hits	At Bats
Arizona Diamondbacks	1366	5473
~~Atlanta Braves~~	~~1441~~	~~5463~~
~~St. Louis Cardinals~~	~~1436~~	~~5542~~
Washington Nationals	1355	5418
Total	**22,423**	**87,886**

$$\text{Batting Average} = \frac{\text{Hits}}{\text{At bats}} = \frac{20,131}{77,467} \approx 0.260 \qquad \text{Batting Average} = \frac{\text{Hits}}{\text{At bats}} = \frac{22,423}{87,886} \approx 0.255$$

Note that in the tables below, fractions are used for the innings pitched while decimals are used in the original data at *mlb.com*. The decimals represent the outs in an inning. So, 0.1 is 1 out or 1/3 of an inning, and 0.2 is 2 outs or 2/3 of an inning.

American League		
Team	Earned Runs	Innings Pitched
Baltimore Orioles	733	$1436\frac{1}{3}$
~~Boston Red Sox~~	~~679~~	~~$1456\frac{2}{3}$~~
~~Texas Rangers~~	~~656~~	~~$1455\frac{2}{3}$~~
Toronto Blue Jays	676	$1440\frac{2}{3}$
Total	**9,295**	**20,217**

National League		
Team	Earned Runs	Innings Pitched
Arizona Diamondbacks	765	1432
~~Atlanta Braves~~	~~569~~	~~$1439\frac{1}{3}$~~
~~St. Louis Cardinals~~	~~577~~	~~$1455\frac{2}{3}$~~
Washington Nationals	658	1435
Total	**10,300**	**$23,088\frac{1}{3}$**

$$\text{ERA} = \frac{\text{Earned runs}}{\text{Innings pitched}} \times 9 = \frac{9295}{20,217} \times 9 \approx 4.14 \qquad \text{ERA} = \frac{\text{Earned runs}}{\text{Innings pitched}} \times 9 = \frac{10,300}{23,088\frac{1}{3}} \times 9 \approx 4.02$$

Checkpoint Solution

Sample answer:

Batting average is defined by Major League Baseball as the total number of safe hits divided by the total number of times at bat. Derek Jeter had a high number of times at bat in 1996 compared to 1995, so his combined average is closer to his average in 1996. David Justice had a high number of times at bat in 1995 compared to 1996, so his combined average is closer to his average in 1995. Jeter's average in 1996 is higher than Justice's average in 1995, so when you combine the two years, Jeter's average ends up being higher.

Example 2 Instructor Notes

Here are some observations about the strike zone for Ted Williams on page 475.

- Remember that this is his estimate. It is not his actual averages for these locations in the strike zone.

- The weakest area is the 12 baseballs in the lower right corner. So, the weakest area takes up $\frac{12}{77}$ or about 15.6% of the strike zone.

- Balls towards the center of the strike zone have the highest averages. This is the case for most players because the player doesn't have to make any adjustments compared to when a ball is on the outer edge, they might have to lean to reach it.

- His career batting average was .344. There are 19 baseballs with averages higher than that, which is $\frac{19}{77}$ or about 24.7% of the strike zone.

- The strike zone is not the only area where players get hits. Players also swing at pitches that are outside of the strike zone.

Checkpoint Solution

Sample answer:

Ted Williams considered the center of the strike zone to be his strongest.

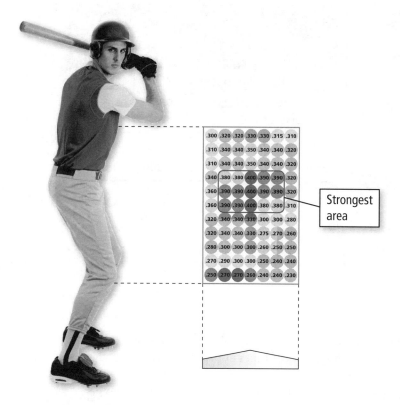

Ted Williams must have believed that he could hit balls best when they were pitched waist-high and to the center. He did not have to extend his arms downward or upward and could obtain the power he wanted.

Example 3 Instructor Notes

Students can read more information about passer rating in the Math Help at *Math.andYou.com*.

Checkpoint Solution

Students can calculate the passer rating for each quarterback as shown in the Checkpoint Solution at *Math.andYou.com*. The calculations for Ben Roethlisberger are shown below.

Ben Roethlisberger:

$$a = 5\left(\frac{\text{completions}}{\text{attempts}} - 0.3\right) = 5\left(\frac{16}{20} - 0.3\right) = 2.5 \qquad \text{Lowered to 2.375.}$$

$$b = 0.25\left(\frac{\text{yards}}{\text{attempts}} - 3\right) = 0.25\left(\frac{261}{20} - 3\right) = 2.5125 \qquad \text{Lowered to 2.375.}$$

$$c = 20\left(\frac{\text{touchdowns}}{\text{attempts}}\right) = 20\left(\frac{3}{20}\right) = 3 \qquad \text{Lowered to 2.375.}$$

$$d = 2.375 - 25\left(\frac{\text{interceptions}}{\text{attempts}}\right) = 2.375 - 25(0) = 2.375$$

$$\textbf{Passer rating} = 100\left(\frac{a+b+c+d}{6}\right) = 100\left(\frac{2.375 + 2.375 + 2.375 + 2.375}{6}\right) \approx 158.3$$

All four of the quarterbacks had a perfect passer rating because all four quarterbacks had a rating of 158.3.

Example 4 Instructor Notes

Review the meaning of each curve on the win probability graph on page 477. For instance, $+7$ means the team with the ball is winning by 7 points. Remind students that this graph is just for the team that has the ball. Below are some observations about the graph.

- To find the win probability for the team without the ball, subtract the win probability of the team with the ball in the graph from 100%. Because the probability of winning for a team with the ball that is 3 points ahead with 10 minutes remaining is about 85%, the probability of winning for a team without the ball that is 3 points behind with 10 minutes remaining is about $100\% - 85\% = 15\%$.

- Notice that the graph drops off quickly for a team with the ball that is losing by 7 points with about 20 minutes remaining. There are similar drop-offs for a team with the ball that is losing by 1 or 3 points with about 15 minutes to go.

- Notice that for any point in the game, the team with the ball and a lead has a greater than 50% chance of winning.

- Notice that from between 20 minutes remaining and 10 minutes remaining, the probability of a team with the ball winning while losing by 1 point is greater than the probability of a team with the ball winning while winning by 1 point. This seems contradictory to common sense because you would expect the probability while winning to be greater than the probability while losing. One factor that may influence this is that some teams play too conservatively with a small lead and play more aggressively when they are losing.

Checkpoint Solution

Sample answer:

You could use the graph to make decisions such as whether to go for a 4th down and whether to kick a field goal or go for a touchdown depending on the stage of the game. The graph could also help you determine whether to play aggressively or conservatively depending on where you stand and how late it is in the game. For instance, if you lead by 3 points, you do not want to play too conservatively with 10–15 minutes remaining because the win probability graph shows a slight dip during that time. On the other hand, if you are down by 1 near the beginning of the 4th quarter, you should adopt an aggressive strategy and try to take the lead. If you are down by 7, you want to take the lead before the 20-minute mark (close to the end of the 3rd quarter) because there is a dramatic drop-off in win probability. If you are down by 1 or 3, the same applies for a few minutes into the 4th quarter.

Example 5 Instructor Notes

Here are some observations about the U.S. Open and the graph on page 478.

- Here is the order of the rounds: first round, second round, third round, fourth round, quarterfinals, semifinals, and finals. The only time the top four seeds would play each other would be in the semifinals or the finals.

- At least two of the top four seeds reached the fourth round in every year except 1973.

- For any year, the sum of the percents adds up to 100%. This is because the outcomes are win in straight sets, win by dropping one or two sets, or lose.

- Notice that from 1977 to 1988 none of the top four seeds lost in the first three rounds.

Checkpoint Solution

a. The three line graphs always total 100% for a given year. A player can either win the first three sets and win the match, lose one or two of the sets and win the match, or lose the match. Those are the only three possibilities. If you add up the number of straight set wins, wins with one or two dropped sets, and losses and then divide that number by the total number of matches, you must get 1.

b. In the years in which there were no losses, the green value and the red value must add to 100. The green and red lines are mirror images of each other reflected over the 50% line because the following is true for any number X.

$$\begin{array}{r} 50 + X \\ + \ 50 - X \\ \hline 100 + 0 \end{array}$$

If the green graph is a certain distance above the 50% line, the red graph will be the exact same distance below the 50% line and vice versa.

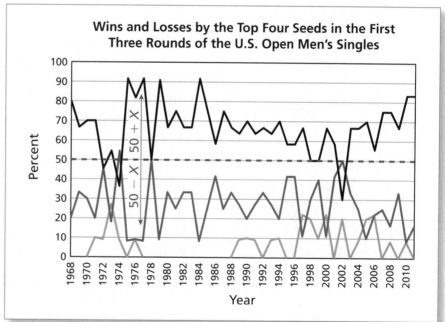

Wins and Losses by the Top Four Seeds in the First Three Rounds of the U.S. Open Men's Singles

Example 6 Instructor Notes

Help your students to see why the graphs at the top of Example 6 make sense. For people with a low skill level, their bowling ball will be all over the lane, so there is a wide dispersion. For people with a high skill level, they will hit the head pin with almost every throw, so there is a narrow dispersion. Notice that the graphs are normal distributions because they are bell-shaped. For more information on dispersion and normal distributions, students can refer to Section 9.3, pages 424 and 426.

Checkpoint Solution

Sample answer:

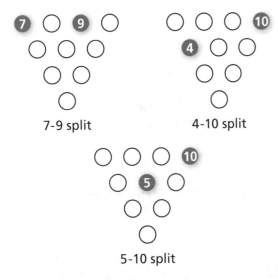

7-9 split

4-10 split

5-10 split

Section 10.4 Outdoor Sports

Example 1 Instructor Notes

Explain to students that grade refers to the amount of inclination of a road, trail, railroad track, or other surface (see figure). In some instances, you might see grade called slope or incline. Slope can be calculated using the ratio

$$\frac{\text{Rise}}{\text{Run}}.$$

Grade is usually listed as a percent. For instance,

$$\frac{\text{Rise}}{\text{Run}} = 0.20 = 20\%.$$

Note that the horizontal axis in Example 1 shows each grade as a decimal. As a percent, each grade would be (from left to right)

$$-60\%, -40\%, -20\%, 0\%, 20\%, 40\%, \text{ and } 60\%.$$

Notice the following about grade.

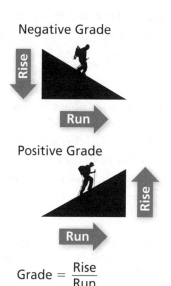

Grade $= \dfrac{\text{Rise}}{\text{Run}}$

- A negative grade is "downhill."

- A positive grade is "uphill."

- A zero grade is "level."

- "Large" numbers, such as -60% or 40%, represent grades that are steeper than "smaller" numbers, such as -30% or 20%.

Checkpoint Solution

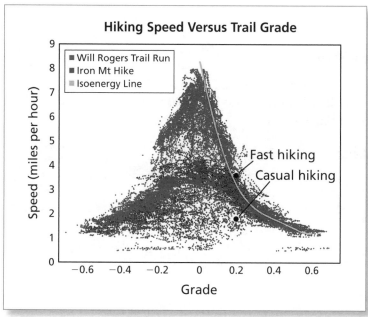

The two speeds fall within the range of the speeds shown in the scatter plot.

Example 2 Instructor Notes

Point out in Example 2 that for the sake of comparison the amount of UV radiation in Seattle is assumed to be 1.

In the solution to Example 2, note that 1.05 represents an increase of 5%. Also, because the UV radiation increases about 5% for every 1000 feet, think of 5000 feet as 5 thousand feet and 20,000 feet as 20 thousand feet. So, the solution to part (b) is 1.05 times itself 5 times, which is written as $(1.05)^5$. The solution to part (c) is 1.05 times itself 20 times, which is written as $(1.05)^{20}$. You can also think of the UV radiation increase with elevation as exponential growth (see Section 4.1), where the initial value is 1 and the rate of growth is 0.05. The model is shown below

$$A = 1(1 + 0.05)^n$$

Initial amount of UV radiation	Number of feet in 1000s

You can evaluate the model $A = (1.05)^n$ for $n = 0$, $n = 5$, and $n = 20$, which is 0 feet, 5000 feet, and 20,000 feet, respectively.

$A = (1.05)^0 = 1$	0 feet
$A = (1.05)^5 \approx 1.276$	5000 feet
$A = (1.05)^{20} \approx 2.653$	20,000 feet

Checkpoint Solution

- For the sake of comparison, assume that the amount of UV radiation in Reno is 1.

- The difference in elevations between the peak of Mount Whitney and Reno is $14,000 - 4000 = 10,000$ feet. Because the peak of Mount Whitney is 10,000 feet higher than Reno, the amount of UV radiation near the peak is

  $$(1.05)^{10} \approx 1.63 \qquad \text{10,000 feet difference in elevations}$$

  or about 63% more than the UV radiation in Reno.

- The difference in elevations between the peak of Mount Everest and Reno is $29,000 - 4000 = 25,000$ feet. Because the peak of Mount Everest is 25,000 feet higher than Reno, the amount of UV radiation near the peak is

  $$(1.05)^{25} \approx 3.39 \qquad \text{25,000 feet difference in elevations}$$

  or about 239% more than the UV radiation in Reno.

Example 3 Instructor Notes

A cubic foot is defined as the volume of a cube with edges one foot long. Explain to students that in *Math & YOU*, cubic foot is abbreviated as ft³.

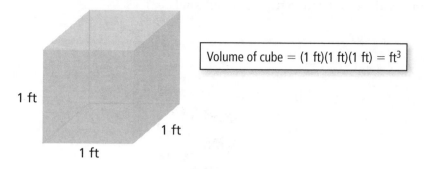

Volume of cube = (1 ft)(1 ft)(1 ft) = ft³

1 ft

1 ft

1 ft

Students can use the *Volume Converter* located in Tools to determine that 1 cubic foot is about 7.5 gallons. (See *http://math.andyou.com/tools/capacity_volume_converter.html.*)

Checkpoint Solution

Sample answer:

The creek has a discharge above 150 cubic feet per second from February 25 through February 26, on March 15, and on March 28. There are about 4 days in the time period that meet your criteria. So, the percent of the days from January 26 through May 26 (121 days) that the creek water is high enough is

$$\frac{\text{Days above 150 ft}^3\text{/sec}}{\text{Total days}} = \frac{4}{121} \approx 0.033.$$

The creek meets your criteria about 3.3% of the time.

Example 4 Instructor Notes

The summary in Example 4 is from an article at *Physlink.com*.
(See *http://www.physlink.com/education/askexperts/ae438.cfm*.) The following illustration shows an example of "tacking," with the boat sailing from left to right, into the wind.

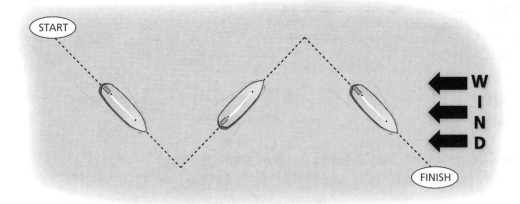

Checkpoint Solution

Sample answer:

The sailboat's weight pulls the ship downward and the sailboat's buoyancy pushes the ship upward with equal force. If the sailboat is tilted, the center of buoyancy will move sideways and the buoyant force will push upward to return the ship to its original position.

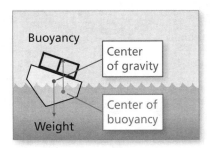

Example 5 Instructor Notes

The graph below was created using data from the National Sporting Goods Association. (See *http://www.nsga.org//i4a/pages/index.cfm?pageid=3479*.) The graph shows the numbers of people (in millions), ages 7 years and older, who participated at least once in the sport listed.

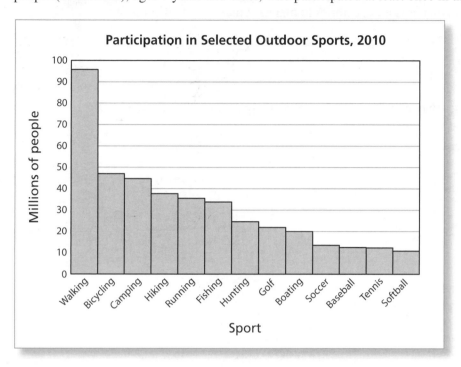

Participation in Selected Outdoor Sports, 2010

Millions of people (y-axis: 0, 10, 20, 30, 40, 50, 60, 70, 80, 90, 100)

Sport (x-axis: Walking, Bicycling, Camping, Hiking, Running, Fishing, Hunting, Golf, Boating, Soccer, Baseball, Tennis, Softball)

Checkpoint Solution

Sample answer:

Students can use a spreadsheet to graphically represent the data. (See *http://math.andyou.com/content/10/04/data/mthu_data_1004_488_05a.xls*.)

- Recreation
- Exercise
- Commute to school/work
- Personal errand
- Visit friend/relative
- Go on a bicycle ride
- Other

Example 6 Instructor Notes

Discuss with students that the graph in Example 6 shows that the number of calories burned by males is greater than the number of calories burned by females for each sport. This is true because, according to the Mayo Clinic, men usually have less body fat and more muscle than women of the same age and weight. The human body burns more calories to maintain muscle, whether during activity or at rest.

Checkpoint Solution

Sample answer:

One reason that the Swedish athletes may have had a higher oxygen uptake than American athletes is because of differences in training and conditioning.

Answers to Exercises

Section 1.1   *(page 8)*

1. $47.08   2. $54.28   3. $39.41

4. Ten payments of $78.58 and one payment of $78.61

5. **a.** 1361.25 cal   6. **a.** 2736 cal
   b. 151.25 cal   **b.** 42.75 cal

7. b; The keystroke sequence in part (a) gives an incorrect total of $3810 because it will multiply 254 by 15. The actual total parking cost is $310.

8. a; The entire numerator gets added before being divided, giving an average book cost of $110.

9. a; Having parentheses around 3×10 and 5×2 clearly indicates the operations being performed, giving a total cost of $40.

10. b; 0.5 must be squared first, and then the result is multiplied by 25,000 so that the value of the car after 6 years is $6250.

11. **a.** 29 bags   **b.** $805.91

12. **a.** 48 gal
    b. Answers will vary. *Sample answer:* The paint is diluted so that each gallon of paint will cover more area.

13. About 499 sec   14. About 15,005 sec

15. Between about 399 seconds and about 1121 seconds

16. Between about 2098 seconds and about 3096 seconds

17. About 36,049 mph

18. Answers will vary. *Sample answer:* A light-year (ly) is a unit of length just under 10 trillion kilometers; The term light-year is used to measure distances between astronomical objects.

19. **a.** $-$21.49
    b. You have overpaid the electric company, so you have a credit of $21.49.
    c. $80.71; Your average monthly payment in the current year is $80.71. So as long as your monthly usage and the rates stay the same, you should make this your monthly payment next year.

20. b; This gives the correct result of $(8)(36) = 288$ cartridges.

21. **a.** Find the area of the base and the wall of the hot tub.
    b. 13,565 tiles

22. Offer A: Min = $49,752, Max = $79,752
    Offer B: Min = $62,400, Max = $77,400

23. Answers will vary. *Sample answer:* Offer B because the minimum compensation is much greater than the minimum compensation for Offer A, but the maximum compensation is only slightly less than the maximum compensation for Offer A. However, there are many non-financial factors that could also affect your decision.

24. Answers will vary.

Section 1.2   *(page 18)*

1. 3900 billion kWh

2. About 3000 billion; less than

3. About 12,829 kWh/person

4. About 16,667 kWh/person; Canada

5. **a.** Top-freezer: $63.59; Side-by-side: $76.21
   b. $12.62

6. **a.** $74.40   **b.** $10.81

7. **a.** $588.98   **b.** $445.13
   c. No, the difference in electricity costs is only $143.85.

8. $0.11

9. 1.2×10^{-3} m; meso-plankton

10. 9.1×10^{-6} m; nano-plankton

11. 0.0000002 m; femto-plankton

12. 600,000 lb; 6.0×10^5 lb

13. In 2009, the population of Texas was about 25 million; It is difficult to determine exact populations.

14. The price could be rewritten as $240,000. A difference of $100 does not make a difference for this amount of money.

15. The weight of a bag of sugar is about 5 pounds; You cannot be sure of the accuracy of the weight, plus most people would not care about the extra 0.01 pound.

16. The number of calories in a sandwich is about 300; It is difficult to determine exactly how much of each ingredient is contained in a sandwich, so the number of calories is an estimate.

17. **a.** 297 ft^2 **b.** $1036.53

18. a. 200 ft²; No, you cannot put linoleum under the counters because they are mounted to the floor.

   b. $250.00

19. When rounding each item to the nearest dollar, the sum is $31. So the grocery bill total of $31.62 is reasonable.

20. When rounding each item to the nearest dollar, the sum is $16. So the grocery bill total of $23.11 is not reasonable. (The actual total is $16.81.)

21. About 200 mi

22. Answers will vary. *Sample answer:* about 310 mi

23. Using a distance of 310 miles, the fuel cost for the trip will be about $42.

24. Answers will vary. *Sample answer:* about 4200 mi²

25. Answers will vary.

1.1–1.2 Quiz *(page 22)*

1. b; The keystroke sequence in part (a) gives an incorrect total of 1072 ft² because it will multiply 134 by 8. The actual area that you are adding to the patio is 92 ft².

2. About 2 hr, 2 min

3. a. About 3.4 people/km² **b.** About 3.75 people/km²

   c. Answers will vary. *Sample answer:* Either the total area or land area can be used, as long as it is specified as to which is being used.

4. a. About 6.2 people/km²

   b. The population density almost doubles; The northern territories cover a large area but not many people live there.

5. a. About 3968 people/km²

   b. Toronto has about 1000 times the population density of Canada.

6. Answers will vary.

Section 1.3 *(page 30)*

1. 67,860,000 men   **2.** 63,960,000 women

3. Method I: Add the populations of men and women, and then find 4% of that total.

   Method II: Separately find the number of men and women who have no opinion and add the two results.

   No; Method I gives a result of 9,600,000 people, while Method II gives a result of 8,430,000 people. The difference is probably due to round-off error when summarizing the poll results.

4. Answers will vary.   **5.** About 1,288,219 people

6. About 760,049 people   **7.** Answers will vary.

8. Answers will vary.   **9.** About 73.7%

10. About 48.3%   **11.** About 4.9%

12. About 24.8%   **13.** About 51.5%

14. Answers will vary. *Sample answer:* Using 0.75 centimeter for the length of the stapes, the length of an adult femur is about 6400% of the length of the stapes.

15. 18.75%   **16.** About 15.8%

17. 2.00 carats; The price range for a 2.00-carat diamond is $6892 to $16,092. $11,499 is in this range.

18. $2026 to $6892

19. A 2.00-carat diamond ring could cost anywhere from $0 to $14,066 more than a 1.00-carat diamond ring.

20. Answers will vary. *Sample answer:* A 0.50-carat diamond ring costs $2026, which is about 208.7% more than a 0.30-carat diamond ring that costs $971.

21. When comparing weights, a 0.50-carat diamond is about 67% heavier than a 0.30-carat diamond. However, when comparing diameters, a 0.50-carat diamond (5.2 mm) is not more than 60% larger than a 0.30-carat diamond (4.3 mm).

22. a. About 340%   **23. a.** 100% increase
   b. About 233%   **b.** 100% increase
   c. About 183%   **c.** 50% increase

24. In general, the higher the carat weight, the more the ring costs.

25. False; A loss of 20% of $1250 leaves you with $1000. A 20% increase of $1000 only takes you up to $1200.

26. False; Each year, the 3% increase is being taken on a larger base value, so your pay over a 5-year period will increase by more than 15%.

27. False; The 1% decrease is being taken from a larger amount than the 5% increase was taken, so the overall increase will be slightly less than 4%.

28. False; Because the coupon is for 10% off the purchase price, not the original price, you will receive less than 50% off the original price.

29. $1530

30. No; This would result in a negative dollar value for spending, which is not possible.

31. 92%

32. 5.5%; 10% of the amount allocated is 10% of the 5%, which is 0.5%. So, 5.5% of the company profits will go to the profit sharing plan.

Section 1.4 *(page 40)*

1. $2.45

2. $293.70

3. $10.40

4. $166.60

5. a. $300.51

    b. It will cost more to order the treadmill online.

    c. No; yes

6. a. 25 lb; no   **b.** Answers will vary.

7. b; 72 min

8. About 112.6 min

9. 0.625 lb

10. 38 oz

11. About 5.47 qt

12. 1968.75 gal

13. 0.8 sec

14. 75 beats/min; yes

15. About 20,321.5 ft

16. Mt. Everest, Mt. Aconcagua, Mt. McKinley, Mt. Kilimanjaro, Mt. Elbrus, Mt. Vinson, Mt. Carstensz

17. About 10 ft/min

18. Lower; Converting from meters to feet, Mt. Kosciuszko is only about 7310 feet high, while Mt. Carstensz is 16,024 feet high.

19. a. 156.2°F

    b. Yes; You could boil a potato, but it would take longer then normal to be cooked because it is at a lower boiling temperature than the normal boiling temperature of 100°C.

20. About −152.9°F

21. $352.63

22. $26.79

23. About $53.97

24. a. 3071.70 Canadian dollars

    b. 1729.74 British pounds

    c. 1652.62 European euros

    d. 61,367.08 Indian rupees

    e. 90,540.85 Japanese yen

    f. $960; $2040

1.3–1.4 Quiz *(page 44)*

1. 14,040,000 people

2. About 12%

3. The percent of the disabled population who are 65 years old and over is 3 times higher than the percent of the general population who are 65 and over. Answers will vary. *Sample answer:* As people get older, they are more likely, and have more opportunity, to develop some type of disability.

4. Answers will vary. *Sample answer:* Younger people have better immune systems and have had less of an opportunity to develop some type of disability.

5. 60 in.

6. About 80.67 ft/sec

7. 12 furlongs

8. About 38.33°C

Chapter 1 Review *(page 46)*

1. a; The keystroke sequence in part (b) gives an incorrect total cost of $480 because it will multiply 2 by 240. The actual total cost is $300.

2. Answers will vary.

3. About 3.5 hr

4. 10 hr

5. About 234.375 mi/yr

6. Answers will vary. *Sample answer:* The train probably makes some stops and slows down in residential areas.

7. a. 19,500,000 barrels/day   **b.** Answers will vary.

8. About 9.75×10^6

9. a. About 0.006 barrels/person/day

    b. The number of gallons of oil consumed by the United States is about 0.064 barrel/person/day, which is about 10 times more than the amount consumed by China per person per day.

10. Russia: About 6,750,000 net exports
Japan: About −4,700,000 net exports

A negative value indicates that a country must be importing oil from other countries or they have excess oil produced in previous years.

11. 189,800,000 barrels; Japan is one of Iran's top imports because Japan does not produce much oil but continues to consume oil.

12. $208,219,178.10 per day

13. 9,975,000 mi^3

14. 6,852,825 mi^3

15. About 51.6%

16. About 1.68%

17. About 20.1% increase

18–20. Answers will vary.

21. Monitor

22. 36 ft

23. **a.** 3.45 mi

    b. Territorial waters are now defined to be at most 12 nautical miles from the baseline of a coastal state.

24. **a.** 69,000 mi

    b. 20,000 leagues is the distance traveled under the sea, not the depth of the sea.

25. 30 ft   **26.** 2 fathoms

Section 2.1 *(page 58)*

1. About $0.17 per oz   **2.** About $0.06 per oz

3. About $0.05 per fl oz   **4.** About $2.99 per qt

5. **a.** $0.98 per lb   **b.** About 38%

6. **a.** $0.64 per lb   **b.** About 48%

    c. 1991; Farmers earned about 48% of the average retail price in 1991 compared to about 38% in 2009.

7. Brand A: About $0.09 per oz
Brand B: About $0.05 per oz
Brand C: $0.06 per oz

    Brand B is the best buy because it has the least unit price.

8. **a.** Brand D: About $0.07 per oz
No; Brand D is the biggest bottle, but Brands B and C have a lower unit price.

    b. No; You should buy the 20-oz bottle because it contains all the ketchup you need and it has the lowest retail price of $1.89.

9. **a.** About $0.07 per fl oz

    b. Answers will vary. *Sample answer:* Because it results in a lower unit price.

10. **a.** The unit price of homemade ketchup is about $0.20 per ounce, so Brand A has a lower unit price.

    b. About $0.03 per oz

11. $55.73   **12.** $75.57

13. **a.** $17.55   **14.** **a.** $7.88
    b. $45.75   **b.** $15.75

15. About $0.05   **16.** About $0.01

17. Decreasing the amount of product in a package but keeping the same price will increase the unit price, as shown in Exercises 15 and 16.

18. Yes, as long as the percent reduction of the size is greater than the percent reduction of the price.

19. **a.** $2.34

    b. The unit price in part (a) is $0.35 greater than the unit price on the package.

20. **a.** Brand A: $2.39 per gal
Brand B: $1.49 per gal
Brand B is the better buy.

    b. 192 fl oz

    c. Brand A: $1.19
Brand B: $1.49
Brand A is the better buy.

Section 2.2 *(page 68)*

1. About 122%   **2.** About 83%

3. About 64%   **4.** About 26%

5. $20   **6.** $37.50

7. About 48%

8. No; You must subtract $26 \times \$35 = \$910$ from the revenue to find the profit.

9. **a.** 3

    b. You can make a profit as long as the total revenue is greater than what you paid for the inventory. If you sell enough items above the wholesale price, then you can afford to sell some below the retail price and still make a profit.

10. **a–b.** Answers will vary.

    c. You need to make sure that you sell enough statues above the wholesale price such that you will make a profit even if you sell some at or below the wholesale price.

11. About 62%   **12.** About 20%

13. **a.** $298   **b.** $301.75

14. **a.** $303   **b.** $306   **c.** $258.40

15. **a.** 25%   **b.** $17.94

16. **a.** 20%   **b.** $18.26

17. 40%   **18.** About 17%

19. About 21%   **20.** About 8%

21. **a.** $13.20   **b.** 44%

    c. Answers will vary. *Sample answer:* Having a 30% off sale combined with an additional 20% off makes it appear that the store is having a 50% off sale, when it is actually having a 44% off sale.

22. Answers will vary. *Sample answer:* The first 50% off takes the price from $40 to $20. The second 50% off takes the price from $20 to $10.

2.1–2.2 Quiz   *(page 72)*

1. Brand A: About $0.27 per oz
   Brand B: About $0.12 per oz
   Brand C: About $0.09 per oz
   Brand A has the greatest unit price. Brand C has the least unit price.

2. $23.04   **3. a.** $1   **b.** About 101%

4. **a.** $2.15

   b. It reduces the unit price to 2.15/19.95 < $0.11 per oz.

   c. No; Brand C still gives you the most hand soap for your money because it is only $0.09 per oz.

5. **a.** About $0.01 per oz   **b.** About 89%

Section 2.3   *(page 80)*

1. $103.87   2. $53.19

3. 6%   4. 7%

5. Mississippi: $88.13
   Alabama: $50.36
   The best option would be to drive to Alabama. You would save $88.13 − $50.36 = $37.77 in sales tax. You would not spend nearly that much in gas for the 40-mile round trip.

6. Answers will vary. *Sample answer:* It would be beneficial to drive to another state when the cost of transportation does not come close to the amount of sales tax saved, as shown in Exercise 5.

7. City sales tax: 1.2%   8. Answers will vary.
   State sales tax: 6%

9. Wyoming; Alaska   10. $15.66; $2.33

11. $0.60   12. $1.19

13. About 19%

14. Rather than being a certain percent like sales tax, excise taxes are often a fixed dollar amount per sales unit.

15. $1380

16. Raw materials: $420
    Manufacturer: $660
    Dealer: $300
    The total tax is the same.

17. $24,380   18. $2805

19. Raw materials: $907.50
    Manufacturer: $1320
    Dealer: $577.50
    The total tax is the same.

20. $36,805

21. The gasoline excise tax in the United States is about 9% of the gasoline excise tax in Germany.

22. Answers will vary.   23. 1%

24. Answers will vary; Your friend's cost will most likely be higher because she will have to pay a shipping charge.

25. Bottle of cough syrup

26. Answers will vary.

27.

	Value-Added Tax	New Value
Raw materials	$90.00	$1,290.00
Manufacturer	$172.50	$3,762.50
Finisher	$37.50	$4,300.00
Retailer	$105.00	$5,805.00
Total	**$405.00**	

   7.5%

28. Answers will vary.

Section 2.4   *(page 90)*

1. 0.00   2. 225.00   3. 3055.00

4. (31.66)   5. 69.50   6. 100.00

7. 250.00

8. It means that you spent $80.19 less than what you budgeted.

9. $540.26   10. $431.84

11. Yes; check #220

12. This means that checks #218, #219, and #220 are also bad checks, which will cause you to have additional bank charges.

13. $319.01   14. $240   15. $54,000

16. About 12%   17. About 6%

18. Answers will vary. *Sample answer:* Not having any entertainment and miscellaneous expenses would eliminate about 11% of your expenses.

19. No   20. Answers will vary.

21. The budget compares well with the guidelines. The only areas of concern are that you are a little high on entertainment and a little low on retirement.

22. Answers will vary.

23. $50

24. Answers will vary. *Sample answer:* You should transfer the money to your savings because if you leave it in your checking account, then you might spend it on something else.

25. Answers will vary. *Sample answer:* You could reduce unnecessary expenses, such as entertainment and miscellaneous.

26. Answers will vary. *Sample answer:* Either cut back on that expense or reduce one of the other expenses in your budget.

27. If you do not account for the bank fees in your checkbook register, then you will think you have more money in your checking account than you actually do.

28. Answers will vary.

2.3–2.4 Quiz (page 94)

1. **a.** 4.5%
   b. 1%
   c. Oklahoma

2. **a.** $3.09
   b. About 16%

3. **a.** $1.7
   b. About 5.5%

4. Answers will vary. *Sample answer:* The magazine and cigarettes would be entered as miscellaneous, the sports drink and potato chips would be entered as food, and the gasoline would be entered as transportation.

5. $522.35

6. **a.** It means that check #363 is a bad check.
   b. $418.35

Chapter 2 Review (page 96)

1. 2-liter bottle: About $0.013 per fl oz
   6-pack: About $0.027 per fl oz
   Case: About $0.026 per fl oz

2. About $0.08 per fl oz; The 2-liter bottle has a much lower unit price.

3. $358.40

4. **a.** The unit price of four cases with the deal is about $0.017 per fluid ounce, which is less than the unit price for one case without the deal.
   b. $1.29

5. Bubble A will get larger.

6. Bubble C will get larger.

7. Bubble B; It is the smallest bubble, which means it has the least unit price.

8. Bubble A; It is the largest bubble, which means it has the greatest unit price.

9. $60

10. About 71%

11. $30

12. About 49%

13. 25%

14. **a.** Initial retail price; The initial retail price was $60, and the price after the third discount is $30, so it is 50% off the initial retail price.
    b. About 33%

15. $49.50

16. **a.** $27.50   **b.** $25

17. $0.16

18. 4%

19. $6.52

20. About 70%

21. Excise taxes are often a fixed dollar amount per sales unit, and a value-added tax is a certain percent added to a product at each stage of its manufacture or distribution.

22. **a.** There was about a 321% increase in the federal excise tax from 1995 to 2010.
    b. Answers will vary.

23. January: $10, February: $19, March: ($5), April: $25, May: $23, June: $17

24. It increases the budget shortage because you are spending more than you budgeted.

25. You will need to increase your budgeted amount for cell phone expenses. If you do not want to do this, then you are going to have to find a way to reduce your cell phone expenses.

26. $144.98

27. Yes. Even though the ratio for the 36% rule is about 36.1%, most banks would determine that you qualify for the home mortgage.

28. Answers will vary.

Section 3.1 (page 108)

1.

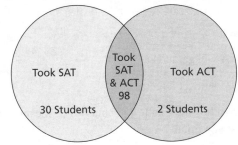

2. 130 **3.** 17 **4.** 27

5. 7 **6.** 4

7. Not likely; Of the 12 colleges with an enrollment of less than 2000, only 3 have tuitions less than $20,000 per year. This is reasonable in real life because small colleges need to charge a substantial amount in tuition to meet their expenses.

8. Answers will vary. *Sample answer:*

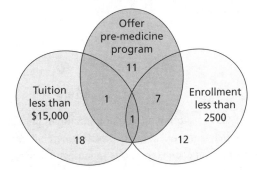

9.

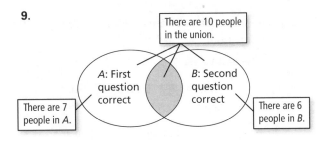

10. 3 **11.** 6

12. 6 **13.** 4

14. 12 **15.** 14

16. a. $15,000; Answers will vary. *Sample answer:* You should try to sell the boat to cover the cost of the taxes.

b. No, you might not be able to sell the boat for $15,000; Answers will vary.

17.

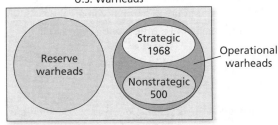

18. 2645 **19.** 2096

20. No; You do not know the number of Russia's reserve warheads.

21. a. The numbers in each category will be lower.

b. Answers will vary. The graph will continue to decrease.

22. Answers will vary.

23. 15

24. The first diagram; The first diagram shows all 15 possible results, but the second diagram does not show "*A* and *C*" or "*B* and *D*."

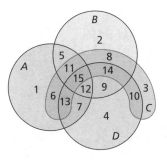

25. 97 **26.** 71 **27.** 47

28. Answers will vary. *Sample answer:* Prior to the U.S. financial crisis, the set diagram may have shown a larger set to U.S. companies that were also banking companies.

Section 3.2 (page 118)

1.

2.

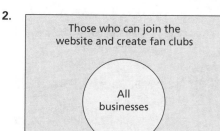

Those who can join the website and create fan clubs

All businesses

3.

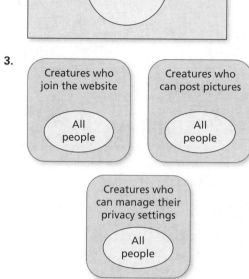

Creatures who join the website

All people

Creatures who can post pictures

All people

Creatures who can manage their privacy settings

All people

4.

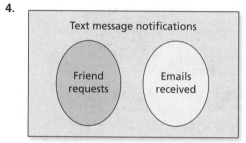

Text message notifications

Friend requests

Emails received

5.

Things that will be terminated

Unauthorized contests held on the website

or

Illegal activity

Unauthorized contests held on the website

6.

Avocado burger fans

Members who will receive coupon for a free burger

Jalapeno burger fans

7.

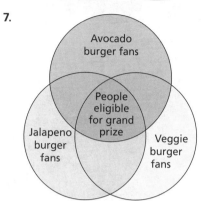

Avocado burger fans

People eligible for grand prize

Jalapeno burger fans

Veggie burger fans

8. a.

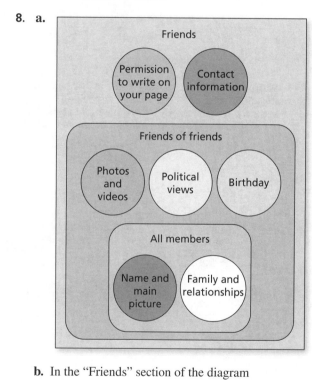

Friends

Permission to write on your page

Contact information

Friends of friends

Photos and videos

Political views

Birthday

All members

Name and main picture

Family and relationships

b. In the "Friends" section of the diagram

9.

Midget submarines

Japanese midget subs that were destroyed in the attack

Japanese machinery that was destroyed in the attack

10.

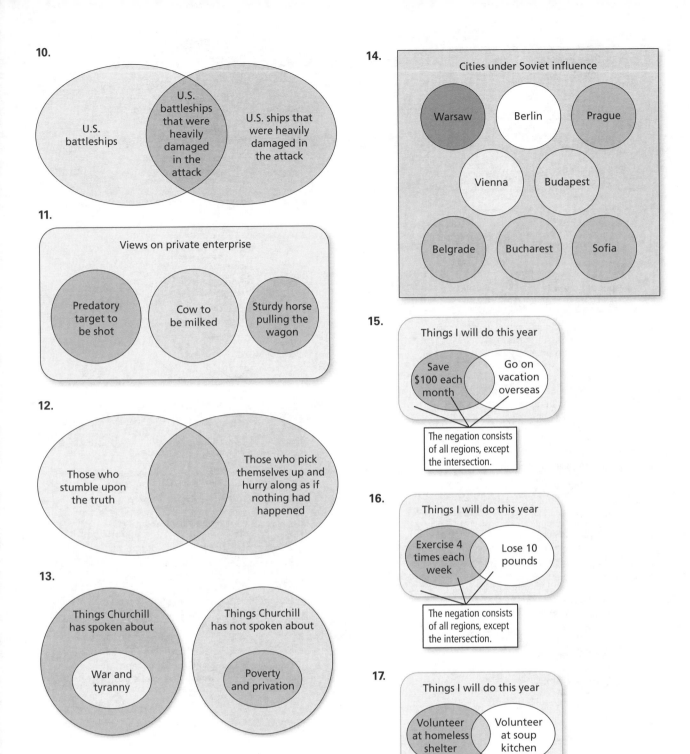

11.

12.

13.

14.

15.

16.

17.

18.

Things I will do this year

Stop biting my fingernails / Stop cracking my knuckles

The negation is when you do not stop either habit.

19.

Employees

Will not be paid for any holidays

Will not be paid for any vacation days

Will not be paid for any sick days

The shaded region is the complement of the intersection of the three sets. The negation is true if at least one employee is in the shaded region.

20.

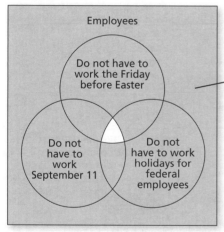

Employees

Do not have to work the Friday before Easter

Do not have to work September 11

Do not have to work holidays for federal employees

The shaded region is the complement of the intersection of the three sets. The negation is true if at least one employee is in the shaded region.

21.

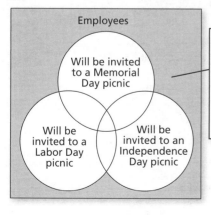

Employees

Will be invited to a Memorial Day picnic

Will be invited to a Labor Day picnic

Will be invited to an Independence Day picnic

The shaded region is the complement of the union of the three sets. The negation is true if at least one employee is in the shaded region.

22.

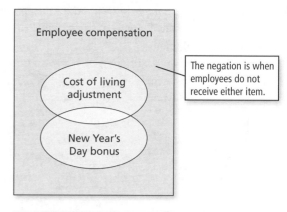

Employee compensation

Cost of living adjustment

New Year's Day bonus

The negation is when employees do not receive either item.

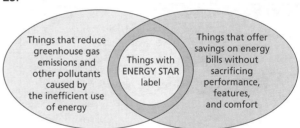

Employee compensation

Cost of living adjustment

New Year's Day bonus

Negation

23.

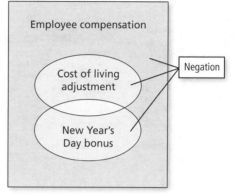

Things that reduce greenhouse gas emissions and other pollutants caused by the inefficient use of energy

Things with ENERGY STAR label

Things that offer savings on energy bills without sacrificing performance, features, and comfort

24.

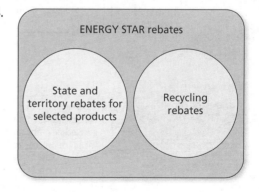

ENERGY STAR rebates

State and territory rebates for selected products

Recycling rebates

25. Answers will vary. *Sample answer:* All of the products shown emit less than 50 grams of CO_2e, while some emit less than 10 grams.

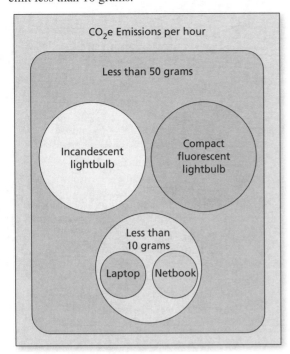

26.

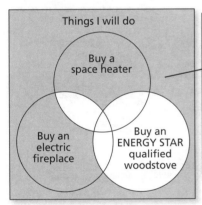

The shaded region is the complement of the union of the set where you buy both a space heater and an electric fireplace and the set where you buy an ENERGY STAR qualified woodstove. The negation is true if your actions are in the shaded region.

27.

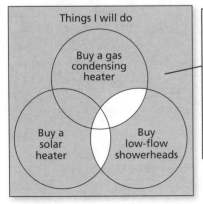

The shaded region is the complement of the intersection of the set where you will buy at least one water heater and the set where you will buy low-flow showerheads. The negation is true if your actions are in the shaded region.

28.

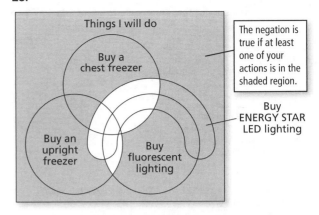

The negation is true if at least one of your actions is in the shaded region.

Buy ENERGY STAR LED lighting

3.1–3.2 Quiz   *(page 122)*

1. 311   **2.** 45   **3.** 387   **4.** 155,004

5.

People who are presumed innocent

All defendents who are accused of a crime

6.

People who commited crimes

People convicted of crimes

People convicted of crimes that they did not commit

7.

People protected by habeas corpus

People who can be jailed without being charged with a crime

8.

Rights of accused in all criminal prosecutions

Speedy trial   Public trial

The negation is true when the accused has just a speedy trial, just a public trial, or neither.

Section 3.3 *(page 130)*

1. All segregated public schools are unconstitutional.

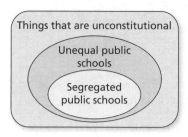

2. Any law that limits corporate spending on independent political broadcasts is unconstitutional.

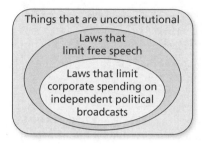

3. The Constitution will govern the case to which they both apply.

4. Answers will vary. *Sample answer:* The first premise, "If an ordinary law conflicts with the Constitution, then because the Constitution is superior to ordinary law, the Constitution will govern the case to which they both apply" is not true. Then the conclusion, "The Constitution will govern the case to which they both apply," which is the deduction, cannot be inferred to be true.

5. Premise: All unequal treatment of individuals that is based on gender is unconstitutional.
   Premise: The Virginia Military Institute's male-only admission policy was an unequal treatment of individuals that was based on gender.
   Conclusion: The Virginia Military Institute's male-only admission policy was unconstitutional.

6. Premise: If an individual is not advised of his or her Fifth Amendment rights before making any statements, then the statements are inadmissible.
   Premise: Ernesto Miranda was not advised of his Fifth Amendment rights before he made his statements.
   Conclusion: Ernesto Miranda's statements were inadmissible.

7. Premise: If any resident of a house objects to a police search without a warrant, then it is unconstitutional for the police to search the house.
   Premise: In the case of *Georgia v. Randolph*, one resident objected to a police search of the house without a warrant.
   Conclusion: The police search of the house without a warrant was unconstitutional.

8. Premise: "Cruel and unusual punishment" is unconstitutional.
   Premise: The execution of an offender who was under 18 years old at the time of the crime was "cruel and unusual punishment."
   Conclusion: The execution of the offender who was under 18 years old at the time of the crime was unconstitutional.

9. "town" and "road"

10. No; A road can have curves and still pass through two towns.

11. Premise: If there are two towns, then there is a road that passes through them.
    Premise: There are two towns.
    Conclusion: There is a road that passes through the two towns.

12. Premise: If there is a road, then there is at least one town that the road does not pass through.
    Premise: There is a road.
    Conclusion: There is a town that the road does not pass through.

13. 1. There exists two towns.
    2. There exists a road passing through the two towns.
    3. There exists a town that the road does not pass through.
    4. The town in Step 3 is different from the towns in Step 1.
    5. So, there exists at least three towns.

14. a. Valid
    b. Valid
    c. Invalid; Postulate 2; The green road passes through all three towns.
    d. Valid

15. No; The model shown satisfies all three postulates and has an intersection of two roads at which there is no town.

16. a. Premise: If there is a town, then there is at least one road that does not pass through the town.
Premise: There is a town.
Conclusion: There is at least one road that does not pass through the town.

b. 2; Postulate 3 states that there are at least two towns.

c. 2; Postulate 3 states that there are at least two towns. Postulate 1 states that there is a road that passes through the towns. The new Postulate 2 states that there is a second road that does not pass through either town.

17. *Troodon*: The only places that *Troodon* fossils have been found are Wyoming, Montana, Alberta, and Alaska. Therefore, the only places that *Troodon* lived were Wyoming, Montana, Alberta, and Alaska.

Velociraptor: The only places that *Velociraptor* fossils have been found are China and Mongolia. Therefore, the only places that *Velociraptor* lived were China and Mongolia.

Giganotosaurus: The only place that *Giganotosaurus* fossils have been found is Argentina. Therefore, the only place that *Giganotosaurus* lived was Argentina.

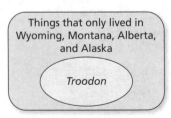

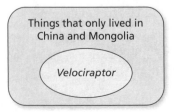

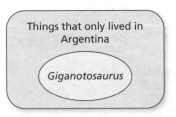

18. No; It could be that *Velociraptors* did live in North America but just that no fossils were ever found.

19. All *Giganotosaurus* fossils have been dated to about 100 to 95 million years ago. Therefore, *Giganotosaurus* lived about 100 to 95 million years ago.

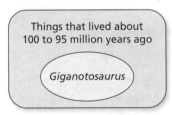

20. All *Troodon* fossils have been dated to a period of time from 75 million years ago to 65 million years ago. Therefore, the only time period in which the dinosaur species *Troodon* lived was from 75 million years ago to 65 million years ago.

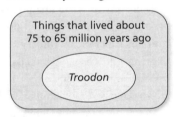

21. It is extremely unlikely that *Velociraptor* encountered *Giganotosaurus* because the two species lived millions of years apart. It is unlikely that *Velociraptor* encountered *Troodon* because they lived in different parts of the world.

22. It is likely that *Tyrannosaurus rex* encountered *Troodon* because *Tyrannosaurus rex* lived in western North America about 65 million years ago.

23. Premise: All discovered alkali metals react strongly with water.
Premise: Potassium is an alkali metal.
Conclusion: Potassium reacts strongly with water.

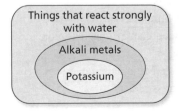

24. Premise: All discovered noble gases are odorless.
Premise: Xenon is a noble gas.
Conclusion: Xenon is odorless.

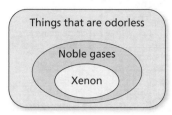

25. Premise: All discovered alkaline earth metals are solid at room temperature.
Premise: Radium is an alkaline earth metal.
Conclusion: Radium is solid at room temperature.

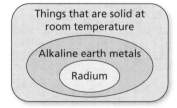

26. Premise: All actinides are radioactive.
Premise: Thorium is an actinide.
Conclusion: Thorium is radioactive.

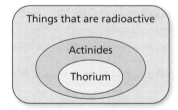

27. All discovered alkali metals react strongly with water. Therefore, all alkali metals (discovered or undiscovered) react strongly with water.

28. All discovered alkaline earth metals are solid at room temperature. Therefore, all alkaline earth metals (discovered or undiscovered) are solid at room temperature.

29. Premise: All alkali metals (discovered or undiscovered) react strongly with water.
Premise: Unununennium is an undiscovered alkali metal.
Conclusion: Unununennium reacts strongly with water.

30. Premise: All alkaline earth metals (discovered or undiscovered) are solid at room temperature.
Premise: Unbinilium is an undiscovered alkaline earth metal.
Conclusion: Unbinilium is solid at room temperature

Section 3.4 *(page 140)*

1. Premise: If something is not there, you will not find it.
Premise: We did not find weapons of mass destruction in Iraq.
Conclusion: Therefore, there are no such weapons in Iraq.
Affirming the consequent

2. Premise: If Saddam had shipped his weapons out of Iraq, we would not have found them.
Premise: We didn't find Saddam's weapons.
Conclusion: Therefore, Saddam must have shipped his weapons out of Iraq.
Affirming the consequent

3. Premise: If we found weapons of mass destruction in Iraq, it would prove that Iraq had such weapons.
Premise: We have not found weapons of mass destruction in Iraq.
Conclusion: Therefore, Iraq did not have weapons of mass destruction.
Denying the antecedent

4. Premise: If the war in Iraq made America safer, there will have been no major terrorist attack since we invaded.
Premise: There hasn't been a major terrorist attack since we invaded.
Conclusion: Therefore, the war made America safer.
Affirming the consequent

5. Premise: If you support the war in Iraq, you support America.
Premise: The senator does not support the war.
Conclusion: Therefore, the senator does not support America.
Denying the antecedent

6. Premise: If a person is a great leader, then that person will do what they believe is right.
Premise: George W. Bush did what he believed was right.
Conclusion: Therefore, George W. Bush was a great leader.
Affirming the consequent

7. Premise: If we had overthrown Saddam's regime in 1991, then we would not be fighting in Iraq today.
Premise: We did not overthrow Saddam's regime in 1991.
Conclusion: Therefore, we are still fighting in Iraq today.
Denying the antecedent

8. Premise: The United States invaded Iraq on the premise that Saddam Hussein had weapons of mass destruction.

Premise: Saddam did not have weapons of mass destruction.

Conclusion: The United States should not have invaded Iraq.

Fallacy of false cause

9.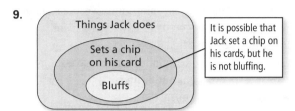

10.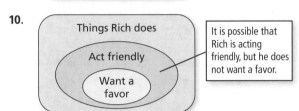

11.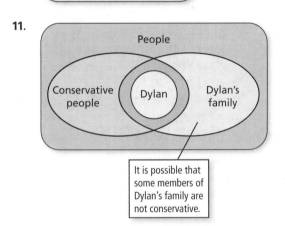

12.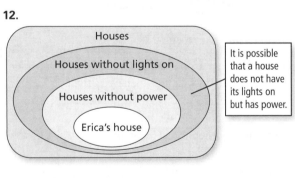

13.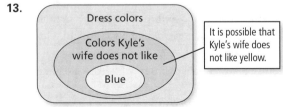

14.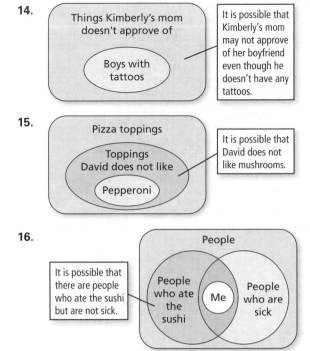

15.

16.

17. The ad implies that if you use the toothpaste, then your teeth will be as white as those shown. It also implies that some type of survey was conducted with dentists.

18. The ad implies that if you use the machine, then you will look like the person shown. It also implies that the machine can perform any exercise (all-in-one)

19. The ad implies that the shoes can make you a good athlete.

20. The ad implies other companies may not put safety first.

21. The ad appeals to emotion by displaying the American flag and by using the colors of the flag. It also contains an appeal to authority by having the candidate pointing and saying "I want you" like Uncle Sam.

22. The ad appeals to emotion by displaying the American flag and by using the colors of the flag. It also begs the question by assuming that people have not declared their independence.

23. The ad appeals to celebrity by implying that if President Obama wears this jacket, then you should wear it.

24. Answers will vary.   25. Ad hominem

26. Appeal to novelty   27. Self-refuting idea

28. False dilemma   29. Ad populum

30. Composition

3.3–3.4 Quiz   *(page 144)*

1. a. 100°C

b. All water boils at 100°C.

c.

```
Characteristic of
all water
  ┌──────────────┐
  ( Boils at 100°C )
  └──────────────┘
```

2. a. About 87°C

b. All water boils at 87°C.

c.

```
Characteristics of
all water
  ┌──────────────┐
  ( Boils at 87°C )
  └──────────────┘
```

3. Premise: If water at sea level is heated to a temperature of 100°C, then it will boil.
Premise: Water at sea level is heated to a temperature of 100°C.
Conclusion: The water boils.

4. Premise: The boiling point of water at about 3600 meters above sea level is about 87°C.
Premise: Some water at about 3600 meters above sea level is heated to a temperature of about 87°C.
Conclusion: The water boils.

5. Premise: If you move from sea level to a higher elevation, then the boiling point of water will be less than 100°C.
Premise: You move from sea level to a higher elevation.
Conclusion: The boiling point of water is less than 100°C.

6. Invalid

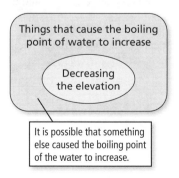

7. Premise: If you move from sea level to a higher elevation, then the atmospheric pressure decreases.
Premise: You move from sea level to a higher elevation.
Conclusion: The atmospheric pressure decreases.

8. Outside the pressure cooker, all water at 5000 meters boils at about 83°C. When the pressure increases, but the height remains the same, the boiling point decreases. Therefore, atmospheric pressure affects the boiling point of water. As elevation increases, atmospheric pressure decreases. The decrease in atmospheric pressure as elevation increases is what causes the boiling point of water to decrease.

Chapter 3 Review   *(page 146)*

1.

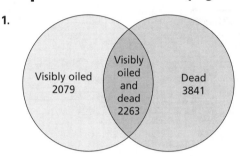

2. 8183   **3.** 14   **4.** 30

5. 6   **6.** 36

7.

Personnel Costs	USCG Aircraft Costs	USCG Vehicle Costs
	$25,623.00	$43,484.92

8. $9,774,378.85

9.

```
Radiation that is made up of small particles that
travel in a wave-like pattern at the speed of light
  ┌──────────────────────────┐
  (       EM radiation        )
  (   ┌──────────────┐        )
  (   ( UV radiation )        )
  (   └──────────────┘        )
  └──────────────────────────┘
```

10.

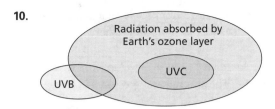

Radiation absorbed by Earth's ozone layer

UVC

UVB

11.

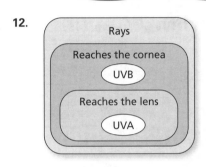

Things that damage DNA in cells

UV radiation

Things that can cause premature skin aging and skin cancer

12.

Rays

Reaches the cornea

UVB

Reaches the lens

UVA

13.

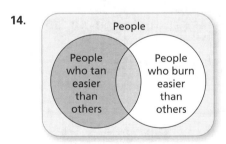

Things that reduce the amount of UV radiation that penetrates skin

Broad-spectrum sunscreen

14.

People

People who tan easier than others

People who burn easier than others

15.

Characteristics of my friend

Has a farmer's tan

Has a trucker's tan

The negation is when my friend does not have a farmer's tan and also does not have a trucker's tan.

16.

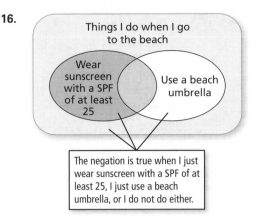

Things I do when I go to the beach

Wear sunscreen with a SPF of at least 25

Use a beach umbrella

The negation is true when I just wear sunscreen with a SPF of at least 25, I just use a beach umbrella, or I do not do either.

17. Newton observed something falling and noticed that it fell in a path that is perpendicular to the center of Earth; inductive; Newton's conclusion was based on repeated patterns.

18. Premise: Matter draws matter.
Premise: The apple and Earth are matter.
Conclusion: The apple draws Earth, as well as Earth draws the apple.
Deductive

19. Inductive; As is true of almost all scientific laws, Newton based his laws of motion on observed patterns.

20. Deductive; He used premises to draw conclusions.

21. Premise: If an object is in uniform motion and no external force acts on it, then it will remain in uniform motion.
Premise: An object is in uniform motion and no external force is acting on it.
Conclusion: The object will remain in uniform motion.

22. Premise: If there is an action, there is an equal and opposite reaction.
Premise: There is an action.
Conclusion: There is an equal and opposite reaction.

23. This is an example in which you can reach a false conclusion using inductive reasoning because the reasoning was not based on a large enough and diverse enough sample.

24. Inductive reasoning can be used to arrive at scientific conclusions. Then deductive reasoning can be used to apply them.

25.

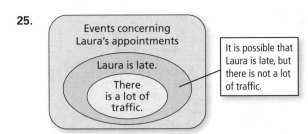

26.

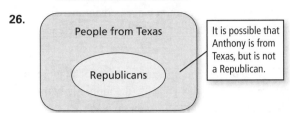

27.

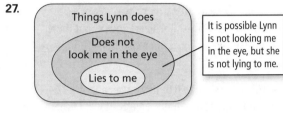

28.

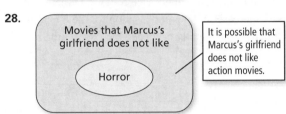

29. The ad implies that the golf clubs can make you a good golfer.

30. The ad implies that it is best to drink orange juice that is 100% natural.

31. This ad appeals to emotion by displaying the American flag and by using the colors of the flag. It also begs the question by assuming that we need change.

32. This ad appeals to emotion by displaying a farmland. It also begs the question by assuming that we need to take back America.

Section 4.1 *(page 158)*

1. $A = 3(1.25)^n$

2.

Time, n	Informed People
0 hr	3
2 hr	5
4 hr	7
6 hr	11
8 hr	18

3. 635 people **4.** No; Answers will vary.

5.

	A	B
1	Minutes, n	Informed People
2	0	100
3	3	305
4	6	929
5	9	2,833
6	12	8,638
7	15	26,334
8	18	80,283
9	21	244,753
10	24	746,160
11	27	2,274,763
12	30	6,934,898

6. Answers will vary. *Sample answer:* Social networking websites and blogs may be a fast, or even instantaneous (real time) way to communicate, but their reliability may be questionable at times.

7. 8032 people

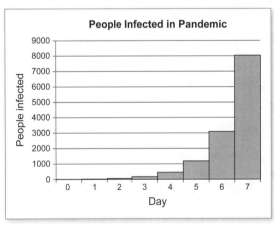

8. 40,159 people

9. 4374 people

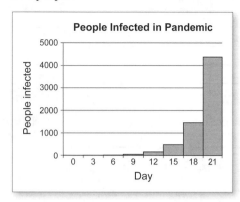

People Infected in Pandemic

10. 9,565,938 people

11. The graph of an exponential growth model is a curve that rises more and more rapidly as *n* increases.

12. Answers will vary. *Sample answer:* Some factors could be water treatment facilities, population density, and education. These factors could increase or decrease the growth rate depending on the quantity and quality of each.

13. 1%   **14.** 0.2%

15. a. $1350.50   **b.** $1461.00

16. a. $2605.20   **b.** $7528.30

17. $r \approx 0.732$, or about 73.2%

18. $r \approx 0.118$, or about 11.8%

19. Linear; The balance is increasing by about the same amount each year.

20. Answers will vary. *Sample answer:* I would invest the $10,000 in a low-interest guaranteed savings account.

21. Exponential growth continues to increase more and more rapidly as time increases. Logistic growth starts off like exponential growth, but then the rate of growth begins to decrease and eventually approaches zero.

22. Answers will vary. *Sample answer:* The size of a population over time is better represented by a logistic growth model because populations tend to level off at a certain point.

23. The blue part; The growth rate is decreasing.

24. $r \approx 0.442$, or about 44.2%

25. $r \approx 0.154$, or about 15.4%

26. $12,681.98

Section 4.2 *(page 168)*

1. a. About 39.4%   **b.** About 146.2%
   c. About 64.1%   **d.** About 229.0%

2. a. About 26.4%   **b.** About 94.3%
   c. About 90.8%   **d.** About 173.6%

3. 1990–2009; The minimum wage percent increase (90.8%) was higher than the CPI percent increase (64.1%).

4. Answers will vary. *Sample answer:* Yes; The more the Consumer Price Index goes up, the more likely there will be an increase in the minimum wage.

5. No; From 1992 to 2010, there was about a 55.5% increase in the Consumer Price Index, but there was only about a 46.6% increase in the company's starting wage.

6. Yes; From 1980 to 2010, there was about a 164.7% increase in the Consumer Price Index, and there was a 500% increase in the compensation for the CEO. So the compensation actually exceeded the rise in inflation.

7. 2005

8.

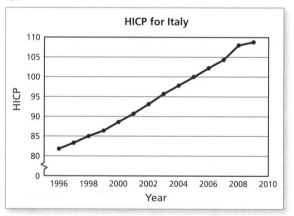

HICP for Italy

The rate of inflation was steadily increasing.

9.

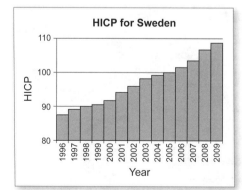

HICP for Sweden

The rate of inflation was steadily increasing.

10. Sweden; For the years shown, Italy's HICP ranged from 81.8 to 108.8, while Sweden's only ranged from 87.5 to 108.7.

11. Yes; The HICP increased in all of the countries from year to year.

12. Answers will vary. *Sample answer:* I do not agree with this argument. Although the HICP excludes owner-occupied housing costs in its calculations, it does incorporate rural and urban consumers. The HICP is an internationally comparable measure of inflation.

13.

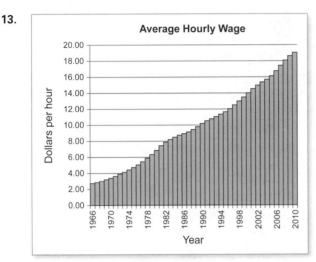

1966–1984: Exponential growth pattern
1985–1998: Linear growth pattern
1999–2010: Steeper linear growth pattern

14. Answers will vary. *Sample answer:* Yes; In general, as the CPI increased over the years, so did the hourly wage.

15. No; From 1970 to 1990, the CPI had about a 237% increase, but the hourly wage only had a 200% increase.

16. Yes; From 1990 to 2010, the CPI had about a 67% increase, but the hourly wage had about an 87% increase.

17. $50,000 in 1990; From 1990 to 2010, the CPI had about a 67% increase, but your salary only had a 50% increase.

18. Answers will vary. *Sample answer:* The discrepancy has increased because the average hourly rate has increased at a greater rate than the federal minimum hourly wage since 1978.

19.

Year	Gasoline Index	Diesel Index
1995	100.0	100.0
1996	107.0	111.7
1997	107.0	108.1
1998	92.2	93.7
1999	101.7	100.9
2000	131.3	134.2
2001	127.0	126.1
2002	118.3	118.9
2003	138.3	136.0
2004	163.5	163.1
2005	200.0	216.2
2006	225.2	244.1
2007	243.5	260.4
2008	284.3	342.3
2009	204.3	222.5

20.

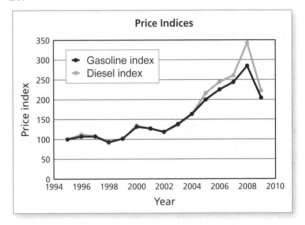

The rate of inflation for gasoline was generally close to the rate of inflation for diesel fuel. After 2004, the rate for gasoline was less than the rate for diesel fuel.

21. Both gasoline and diesel fuel prices increased at a higher rate than the Consumer Price Index.

22. Gasoline engine; For instance, 500 gallons of diesel fuel would be equivalent to 500(1.3) = 650 gallons of gasoline. In 2008, 650 gallons of gasoline would cost 650(3.27) = $2125.50, while 500 gallons of diesel fuel would cost only 500(3.80) = $1900.

23. Answers will vary.

24. Answers will vary. *Sample answer:* In a positive way, inflation can lead to lower loan interest rates. In a negative way, inflation decreases the value of money.

4.1–4.2 Quiz *(page 172)*

1. $A = 100(1.03)^n$

2.

	A	B
1	Year	CPI
2	1983	100.0
3	1984	103.0
4	1985	106.1
5	1986	109.3
6	1987	112.6
7	1988	115.9
8	1989	119.4
9	1990	123.0
10	1991	126.7
11	1992	130.5
12	1993	134.4
13	1994	138.4
14	1995	142.6

	A	B
15	1996	146.9
16	1997	151.3
17	1998	155.8
18	1999	160.5
19	2000	165.3
20	2001	170.2
21	2002	175.4
22	2003	180.6
23	2004	186.0
24	2005	191.6
25	2006	197.4
26	2007	203.3
27	2008	209.4

	A	B
	Year	CPI
28	2009	215.7
29	2010	222.1
30	2011	228.8
31	2012	235.7
32	2013	242.7
33	2014	250.0
34	2015	257.5
35	2016	265.2
36	2017	273.2
37	2018	281.4
38	2019	289.8
39	2020	298.5

3.

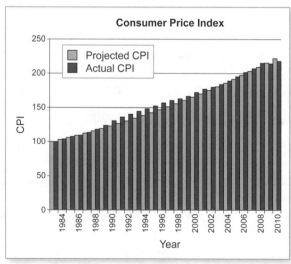

4. About $34,225

5. About $244 billion

6. No; In 2020, the value of your investment will be $13,458.68. That is about a 35% increase. In that same time period, the CPI will have about a 56% increase.

Section 4.3 *(page 180)*

1. $A = 320(0.86)^n$

2.

Year	Size
1900	320
1910	275
1920	237
1930	204
1940	175
1950	151
1960	129
1970	111
1980	96
1990	82
2000	71

3.

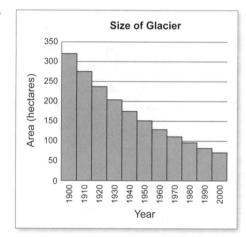

4. About 70 hectares

5. 2130

6. **a.** Answers will vary. *Sample answer:* No; The research suggests that the melting rate of the glacier after 2000 will drastically increase.

  b. An exponential model would be appropriate when the glacier is melting at the same rate each decade. A linear model would be appropriate when the same amount of the glacier is melting each decade.

7. 5 mg

8. 5 mg

9. Saber-toothed cat: 40 hr
Tasmanian tiger: 32 hr

10. About 22,920 years ago

11. 0.94

12. Decrease; The amount of venom left in the bloodstream would be $20(0.5)^4 = 1.25$.

13. 1995

14. 2010

15. 3.2 billion years

16. 2800 years

17. **a.** No; Radon itself has a half-life, so some of the radon will have decayed into polonium.

b. About 4 days; After 2 days, the amount of radon-222 decayed to $34.7/50 = 0.694 = 69.4\%$ of the original amount. After 2 more days, the amount of radon-222 will be $34.7(0.694) \approx 24.1$, which is about half of the original amount.

18. Answers will vary. *Sample answer:* Since radon is a result of the decay of the chain of elements that include uranium, it is recommended that homes be tested and if levels of radon are elevated, safety measures can be installed in the home to vent the radon gases out of the living space.

19. $A = 1024(1.5)^n$

20. 59,049 views

21. $A = 39,366(0.9)^n$

22.

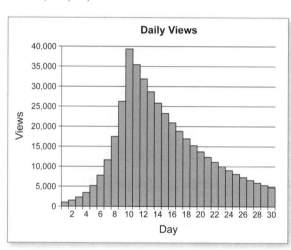

23. Day 30

24. **a.** After one half-life

b. 1 : 3

c. Yes; Yes; The graph of the parent exhibits exponential decay because it is decaying at a slower rate over time. The graph of the daughter exhibits exponential growth because it is growing at a slower rate over time.

d. Answers will vary. *Sample answer:* Since uranium-lead existed long before carbon-14, it could be used to date older objects.

Section 4.4 *(page 190)*

1.

	A	B	C	D
1	Year	Value before Depreciation	Depreciation	Value after Depreciation
2	1	$1,100.00	$100.00	$1,000.00
3	2	$1,000.00	$100.00	$900.00
4	3	$900.00	$100.00	$800.00
5	4	$800.00	$100.00	$700.00
6	5	$700.00	$100.00	$600.00
7	6	$600.00	$100.00	$500.00
8	7	$500.00	$100.00	$400.00

2.

	A	B	C	D
1	Year	Value before Depreciation	Depreciation	Value after Depreciation
2	1	$14,500.00	$1,200.00	$13,300.00
3	2	$13,300.00	$1,200.00	$12,100.00
4	3	$12,100.00	$1,200.00	$10,900.00
5	4	$10,900.00	$1,200.00	$9,700.00
6	5	$9,700.00	$1,200.00	$8,500.00
7	6	$8,500.00	$1,200.00	$7,300.00
8	7	$7,300.00	$1,200.00	$6,100.00
9	8	$6,100.00	$1,200.00	$4,900.00
10	9	$4,900.00	$1,200.00	$3,700.00
11	10	$3,700.00	$1,200.00	$2,500.00

3. $5000

4. $3000

5. Year 5: $1000
Year 6: $2000
Year 7: $3000
Year 8: $4000

6. Year 1: $5000
Year 2: $4000
Year 3: $3000
Year 4: $2000
Year 5: $1000

7.

	A	B	C	D
1	Year	Value before Depreciation	Depreciation	Value after Depreciation
2	1	$50,000.00	$20,000.00	$30,000.00
3	2	$30,000.00	$12,000.00	$18,000.00
4	3	$18,000.00	$7,200.00	$10,800.00
5	4	$10,800.00	$800.00	$10,000.00
6	5	$10,000.00	$0.00	$10,000.00

8.

	A	B	C	D
1	Year	Value before Depreciation	Depreciation	Value after Depreciation
2	1	$60,000.00	$15,000.00	$45,000.00
3	2	$45,000.00	$11,250.00	$33,750.00
4	3	$33,750.00	$8,437.50	$25,312.50
5	4	$25,312.50	$6,328.13	$18,984.37
6	5	$18,984.37	$4,746.09	$14,238.28
7	6	$14,238.28	$2,238.28	$12,000.00
8	7	$12,000.00	$0.00	$12,000.00
9	8	$12,000.00	$0.00	$12,000.00

9. $144,675.93   **10.** $100,469.39

11. $11,628.40   **12.** $3647.00

13. $56,275.53   **14.** No

15.

	A	B	C	D
1	Year	Value before Depreciation	Depreciation	Value after Depreciation
2	1	$4,500.00	$1,500.00	$3,000.00
3	2	$3,000.00	$1,200.00	$1,800.00
4	3	$1,800.00	$900.00	$900.00
5	4	$900.00	$600.00	$300.00
6	5	$300.00	$300.00	$0.00
7				

16.

	A	B	C	D
1	Year	Value before Depreciation	Depreciation	Value after Depreciation
2	1	$400.00	$87.50	$312.50
3	2	$312.50	$75.00	$237.50
4	3	$237.50	$62.50	$175.00
5	4	$175.00	$50.00	$125.00
6	5	$125.00	$37.50	$87.50
7	6	$87.50	$25.00	$62.50
8	7	$62.50	$12.50	$50.00

17. Double-declining balance

18. Straight-line

19. $103,636.36

20. Straight-line: $60,000 loss
Double-declining balance: $45,200 gain
Sum-of-the-years digits: $43,636.37 gain

21. **a.** Year 4   **22.** **a.** Year 3
     b. Year 7   **b.** Year 5

23.

	A	B	C	D
1	Year	Value before Depreciation	Depreciation	Value after Depreciation
2	1	$4,000.00	$800.00	$3,200.00
3	2	$3,200.00	$1,280.00	$1,920.00
4	3	$1,920.00	$768.00	$1,152.00
5	4	$1,152.00	$460.80	$691.20
6	5	$691.20	$460.80	$230.40
7	6	$230.40	$230.40	$0.00
8				

24.

	A	B	C	D
1	Year	Value before Depreciation	Depreciation	Value after Depreciation
2	1	$10,000.00	$2,000.00	$8,000.00
3	2	$8,000.00	$3,200.00	$4,800.00
4	3	$4,800.00	$1,920.00	$2,880.00
5	4	$2,880.00	$1,152.00	$1,728.00
6	5	$1,728.00	$1,152.00	$576.00
7	6	$576.00	$576.00	$0.00

25.

	A	B	C	D
1	Year	Value before Depreciation	Depreciation	Value after Depreciation
2	1	$24,000.00	$3,428.57	$20,571.43
3	2	$20,571.43	$5,877.55	$14,693.88
4	3	$14,693.88	$4,198.25	$10,495.63
5	4	$10,495.63	$2,998.75	$7,496.88
6	5	$7,496.88	$2,141.97	$5,354.91
7	6	$5,354.91	$2,141.96	$3,212.95
8	7	$3,212.95	$2,141.97	$1,070.98
9	8	$1,070.98	$1,070.98	$0.00

26.

	A	B	C	D
1	Year	Value before Depreciation	Depreciation	Value after Depreciation
2	1	$3,000.00	$428.57	$2,571.43
3	2	$2,571.43	$734.69	$1,836.74
4	3	$1,836.74	$524.78	$1,311.96
5	4	$1,311.96	$374.85	$937.11
6	5	$937.11	$267.75	$669.36
7	6	$669.36	$267.74	$401.62
8	7	$401.62	$267.75	$133.87
9	8	$133.87	$133.87	$0.00

4.3–4.4 Quiz   *(page 194)*

1. **a.** 54 ppb   **b.** 5 filters

2. **a.** 125 ppb   **b.** 8 filters
   c. No; After each pass through a filter, the concentration of pollutants gets closer and closer to zero but never reaches zero.

3. 7 filters   **4.** 51.2 ppb

5.

	A	B	C	D
1	Year	Value before Depreciation	Depreciation	Value after Depreciation
2	1	$10,000.00	$1,800.00	$8,200.00
3	2	$8,200.00	$1,800.00	$6,400.00
4	3	$6,400.00	$1,800.00	$4,600.00
5	4	$4,600.00	$1,800.00	$2,800.00
6	5	$2,800.00	$1,800.00	$1,000.00
7				

6. $8192

7. Sum-of-the-years digits; The values are not decreasing by the same amount or by the same percent each year.

Chapter 4 Review   *(page 196)*

1. $A = 415{,}000(1.115)^n$

2.

Year	Population per Representative
1960	415,000
1970	462,725
1980	515,938
1990	575,271
2000	641,427
2010	715,192

3.

Year	Population per Representative
2020	797,439
2030	889,144
2040	991,396
2050	1,105,406
2060	1,232,528
2070	1,374,269
2080	1,532,310
2090	1,708,525
2100	1,905,006

4.

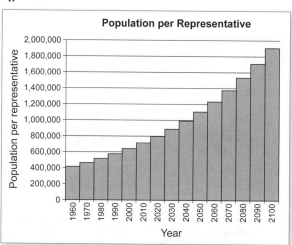

5. About 11.8%; The populations are relatively close, while the rate of growth is slightly greater.

6. About 37.9 million people

7. 1970s; The CPI increased over 40 units in the 1970s but less than 40 units in the 1980s and 1990s.

8. 1986, 1987, 1988, 1995, 1998, 1999, 2002, 2007, and 2009

9.

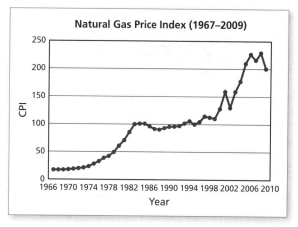

Answers will vary.

10. Answers will vary.

11. $1.09 per thousand cubic feet

12. $6.06 per thousand cubic feet

13. $115.50 in 2004; From 1990 to 2004, the CPI had about a 45% increase but your natural gas bill only had about a 23% increase.

14. Answers will vary. *Sample answer:* Yes; Prices are always going to rise, so it is better to know if they are rising at the current rate of inflation.

15. $A = 100(0.9)^n$

16.

Week	Dosage (mg)
1	100.0
2	90.0
3	81.0
4	72.9
5	65.6
6	59.0
7	53.1
8	47.8
9	43.0
10	38.7

17.

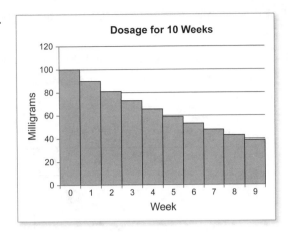

18. About 19.4 mg   **19.** 15 g

20. 13.5 years

21. 6 years; It took 6 years for the amount to decay from 10 grams to 5 grams.

22. Because technetium-99m has a half-life of only 6 years, it will lose its effectiveness in a short period of time.

23.

	A	B	C	D
1	Year	Value before Depreciation	Depreciation	Value after Depreciation
2	1	$2,500.00	$400.00	$2,100.00
3	2	$2,100.00	$400.00	$1,700.00
4	3	$1,700.00	$400.00	$1,300.00
5	4	$1,300.00	$400.00	$900.00
6	5	$900.00	$400.00	$500.00
7				

24.

	A	B	C	D
1	Year	Value before Depreciation	Depreciation	Value after Depreciation
2	1	$4,000.00	$400.00	$3,600.00
3	2	$3,600.00	$400.00	$3,200.00
4	3	$3,200.00	$400.00	$2,800.00
5	4	$2,800.00	$400.00	$2,400.00
6	5	$2,400.00	$400.00	$2,000.00
7	6	$2,000.00	$400.00	$1,600.00
8	7	$1,600.00	$400.00	$1,200.00

25. $14,285.71   **26.** $6640.52

27. $8413.15   **28.** $10,714.27

Section 5.1 *(page 208)*

1. $1666   **2.** $85,000   **3.** $1088

4. $2610   **5.** Not taxable   **6.** Not taxable

7. Taxable   **8.** Taxable

9. Regressive; As the earnings over $106,800 increases, the percent of the Social Security tax paid on the earnings decreases.

10. Progressive; The tax rate is 0% for incomes of $12,500 or less, and the tax rate is 17% for all income over $12,500. So the tax rate increases as the income increases.

11. Flat; The same percentage is paid on all incomes.

12. Regressive; People with lower incomes pay a higher percentage of their income in sales tax.

13. Sales & Excise Taxes: $2030
Property Taxes: $2436
Income Taxes: $1682

14. Sales & Excise Taxes: $22,120
Property Taxes: $28,440
Income Taxes: $158,000

15. Sales & Excise Taxes: Regressive
Property Taxes: Regressive
Income Taxes: Progressive

16. Regressive; Adding the percentages in each column shows that the general trend is that the percentages decrease as the income increases.

17. $1.25; The retailer doubles the price to $30. Because 30(0.04166) = $1.25, the consumer pays $31.25 for the lei. Of this, $1.25 is the general excise tax.

18. $20.83; The retailer marks up the price to $500. Because 500(0.04166) = $20.83, the consumer pays $520.83 for the surfboard. Of this, $20.83 is the general excise tax.

19.

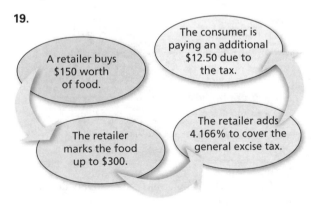

Regressive

20.

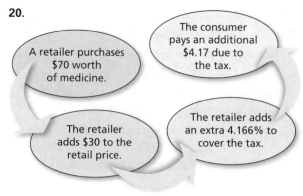

Regressive

21. The state requires a general excise tax of 4% on the entire retail price, including the extra charge to cover the tax. So just charging an extra 4% of the marked-up price would not totally cover the tax. Retailers are allowed to add 4.166% of the marked-up price to compensate for this.

22. Answers will vary. *Sample answer:* An extra 0.5% surcharge to the general excise tax to fund a mass transit system could help people who are paying it by maintaining the equipment so it is operational; adding stops to the system where authorities determine the system could expand; adding convenience features to the vehicles, such as Wi-Fi and stereo systems; and adding convenience features to the waiting areas at the stops.

23. $4900

24. $7504

25. $6590

26. $7156

27. Tax credit of $1000; A tax credit saves the taxpayer $1000. A tax deduction of $1000 only saves the taxpayer $1000(0.14) = $140.

28.

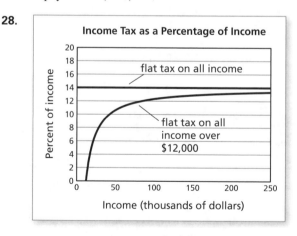

With deductions, people with lower incomes pay a smaller percent of their income toward the flat tax.

29. **a.** Receives a check; $280 **b.** $42,000

30. **a.** Owes income taxes; $3220 **b.** $49,000

Section 5.2 *(page 218)*

1. $7975; about 13.6%

2. A single taxpayer pays $14,931.25. You and your spouse pay $11,112.50. So a single taxpayer pays $3818.75 more.

3. $23,062.50; about 18.8%

4. **a.** $42,927.50; about 22.0%

   b. $56,781.50; about 27.8%; about 5.8% higher

5. No; Filing "separately," you would be in the income bracket with a marginal tax rate of 25%. Filing "jointly," you would be in the bracket with a rate of only 15%.

6. No; The effective tax rate will go up as the amount of money being taxed in the bracket increases.

7. South Carolina's state income tax is a graduated income tax system. The top 25% of all wage earners in South Carolina pay 84.9% of all the state income tax paid. This seems equitable because the top 25% of all wage earners in South Carolina earn 79.6% of all the income.

8. South Carolina's state income tax is comparable to the federal income tax because the top 25% of all wage earners in South Carolina pay 84.9% of all the state income tax paid, while the top 25% of wage earners in the United States pay 86% of all the federal income tax paid, a difference of only 1.1%.

9. About 22% **10.** About 35%

11. The sources are quite different. The two largest sources of tax revenue for South Carolina are property taxes and sales taxes. The federal government does not collect either of these taxes. The two largest sources of tax revenue for the federal government are Social Security and Medicare taxes and individual income taxes. South Carolina does not collect Social Security and Medicare taxes.

12. **a.**

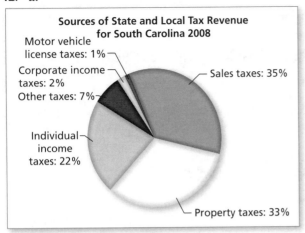

b. Answers will vary. *Sample answer:*

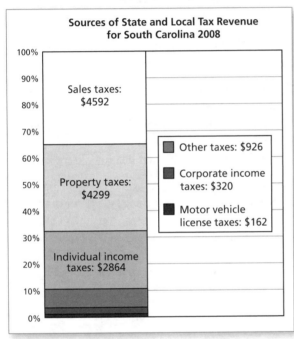

c. Answers will vary.

13. California could raise this amount of income tax revenue by using a flat tax rate of $58{,}000{,}000{,}000 / 1{,}610{,}000{,}000{,}000 \approx 0.03602 \approx 3.6\%$.

14. Using a graduated tax on total income would increase the total income tax revenue because the taxable income does not allow for any deductions like the marginal tax rates do. Therefore, the marginal tax rates would be lower.

15. $11,251,000,000; 4.3%

16. **a.** $35,042,490,000; 2.2%
 b. $46,293,490,000; 2.9%

17. Income tax: $4321.25
 Effective tax rate: About 12.1%

18. Income tax: $32,959.25
 Effective tax rate: About 18.8%

19. **a.** Income tax: $307,643.75
 Effective tax rate: About 30.8%

 b. Income tax: $227,643.75
 Effective tax rate: About 22.8%

 c. As more and more income moves from ordinary income to capital gains, the effective tax rate moves closer and closer to the capital gains rate of 15%.

20. A taxpayer in a higher income bracket can have a lower effective tax rate than a taxpayer in a lower income bracket when the taxpayer in the higher bracket has a much larger amount of capital gains. This is because the capital gains are taxed at 15% but ordinary income is taxed as high as 35%.

5.1–5.2 Quiz   *(page 222)*

1. Sales & Excise Taxes: $1775
 Property Taxes: $275
 Income taxes: $575

2. **a.** Regressive **b.** Flat

3. Income tax: $1460
 Effective tax rate: About 4.9%

4. Income tax: $4920
 Effective tax rate: About 4.9%

5. Answers will vary.

Section 5.3   *(page 230)*

1. **a.** $5816.16   **b.** About 2.9%

2. **a.** $9880   **b.** About 4.9%

3. **a.** $10,314   **b.** About 5.2%

4. **a.** $1688.70   **b.** About 0.8%

5. **a.** $3813   **b.** About 1.9%

6. **a.** $5935.68   **b.** About 3.0%

7. **a.** Cohoes; $1295.23

 b. Answers will vary. *Sample answer:* The house in Cohoes is the most economical choice. The additional cost of fuel in commuting from Sarasota Springs will overshadow the difference in property tax. Plus, the house in Cohoes costs $10,000 less.

8. **a.** About 3.6%   **9.** $2070; $725
   b. $4324.80; $856.80
   c. $18.42; $340.58

10. Answers will vary. *Sample answer:* Yes; If the assessed value of her home was decreased to $100,000, then Clarice would save $375 a year in property taxes. She would save a total of $750 if it took her 2 years to sell the house.

11. Answers will vary. *Sample answer:* No; Fred's assessment is similar to that of his neighbors. Plus, because the one house is assessed at $60,000, there is a chance that his assessment could actually be increased.

12. $2725   **13.** $1300

14. Answers will vary. *Sample answer:* Municipalities can raise the assessment level.

15. About 42%   **16.** About $2,580,000

17. $4,398,900,000   **18.** $1912.50

19. $1120   **20.** **a.** $15,000   **b.** $135

21. 12 mills   **22.** 50 mills   **23.** $468.75

24. Town A: $20,000,000   **25.** Town A: 40%
   Town B: $20,000,000   Town B: 40%
   Town C: $10,000,000   Town C: 20%

26. Town A: $400,000; 40 mills
   Town B: $400,000; 40 mills
   Town C: $200,000; 20 mills

27. Answers will vary. *Sample answer:* It would be unfair because Town C would be paying a disproportionate amount based on market value.

28. Answers will vary. *Sample answer:* It would require a detailed analysis of which parts of each town are in the school district. This information would be needed to determine the proper levy for each portion of each town in the school district.

Section 5.4 *(page 240)*

1. $2309.19   **2.** $540.05   **3.** $1672.71

4. $37,245.00   **5.** About 22.8%

6. **a.** $45,082.35   **b.** $27,635.35

7. $1657   **8.** $2151   **9.** $1410

10. Answers will vary.

11. Age 82   **12.** Age 84

13. The primary reason that the total dependency ratio is projected to increase is that people are projected to live longer.

14. About 67%

15. The working age population will decrease.

16. Answers will vary. *Sample answer:* A high economic dependency ratio can cause serious problems for a government. The largest proportion of a government's expenditure is on health, Social Security, and education, which are most used by the young and old populations.

17. 2050; The old-age dependency ratio is projected to be more than twice as much in 2050 as it was in 1965. This means that there will be higher expenditures for both Social Security and Medicare.

18. Answers will vary. *Sample answer:* Some possibilities to try to fix the imminent challenges of the Social Security system are to continue to raise the retirement age and/or increase the amount of deductions from the working population.

19.

Year	Indexed Earnings	Year	Indexed Earnings
1975	$19,160.00	1987	$32,551.68
1976	$18,569.60	1988	$66,768.00
1977	$18,079.02	1989	$66,369.08
1978	$28,537.60	1990	$65,687.68
1979	$27,057.60	1991	$65,455.00
1980	$25,548.60	1992	$69,381.00
1981	$24,006.00	1993	$71,390.57
1982	$34,662.20	1994	$71,924.64
1983	$34,370.93	1995	$71,477.67
1984	$33,717.76	1996	$70,750.40
1985	$33,667.56	1997	$69,114.21
1986	$33,715.73	1998	$97,812.00

Year	Indexed Earnings
1999	$98,736.00
2000	$98,298.00
2001	$101,304.00
2002	$105,276.00
2003	$105,270.00
2004	$101,964.00
2005	$100,800.00
2006	$100,794.00
2007	$99,450.00
2008	$102,000.00
2009	$106,800.00

20. $5405   **21.** $1523

22. The Social Security benefit formula is designed to pay a higher percent for lower AIMEs so that lower income workers recoup a larger percent of the money that they contributed to the Social Security system.

23. In principle, the economic dependency ratio is supposed to measure the ratio of "nonworking people" to "working people" by using age groups. The problem is there are people who work even though they are either under the age of 20 or 65 and over, while there are people who do not work even though they are between the ages of 20 and 64.

24. Answers will vary.

5.3–5.4 Quiz *(page 244)*

1. 68.100 mills   **2.** $1225.80

3. About 1.4%   **4.** $1215.31

5. Local: $8.45   **6.** Social Security: $52.39
State: $25.94   Medicare: $12.25

7. About 18%   **8.** Age 83

Chapter 5 Review *(page 246)*

1. $2385   **2.** $53,000

3. Sales & Excise Taxes: $1537
Property Taxes: $1802
Income Taxes: $2014

4. Sales & Excise Taxes: $13,000
Property Taxes: $26,000
Income Taxes: $114,400

5. Sales & Excise Taxes: regressive
Property Taxes: regressive
Income Taxes: progressive

6. Regressive; Adding the percentages in each column shows that the general trend is the percentages decrease as the income increases.

7. Answers will vary.

8. Answers will vary. *Sample answer:* Smoking cigarettes can lead to health problems, such as lung cancer. So, many smokers will need to use health insurance.

9. $489.40; about 2.7%   **10.** $1391.69; about 3.0%

11. $2611.73; about 3.5%   **12.** $8699.30; about 4.1%

13. About 14.8%   **14.** About 29.2%

15. Arizona: About 48.3%; South Carolina: About 34.9%

16. About 1.52%   **17.** $256

18. $2522.40   **19.** 0.7%

20. Adams County, Colorado: about 0.21%
Chicot County, Arkansas: 0.2%
The effective tax rate is slightly greater in Adams County.

21. $893.20   **22.** $840   **23.** $3596

24. Employed: $841; Self-employed: $7192

25. $1473   **26.** 81 years old

27. No; A person needs at least 40 credits (10 years of work) to qualify for Social Security retirement benefits.

28. Yes; The SSA policy states "Social Security survivors' benefits can be paid to a widow or widower—full benefits at full retirement age, or reduced benefits as early as age 60."

29. Answers will vary.

30. Answers will vary. *Sample answer:* With the elderly population rising and people living longer, more people are receiving benefits than ever before and for a longer period of time. This puts a strain on the Social Security system. Therefore, the dependency ratio will increase, especially the old-age dependency portion. This would result in increasing the retirement age to receive full benefits and possibly decreasing the amount of benefits.

Section 6.1 *(page 258)*

1. a. 2 yr   **b.** $1900

2. a. 90 days   **b.** $11,000

3. May 30, 2012

4. June 18, 2012; $5132.36

5. May 18, 2012; $20,923.04

6. No; February has 29 days in 2012 but only 28 days in 2013, so the note is due on May 19, 2013.

7. $16.75   **8.** $95.28   **9.** $36,825

10. No; No; The original loan amount is not stated.

11. Loan Proceeds: $1750
Other Charges: $0
Amount Financed: $1750
Finance Charge: $41.06
Total Amount Due: $1791.06

12. Loan Proceeds: $4500
Other Charges: $160
Amount Financed: $4660
Finance Charge: $152.84
Total Amount Due: $4812.84
Annual Percentage Rate: 6%

13.

t \ P	$100	$400	$1000
30 days	$3.29	$13.15	$32.88
60 days	$6.58	$26.30	$65.75
180 days	$19.73	$78.90	$197.26
1 year	$40.00	$160.00	$400.00

14. $65.75 **15.** $6.58 **16.** $1436.71

17. a. 40% **18. a.** 48% **19. a.** 25%
b. 68.6% **b.** 49.4% **b.** 41.7%

20. a. $1496.71 **21. a.** 140 days
b. $203.29 **b.** $4345.37

22. 141 days; $4344

23. Ordinary simple interest; No; For instance, ordinary simple interest would be cheaper on a loan from July 15 to August 15 because 30/360 < 31/365.

24. Answers will vary. *Sample answer:* Yes, when both formulas yield approximately the same amount at the end of the year, it seems appropriate to use ordinary simple interest as an approximation of exact simple interest.

25. Lender; The interest rate using the Banker's Rule will be greater because, when converting the length of the loan to years, the denominator will be 360 instead of 365. Decreasing the denominator gives a greater percentage.

26. a. Loan A: $308.22
Loan B: $320.55
Loan C: $308.22

b. Loan A: $28.2%
Loan B: 26%
Loan C: 30.3%

c. Loan A: $2897.72
Loan B: $2895.55
Loan C: $2873.22

d. Loan C; It is the cheapest of the three loans.

Section 6.2 (page 268)

1. a. $660.33

b.

	A	B	C	D	E
1	Payment Number	Balance before Payment	Monthly Interest	Monthly Payment	Balance after Payment
2	1	$35,000.00	$145.54	$660.33	$34,485.21
3	2	$34,485.21	$143.40	$660.33	$33,968.28
4	3	$33,968.28	$141.25	$660.33	$33,449.20
5	4	$33,449.20	$139.09	$660.33	$32,927.97
6	5	$32,927.97	$136.93	$660.33	$32,404.56
57	56	$3,261.05	$13.56	$660.33	$2,614.28
58	57	$2,614.28	$10.87	$660.33	$1,964.82
59	58	$1,964.82	$8.17	$660.33	$1,312.66
60	59	$1,312.66	$5.46	$660.33	$657.79
61	60	$657.79	$2.74	$660.52	$0.00

2. a. $241.53

b.

	A	B	C	D	E
1	Payment Number	Balance before Payment	Monthly Interest	Monthly Payment	Balance after Payment
2	1	$8,000.00	$36.60	$241.53	$7,795.07
3	2	$7,795.07	$35.66	$241.53	$7,589.20
4	3	$7,589.20	$34.72	$241.53	$7,382.39
5	4	$7,382.39	$33.77	$241.53	$7,174.63
6	5	$7,174.63	$32.82	$241.53	$6,965.93
33	32	$1,191.26	$5.45	$241.53	$955.17
34	33	$955.17	$4.37	$241.53	$718.01
35	34	$718.01	$3.28	$241.53	$479.77
36	35	$479.77	$2.19	$241.53	$240.43
37	36	$240.43	$1.10	$241.53	$0.00

3. No; after 13 months **4.** $4628.76

5. a. 2 years: $565.91; 3 years: $386.65;
4 years: $297.85; 5 years: $245.27

b. 2 years: $581.84; 3 years: $919.40;
4 years: $1296.80; 5 years: $1716.20
The cost of credit increases as the term increases.

6. No, the cost of credit will decrease by more than 50%; Yes; The APR would be less, so your cost of credit will go down even more.

7. 53 months; $190.54 **8.** 72 months; $929.68

9. 12 months; $64.24 **10.** $43.78

11. 1-year installment loan; $34.20

12. $100 each month; You can pay off the balance quicker and you will be charged less interest.

13. Yes; The rises and falls of the two rates occur at the same times.

14. Answers will vary; Adjustable-rate loan; Rates could rise dramatically.

15. No; The CPI increased by a slightly greater factor than student loan debt from 2000 to 2004.

16. Yes; Student loan debt increased by a greater factor than the CPI from 1996 to 2008.

17. Yes; Credit card debt increased by a slightly greater factor than the CPI from 2000 to 2008.

18. **a.** Yes

    b. Home mortgage debt; Answers will vary.

19. Yes

20. Gold Card: no; World Card: yes
    The Gold Card was paid in full, but only $500 of the $800 balance was paid on the World Card.

21. April's ending balance of $115 must not have been paid in full during the month of May.

22. About 0.055%

23. Gold Card: $127.67
    World Card: $643.55

24. $10.93

6.1–6.2 Quiz   *(page 272)*

1. 5 years; $100,000

2. $1968.35

3. $118,101; $18,101

4. February 1, 2016

5. After 47 payments

6. $704.40

Section 6.3   *(page 280)*

1. **a.** $130,558.00   **b.** $195,311.20
   An increase of only 2 percentage points increases the interest that you pay by $64,753.20.

2. **a.** $270,855.60   **b.** $356,276.40
   An increase of only 2 percentage points increases the interest that you pay by $85,420.80.

3. **a.** $158,111.60   **b.** $254,843.60
   An increase of only 2 percentage points increases the interest that you pay by $96,732.00.

4. **a.** $318,553.60   **b.** $451,426.00
   An increase of only 2 percentage points increases the interest that you pay by $132,872.40.

5. **a.** $116,778.40
   b. $186,510.40
   c. $262,907.20

6. **a.** $93,409.20
   b. $167,922.00
   c. $208,508.40

7. **a.** 34 months sooner
   b. $24,912.16

8. **a.** 53 months sooner
   b. $51,969.80

9. **a.** $215
   b. Total interest for 25-year mortgage: $160,465.00
      Total interest for 25-year mortgage paid off 5 years early: $124,933.82
      Difference: $35,531.18

10. **a.** $249
    b. Total interest for 20-year mortgage: $110,939.12
       Total interest for 20-year mortgage paid off 5 years early: $80,415.45
       Difference: $30,523.67
    c. Total interest for 15-year mortgage: $80,451.25
       Total interest for 20-year mortgage paid off 5 years early: $80,415.45
       Difference: $35.80

11. Balloon payment: $111,835.67
    Total interest paid: $33,007.07

12. Balloon payment: $106,578.74
    Total interest paid: $43,812.14

13. The cost of renting is $50,668.80 less than the cost of buying.

14. The cost of renting is $9192.24 more than the cost of buying.

15. 16.875

16. 18.571

17. **a.** About $190,000   **b.** About $55,000

18. Fell by 2.2%

19. About 13%

20. 1989 to 1998: About 27%
    1998 to 2007: About 63%
    The percent increase from 1998 to 2007 was more than double the percent increase from 1989 to 1998.

21. **a.** Mortgage A: $760.03
       Mortgage B: $805.23
       With Mortgage B, you are paying $45.20 more per month.
    b. About 66 months, or $5\frac{1}{2}$ years

22. a. Mortgage A: $681.35
Mortgage B: $719.46
With Mortgage B, you are paying $38.11 more per month.

b. About 63 months, or almost $5\frac{1}{4}$ years

23. a. $190,491.80   **b.** $5151.00

24. a.

Year	Interest	Principal
1	$8,826.91	$6,362.57
2	$8,434.49	$6,754.99
3	$8,017.86	$7,171.62
4	$7,575.53	$7,613.95
5	$7,105.92	$8,083.56
6	$6,607.36	$8,582.12
7	$6,078.00	$9,111.48
8	$5,516.07	$9,673.41
9	$4,919.41	$10,270.07
10	$4,285.97	$10,903.51
11	$3,613.46	$11,576.02
12	$2,899.49	$12,289.99
13	$2,141.45	$13,048.03
14	$1,336.68	$13,852.80
15	$482.28	$14,705.88

b.

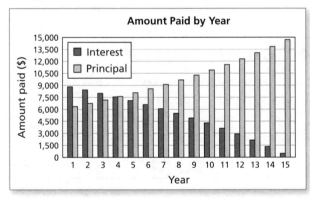

The total amount you pay in interest each year decreases over time, and the total amount you pay toward the principal increases over time.

25. About $112,000

26. ARM reset shock occurs when you suddenly have to begin making monthly payments at a new, higher rate. You can avoid being shocked by planning ahead and preparing for the rate reset.

Section 6.4   *(page 290)*

1. a. $1647.01   **b.** $2712.64

2. a. $1819.40   **b.** $3310.20

3. Your account   **4.** Your friend's account

5. About $6 trillion   **6.** $51,877,742.45

7. $719,536,522.10   **8.** About $515 trillion

9. $57,018.65   **10.** $101,321.86

11. a. $137,799.63
b. $413,398.89
c. The balance in part (b) is three times the balance in part (a).

12. a. $189,629.73
b. $90,052.73
c. The balance in part (b) is $99,577 less than the balance in part (a).

13. a. $396,767.60   **14. a.** $417,239.38
b. $1,432,633.58   **b.** $2,317,857.19
c. $1,829,401.18   **c.** $2,735,096.57

15. a. $750,000   **16. a.** $1,800,000
b. $540,029.59   **b.** $1,279,698.63
c. $790,029.59   **c.** $479,698.63

17. 35.5 years   **18.** 17.7 years

19. 59 years old   **20.** 66 years old

21. a. $440.50   **b.** $172.50

22. a. $58.46   **b.** $71.72

23. a. 6.18%   **b.** 6.17%   **c.** 6.14%
d. 6.09%   **e.** 6%

24. a. 7.25%   **b.** 7.23%   **c.** 7.19%
d. 7.12%   **e.** 7%

25. Annual; When the interest is compounded annually, the APR is the annual rate of increase, which is the definition of APY. Also, substituting $n = 1$ into the formula for APY gives APY $= r$.

26. b

6.3–6.4 Quiz   *(page 294)*

1. a. $401.82   **b.** $807.99

2. a. $74,605.60   **b.** $111,606.40
An increase of only 2 percentage points increases the interest you pay by $37,000.80.

3. a. 75 months sooner   **b.** $20,293.22

4. The cost of renting is $21,471.60 more than the cost of buying.

5. $413,398.89

6. About $7\frac{1}{4}$ years

Chapter 6 Review *(page 296)*

1. October 14   **2.** $117.65

3. Loan Proceeds: $255
Other Charges: $0
Amount Financed: $255
Finance Charge: $45
Total Amount Due: $300
Annual Percentage Rate: 460%
Payable in 1 payment with a term of 14 days.

4. Loan Proceeds: $500
Other Charges: $0
Amount Financed: $500
Finance Charge: $93.10
Total Amount Due: $593.10
Annual Percentage Rate: 226.54%
Payable in 1 payment with a term of 30 days

5. **a.** 460%
b. 226.54%

6. No

7. $487.67

8.

	A	B	C	D	E
1	Payment Number	Balance before Payment	Monthly Interest	Monthly Payment	Balance after Payment
2	1	$50,000.00	$249.58	$487.67	$49,761.92
3	2	$49,761.92	$248.39	$487.67	$49,522.65
4	3	$49,522.65	$247.20	$487.67	$49,282.18
5	4	$49,282.18	$246.00	$487.67	$49,040.51
6	5	$49,040.51	$244.79	$487.67	$48,797.64
141	140	$2,402.24	$11.99	$487.67	$1,926.56
142	141	$1,926.56	$9.62	$487.67	$1,448.51
143	142	$1,448.51	$7.23	$487.67	$968.08
144	143	$968.08	$4.83	$487.67	$485.24
145	144	$485.24	$2.42	$487.67	$0.00
146	Totals		$20,223.63	$70,223.63	

9. $20,224.48   **10.** After 85 payments

11. $928.80   **12.** $618.00

13. 5%: $158,536.00
7%: $237,163.60
An increase of only 2 percentage points increases the interest you pay by $78,627.60.

14. 30 years: $158,536.00
15 years: $71,983.00
The interest you pay on a 15-year loan is $86,553 less than the interest you pay on a 30-year loan.

15. **a.** 39 months sooner
b. $20,343.82

16. Balloon payment: $156,108.60
Total interest paid: $40,864.60

17. The cost of renting is $14,719.00 more than the cost of buying.

18. The prices of homes increase at an abnormal rate;
The prices of homes decrease.

19. **a.** $6155.01
b. $12,628.03

20. Your friend's account   **21.** $1,054,907.98

22. **a.** $1,000,000
b. $751,894.48
c. $806,802.86

23. **a.** $92.10   **b.** $1696.51
c. $31,249.98   **d.** $575,629.52
e. $10,603,184.55   **f.** $22,485,504,530,179.20

24. 68 years old

Section 7.1 *(page 308)*

1. Yes; For every 10 feet of depth, the pressure increases by 4.33 pounds per square inch.

2.

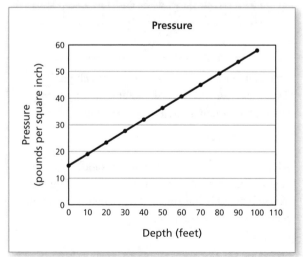

Yes

3. 0.433 pounds per square inch; $\frac{4.33}{10} = 0.433$

4. Pressure in pounds per square inch
$= 0.433$(depth in feet) $+ 14.7$

5.

	A	B	C	D
1	**Depth (feet)**	**Pressure (lb/in.²)**		
2	0	14.70		
3	10	19.15		
4	20	23.60		
5	30	28.05		
6	40	32.50		
7	50	36.95		
8	60	41.40		
9	70	45.85		
10	80	50.30		
11	90	54.75		
12	100	59.20		
13				
14				
15				
16				
17				
18				
19				
20				
21				
22				
23				
24				
25				
26				

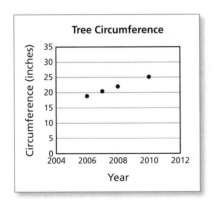

6. 72.55 pounds per square inch

7. 148.2 pounds per square inch

8. 5577.2 pounds per square inch

9.

Tree Circumference

26.70 in.

10. 2006: About 6 in.
2007: About 6.5 in.
2008: About 7 in.
2009: About 7.5 in.
2010: About 8 in.

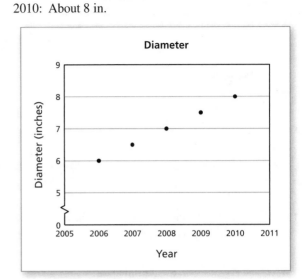

About 8.5 in.

11. From March 10 through May 20, the migration of the black-and-white warbler appears to be linear.

12.

Day	Distance
March 30	0
March 31	20
April 2	60
April 6	140
April 13	280
April 21	440
May 1	640

13. a. For every 1 mg/L of concentration, the absorbance increases by 0.164.

b.

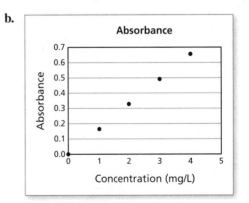

c. 5 mg/L: 0.820

14. a. For every 2 mg/L of concentration, the absorbance increases by 0.312.

b.

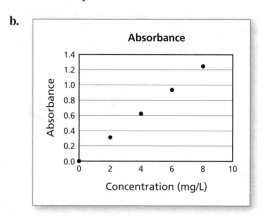

c. 10 mg/L: 1.560

15. a. For every 0.2 cm of path length, the absorbance increases by 0.088.

b.

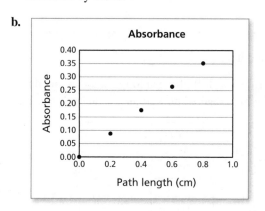

c. 1.0 cm: 0.440

16. a. For every 0.3 cm of path length, the absorbance increases by 0.078.

b.

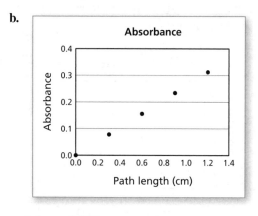

c. 1.5 cm: 0.390

17. 0.265

18. About 0.356

19. a.

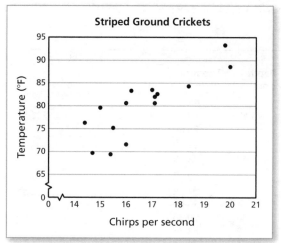

b.

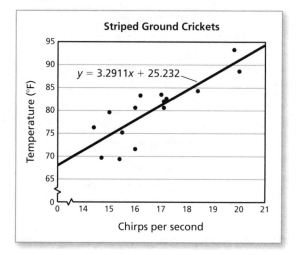

c. About 87.8°F

d. About 97.6°F

20. a.

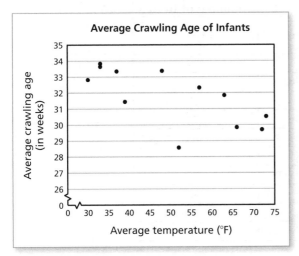

b.

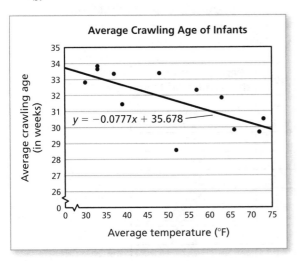

c. About 31.40 weeks

d. About -1.23 weeks; No; No; 475°F is an unrealistic outside temperature and is too far outside the domain to be meaningful. Crawling at -1.23 weeks would mean that the baby was crawling before being born, which is also unrealistic.

Section 7.2 *(page 318)*

1. No; The difference between the surface area values for consecutive weeks is not constant.

2. 40% per week

3.

	A	B	C	D
1	**Week**	**Surface area (square feet)**		
2	0	500		
3	1	700		
4	2	980		
5	3	1,372		
6	4	1,921		
7	5	2,689		
8	6	3,765		
9	7	5,271		
10	8	7,379		
11	9	10,331		
12	10	14,463		
13	11	20,248		
14	12	28,347		
15	13	39,686		
16	14	55,560		
17	15	77,784		
18	16	108,898		
19	17	152,457		
20	18	213,439		
21	19	298,815		
22	20	418,341		
23				
24				
25				
26				
27				
28				
29				
30				
31				
32				
33				
34				
35				

Spreading of Water Hyacinth

The graph shows exponential growth.

4. About 22 weeks

5.

Week	Surface area (square feet)
0	1,500
1	2,400
2	3,840
3	6,144
4	9,830
5	15,729
6	25,166
7	40,265
8	64,425
9	103,079
10	164,927
11	263,883
12	422,212
13	675,540
14	1,080,864
15	1,729,382
16	2,500,000

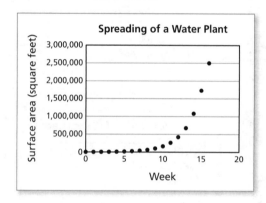

Spreading of a Water Plant

6. About 25 more weeks

7. The initial population

8. About 60% per year

9. 2147 rabbits

10. 5496 rabbits

11. During year 9

12. During year 11

13. 1291 rabbits

14. 492 rabbits

15. About 4000 trout; The population approaches, but does not exceed, 4000 over time.

16.

Year	Change in the number of trout
1	150
2	245
3	371
4	503
5	587
6	577
7	480
8	346
9	225
10	136
11	79
12	45

The yearly increase in the number of trout increases until the population is about half the maximum sustainable population. Then the gain in the trout population begins to decrease.

17.

Year	Percent change in the number of trout
1	75.0
2	70.0
3	62.4
4	52.1
5	40.0
6	28.1
7	18.2
8	11.1
9	6.5
10	3.7
11	2.1
12	1.2

The percent of increase is decreasing each year.

18.

Year	Logistic	Exponential
0	200	200
1	350	320
2	595	512
3	966	819
4	1469	1311
5	2056	2097
6	2633	3355
7	3113	5369
8	3459	8590
9	3684	13,744
10	3820	21,990
11	3899	35,184
12	3944	56,295

Exponential growth is unrealistic in this situation because the lake has limited size and resources.

19. Both species of fish experience a logistic growth pattern. Species A levels off with a population of about 1400 fish. Species B levels off with a population of about 1000 fish.

20. Species A outgrows Species B, although Species A does not grow as fast as when it is in a separate pond. Species B peaks at about 400 fish just after 5 years but then steadily decreases until there is a population of 0.

21. a. 39.2%   **b.** 24%   **c.** 4%

22. a. 45%   **b.** 25%   **c.** 5%

23. 0%; When the population reaches its maximum sustainable population, $r = r_0 \times (1 - 1) = r_0 \times 0 = 0$. This is because when a population is at its maximum, it cannot grow any larger.

24. The growth rate becomes negative. This represents the population size decreasing because it is too large to be supported by available natural resources.

25.

Year	Exponential population	Superexponential population
0	100	100
1	150	150
2	225	240
3	338	413
4	506	769
5	759	1567
6	1139	3517
7	1709	8768
8	2563	24,477
9	3844	77,101
10	5767	276,012

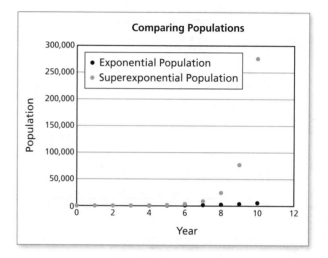

26.

Year	Exponential population	Superexponential population
0	50	50
1	80	80
2	128	133
3	205	229
4	328	412
5	524	774
6	839	1523
7	1342	3141
8	2147	6814
9	3436	15,578
10	5498	37,618

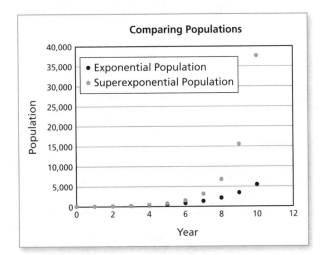

27. Day 29

28. The 6th day

7.1–7.2 Quiz *(page 322)*

1. The pattern for Set A is linear. The deer population is projected to grow at a rate of 24 additional deer each year.

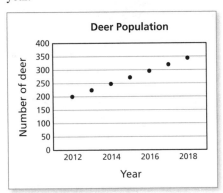

2. 440 deer

3. The pattern for Set B is exponential. The deer population is projected to grow at a rate of about 12% each year.

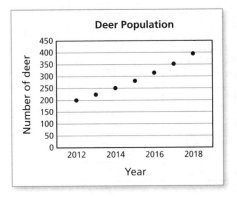

4. 622 deer   **5.** 2025   **6.** 2021

7. Set B; $\dfrac{200}{1.12^5} \approx 113$, but $200 - (5 \times 24) = 80$.

8.

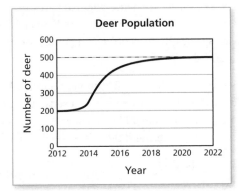

Section 7.3 *(page 330)*

1. The second differences are constant (-8). The pattern is quadratic.

2. The first differences are constant (12.6). The pattern is linear.

3. The second differences are constant (-8). The pattern is quadratic.

4. 27 ft

5.

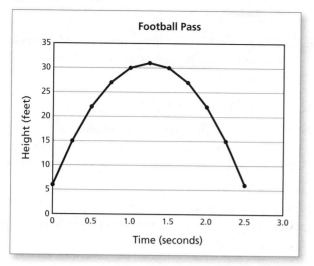

The pattern is quadratic. The graph is a downward U-shaped curve.

6. 1.25 sec

7. Quadratic; The graph is curving upward.

8. Linear; The graph is a line.

9. About 600 ft

10. No; The graph of the braking distance appears to be quadratic, not linear. The breaking distance at 70 miles per hour is about 240 feet, which is 4 times the braking distance at 35 miles per hour.

11. Yes; The second differences are constant (20).

12.

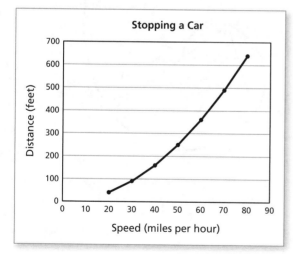

The graph has the same shape as the graph from Exercises 7–10. The only difference is the braking distances are twice as long for the same speeds.

13. Quadratic; The second differences are constant $\left(1\frac{1}{3}\right)$.

14. Quadratic; The second differences are constant (7.4).

15. Quadratic; The second differences are constant (-12.4).

16. Quadratic; The second differences are constant (-86.4).

17.

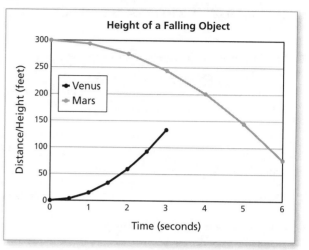

The graph of the data from Venus curves upward. The graph of the data from Mars curves downward. It appears that if the second differences are positive, then the graph curves upward, and if the second differences are negative, then the graph curves downward.

18. 6 times; Earth's distances are 6 times greater than the moon's distances for the same times.

19. Linear; The first differences are about 186.

20. Quadratic; The second differences are about -16.

21. Quadratic; The second differences are about 16.

22. Exponential; The ratio of consecutive prices is about 1.1.

23.

Folds	1	2	3	4	5
Sections	2	4	8	16	32

24.

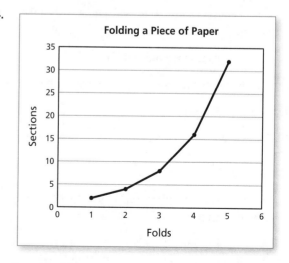

Exponential

25. $S = 2^n$ **26.** 256 sections

Section 7.4   *(page 340)*

1. The number of petals on a daisy is usually a Fibonacci number.

2. Phyllotaxis is the arrangement of leaves on a plant stem. The leaves of plants grow in certain patterns to maximize exposure to sunlight. Some of these patterns follow the Fibonacci sequence.

3. Pineapple scales are patterned into spirals. There are three sets of spirals, and they follow the Fibonacci sequence (5, 8, and 13).

4. The sets of spirals on a pinecone are Fibonacci numbers.

5. The leaves on a sneezewort plant grow in a Fibonacci pattern.

6. Many proportions in the human body have Fibonacci relationships, such as the distances from the hip to the knee and from the knee to the ankle, and the distances from the shoulder joint to the elbow and from the elbow to the finger tips.

7. Yes, credit cards are in the shape of the golden rectangle.

8. Yes, the shape of the TV (including the frame) is a golden rectangle.

9. Yes, the ratio of the height of the mirror to the length of the mirror is approximately equal to the golden ratio.

10. No, the wing span of a butterfly is not in the shape of the golden rectangle.

11. The RF mask identifies several prominent dimensions of the human face. Dr. Marquardt believes that if these dimensions are close to the golden ratio, then the person's face will be perceived as beautiful.

12. It approximates the golden ratio.

13. Yes; Nefertiti's features align perfectly with the mask.

14. Answers will vary.

15. The nth triangular number is the sum of the first n whole numbers ($1, 1 + 2 = 3, 1 + 2 + 3 = 6, 1 + 2 + 3 + 4 = 10$, etc.).

16. Each triangular number corresponds to the number of dots in each figure (1, 3, 6, 10, and 15).

17. No; The first few triangular numbers are 1, 3, 6, 10, 15, 21, 28, 36, 45, 55, 66, 78, 91, 105, and 120.

18. Each number is the sum of the two previous numbers, starting with 1 and 3.

19. The cactus has 11 spirals in one direction and 18 spirals in the other direction. Both 11 and 18 are Lucas numbers.

20. About 1.618 (the golden ratio)

21. About 137.51°; The golden angle is formed by dividing the circumference of a circle into two parts so the ratio of the larger part to the smaller part is equal to the golden ratio.

22. The angle between successive florets and leaves in some flowers and plants is the golden angle. This maximizes exposure to sunlight and rain.

23. **a.** Yes; The triangle is isosceles and $\frac{8}{5} = 1.6$, which is approximately equal to the golden ratio.

    b. No; The triangle is not isosceles.

    c. Yes; The triangle is isosceles and $\frac{55}{34} \approx 1.618$.

    d. No; $\frac{14}{10} = 1.4$, which is not close to the golden ratio.

24.

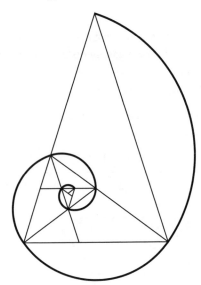

25. The ratio of any diagonal to any side is equal to the golden ratio.

26. 20

7.3–7.4 Quiz   *(page 344)*

1. The second differences are constant (0.16). The pattern is quadratic.

2. 1.26

3.

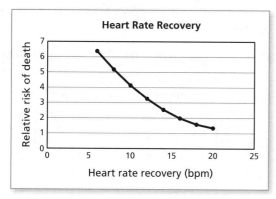

The graph curves downward.

4. The position of the T wave splits the QRS frequency into the golden ratio, as shown by the yellow arrow and the bar on top.

5.

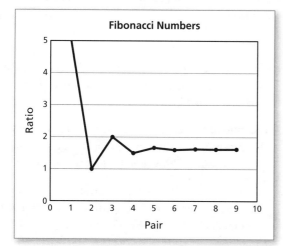

The graph resembles the tail end of the QRS complex shown on the EKG.

6. Answers will vary. *Sample answer:* Studies have shown that people are less likely to have a fatal heart attack when the ratio of the maximum (systolic) pressure to the minimum (diastolic) pressure is close to the golden ratio.

Chapter 7 Review *(page 346)*

1. Yes; For every increase in temperature of 1°C, the resistance increases by 0.38 ohm.

2.

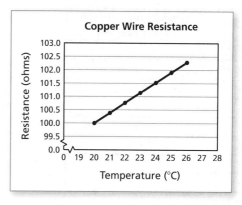

Yes

3. 103.80 ohms   **4.** 110.64 ohms

5. Yes

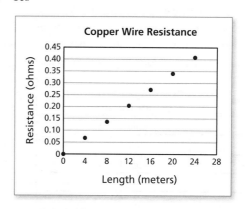

6. a. 0.442 ohm

   b. 0.476 ohm

   c. 0.510 ohm

7. 45 amperes   **8.** 60 amperes

9. 100% per week   **10.** 384 beetles

11. During week 10   **12.** 2 weeks

13. Logistic

14. About 500 flour beetles

15.

Week	Change in the number of flour beetles
1	33
2	54
3	77
4	88
5	79
6	57
7	35
8	20
9	10
10	5
11	2
12	2

The weekly increase in the number of flour beetles increases until the population is about half the maximum sustainable population. Then the gain in the flour beetle population begins to decrease.

16.

Week	Percent change in the number of flour beetles
1	89.2
2	77.1
3	62.1
4	43.8
5	27.3
6	15.5
7	8.2
8	4.3
9	2.1
10	1.0
11	0.4
12	0.4

The percent of increase is decreasing each week.

17. The second differences are constant (56). The pattern is quadratic.

18.

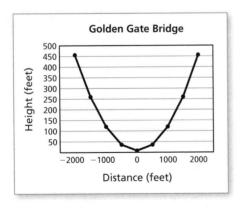

Quadratic; The graph is an upward U-shaped curve.

19. 708 ft; No; The main towers are only 500 feet above the roadway.

20. Quadratic; The second differences are constant (−8).

21.

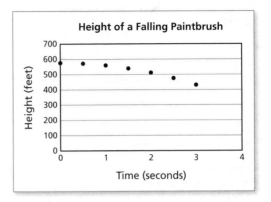

The graph shows a quadratic pattern and curves downward.

22. 6 seconds

23. Each full cycle of a DNA double helix spiral measures 34 angstroms long by 21 angstroms wide. 34 and 21 are numbers in the Fibonacci sequence.

24. The ratio of the length (34 angstroms) to the width (21 angstroms) of a full cycle of a DNA double helix spiral is about 1.619, which is close to the golden ratio.

25. The major groove measures 21 angstroms long, and the minor groove measures 13 angstroms long. 21 and 13 are numbers in the Fibonacci sequence.

26. The ratio of the length of the major groove (21 angstroms) to the length of the minor groove (13 angstroms) is about 1.615, which is close to the golden ratio.

27. By placing two pentagons together and then rotating one of them, you have the shape of the cross-sectional view of a DNA double helix.

28. Each spiral traces out the shape of a pentagon in the cross-sectional view of a DNA double helix. The ratio of any diagonal of a pentagon to any of its sides is equal to the golden ratio.

Section 8.1 (page 358)

1.

Probability of Fears			
	Fraction	Decimal	Percent
Dark	$\frac{1}{20}$	0.05	5%
Heights	$\frac{9}{25}$	0.36	36%
Identity theft	$\frac{25}{38}$	0.66	66%
Thunder or lightning	$\frac{11}{100}$	0.11	11%

The probability of a person being afraid of the dark is very unlikely. The probability of a person being afraid of heights is somewhat unlikely. The probability of a person being afraid of identity theft is likely. The probability of a person being afraid of thunder or lightning is very unlikely.

2.

Probability of Health Issues			
	Fraction	Decimal	Percent
Diagnosed with cancer	$\frac{41}{100}$	0.41	41%
Die from flu	$\frac{1}{345,100}$	0.000003	0.0003%
Has health insurance	$\frac{847}{1000}$	0.847	84.7%
Obese	$\frac{269}{1000}$	0.269	26.9%

The probability of a person being diagnosed with cancer is equally likely to happen or not happen. The probability of a person dying from the flu is next to impossible. The probability of a person having health insurance is very likely. The probability of a person being obese is unlikely.

3. Very unlikely

4. Likely

5. Very likely

6. Very unlikely

7. a. Answers will vary.

   b. Industries differ in fatality rates because occupations that are much more dangerous than others tend to have higher fatality rates.

8. a. Answers will vary.

   b. There are fewer miners than there are people who work in financial activities.

9. Low likelihood, high significance

10. High likelihood, low significance

11. Low likelihood, high significance

12. High likelihood, high significance

13. Low likelihood, high significance

14. High likelihood, high significance

15. The life expectancy for females increased in each country. In Australia, Germany, Spain, and the United States, life expectancy increased at about the same rate. The female life expectancy in Turkey increased at a greater rate than the other countries.

16. The life expectancy for males increased in each country. In Australia, Germany, Spain, and the United States, life expectancy increased at about the same rate. The male life expectancy in Turkey increased at a greater rate than the other countries.

17. 1980: Turkey, Germany, United States, Australia, Spain
2007: Turkey, United States, Germany, Australia, Spain

Germany and the United States switched orders. Spain still has the greatest female life expectancy, and Turkey still has the least female life expectancy.

18. 1980: Turkey, Germany, United States, Australia, Spain
2007: Turkey, United States, Germany, Spain, Australia

Germany and the United States switched orders. Australia passed Spain for the greatest male life expectancy, and Turkey still has the least male life expectancy.

19. In each country in each year, the life expectancy for females is about 5 years greater than for males.

20. Turkey; Turkey

21. a. Event 2; There are 0 numbers less than 1, and there are 5 numbers greater than 1.

   b. Event 2; There are 2 multiples of 3, and there are 3 numbers greater than 3.

22. a. Event 2; There is 1 green area, and there are 2 red areas.

   b. Event 1; There are 3 even numbers, and there are 2 prime numbers.

23. a. Event 2; There are 2 blue areas on spinner A, and there are 3 blue areas on spinner B.

   b. Event 1; There are 3 multiples of 2 on spinner A, and there is 1 multiple of 6 on spinner B.

24. Answers will vary.

Section 8.2 (page 368)

1. $\frac{1}{12}$ **2.** $\frac{1}{12}$ **3.** $\frac{2}{3}$

4. $\frac{1}{4}$ **5.** $\frac{1}{2}$ **6.** $\frac{5}{12}$

7. a. $\frac{1}{1000}$ **b.** $\frac{1}{200}$

8. $0: About 94.7%
$3: About 3.0%
$4: About 1.6%
$7: About 0.6%
$100: About 0.02%
$10,000: 0.001%
$200,000: About 0.0002%
$16,000,000: 0%

9. 64.75%   **10.** About 14.1%

11. About 58.9%   **12.** About 58.9%

13. The probabilities are the same because no matter how the data are presented, the overall probability of saying "No" is the same.

14. Male: About 40.4%; equally likely to happen or not happen

Female: About 47.0%; equally likely to happen or not happen

15. Underweight: About 14.9%; unlikely
Normal weight: About 23.3%; unlikely
Overweight: About 49.0%; equally likely to happen or not happen
Obese: About 59.1%; somewhat likely
Morbidly obese: About 62.1%; likely

16. Females are slightly more likely than males to make losing weight one of their New Year's resolutions. The greater a person's BMI, the more likely the person is to make losing weight a New Year's resolution.

17. About 52.2%   **18.** About 80.4%

19. About 19.6%   **20.** 4

21. 3.5   **22.** About 2.7

23. 25% for all 4 suits

24. Hearts: 34%; Diamonds: 16%; Spades: 26%; Clubs: 24%

25. The experimental and theoretical probabilities for spades and clubs are about the same. The experimental probability for hearts is greater than the theoretical probability. The experimental probability for diamonds is less than the theoretical probability.

26. About 30.8%   **27.** About 53.8%

28. About 42.3%

8.1–8.2 Quiz (page 372)

1.

Month	Fraction	Decimal	Percent
November	$\frac{11}{250}$	0.044	4.4%
December	$\frac{25}{74}$	0.338	33.8%
January	$\frac{81}{1000}$	0.081	8.1%
February	$\frac{301}{1000}$	0.301	30.1%
March	$\frac{5}{34}$	0.147	14.7%

November: Very unlikely
December: Somewhat unlikely
January: Very unlikely
February: Unlikely
March: Very unlikely

2. Unlikely   **3.** Likely

4. Unlikely   **5.** Nearly impossible

6. 10,000   **7.** 70%   **8.** 0.1%

Section 8.3 (page 380)

1. $-$49.70   **2.** $-$50.82

3. $70.95   **4.** $66.92

5. a. $-$100.26   **b.** $100.26   **c.** $1,002,600

6. a. $-$99.75   **b.** $99.75   **c.** $997,500

7.

	Probability	Profit	Expected Value
A	10%	$8 million	0.1($8)
	70%	$4 million	0.7($4)
	20%	$-$2 million	+ 0.2($-$2)
			$3.2 million
B	30%	$8 million	0.3($8)
	50%	$4 million	0.5($4)
	20%	$-$2 million	+ 0.2($-$2)
			$4 million

The company should develop Laptop B.

8.

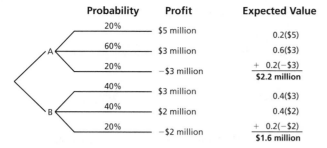

	Probability	Profit	Expected Value
A	20%	$5 million	0.2($5)
	60%	$3 million	0.6($3)
	20%	−$3 million	+ 0.2(−$3)
			$2.2 million
B	40%	$3 million	0.4($3)
	40%	$2 million	0.4($2)
	20%	−$2 million	+ 0.2(−$2)
			$1.6 million

The company should develop MP3 Player A.

9.

	Probability	Profit	Expected Value
A	20%	$7 million	0.2($7)
	45%	$3 million	0.45($3)
	25%	$2 million	0.25($2)
	10%	−$2.5 million	+ 0.1(−$2.5)
			$3 million
B	10%	$8 million	0.1($8)
	40%	$6 million	0.4($6)
	30%	$0	0.3($0)
	20%	−$3 million	+ 0.2(−$3)
			$2.6 million

The company should develop E-reader A.

10.

	Probability	Profit	Expected Value
A	10%	$8 million	0.1($8)
	30%	$5 million	0.3($5)
	20%	$3 million	0.2($3)
	25%	$1 million	0.25($1)
	15%	−$3 million	+ 0.15(−$3)
			$2.7 million
B	20%	$6.5 million	0.2($6.5)
	35%	$4 million	0.35($4)
	25%	$2 million	0.25($2)
	10%	$0	0.1($0)
	10%	−$3 million	+ 0.1(−$3)
			$2.9 million

The company should develop Camera B.

11. Expected value for Option 1: $1000
Expected value for Option 2: $1200
Option 2 has the greater expected value.

12. Expected value for Option 1: −$1000
Expected value for Option 2: −$1100
Option 1 has the greater expected value.

13. Expected value for Option 1: $1400
Expected value for Option 2: $1800
Option 2 has the greater expected value.

14. Expected value for Option 1: $750
Expected value for Option 2: $750
Both options have the same expected value.

15. Expected value for speculative investment: $1600
Expected value for conservative investment: $390

16. Expected value for speculative investment: $1650
Expected value for conservative investment: $250

17. Expected rate of return for Stock V: 11%
Expected rate of return for Stock W: 7%
Stock V has a greater expected rate of return.

18. 9%   **19.** 8.72%   **20.** 8.51%

21. 8.825%   **22.** 8.93%

Section 8.4 *(page 390)*

1. 0.1728%   **2.** 0.1%   **3.** 0.0512%

4. 0.0343%   **5.** 0.0216%   **6.** 0.0125%

7. 0.0008%

8.

	A	B	C	D
1	Event	Probability	Payoff	Expected Value
2	3 cherries	0.1728%	150	0.2592
3	3 bars	0.1%	200	0.2
4	3 watermelons	0.0512%	250	0.128
5	3 lemons	0.0343%	400	0.1372
6	3 plums	0.0216%	1,000	0.216
7	3 oranges	0.0125%	7,500	0.9375
8	3 sevens	0.0008%	12,000	0.096
9	No win	99.6068%	−1	−0.996068
10	Total	100%		0.977832

The expected value of the game is $0.98.

9. About 44.4%   **10.** About 90.7%

11. About 98.4%   **12.** 100%

13. About 45.5%   **14.** About 20.8%

15. About 77.0%   **16.** About 72.2%

17. About 33.3%   **18.** About 66.7%

19. If you do not switch, you win 2 out of 5 times. If you do switch, you win 3 out of 5 times. So, based on probability, you should switch.

20. If you do not switch, you win 50 out of 101 times. If you do switch, you win 51 out of 101 times. So, based on probability, you should switch.

21. 20%   **22.** About 33.3%

23. About 2.0%   **24.** About 11.8%

25. About 74.7%   **26.** About 66.2%

8.3–8.4 Quiz *(page 394)*

1. 2.5 points   **2.** 0.625 point

3. About 5.6%   **4.** About 0.000095%

5. About 1.9%   **6.** About 0.023%

7. About 94.4%

Chapter 8 Review *(page 396)*

1.

Event	Fraction	Decimal	Percent
Being an organ donor	$\frac{4}{15}$	0.267	26.7%
Eats breakfast	$\frac{61}{100}$	0.61	61%
Having a dream that comes true	$\frac{429}{1000}$	0.429	42.9%
Household with television	$\frac{491}{500}$	0.982	98.2%

The probability of being an organ donor is unlikely. The probability of eating breakfast is equally likely to happen or not happen. The probability of having a dream that comes true is equally likely to happen or not happen.

The probability of a household having a television is almost certain.

2. Unlikely   **3.** Almost certain

4. Nearly impossible   **5.** Somewhat unlikely

6. Answers will vary.

7. Because, for each solid, the probability of landing on any one of the faces is the same.

8. Answers will vary.   **9.** 75%

10. A Platonic solid is a solid in which each face is the same regular polygon, with the same number of faces meeting at each vertex.

11. 18–29: About 74.8%; likely

30–49: About 58.3%; equally likely to happen or not happen

50–64: About 31.1%; unlikely

65 and over: About 9.7%; very unlikely

12. Rural: About 30.8%; unlikely

Suburban: About 48.3%; equally likely to happen or not happen

Urban: About 49.0%; equally likely to happen or not happen

13. −$250   **14.** −$270.00

15.

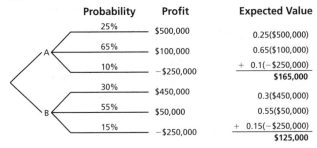

The company should develop Toaster A.

16.

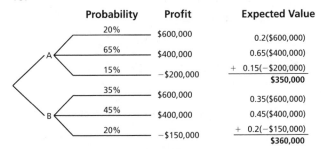

The company should develop Microwave B.

17. Expected value for Option 1: $1000

Expected value for Option 2: $1250

Option 2 has the greater expected value.

18. Expected value for speculative investment: $500

Expected value for conservative investment: $125

19. About 1.56%   **20.** About 23.73%

21. About 86.65%   **22.** About 99.99%

23. 0.81%   **24.** About 11.76%

25. About 91.76%   **26.** About 99.98%

Section 9.1 *(page 408)*

1. Answers will vary. *Sample answer:* The stacked area graph shows the types and quantities of aircraft that composed the USAF fighter force from 1950 through 2009. In general, the number of aircraft has declined since the peak in the 1950s.

2. F-4   **3.** About 24%

4. 2000s; There were only 4 or 5 types of aircraft, in this decade. All previous decades had more variety, as shown by the many different colors in the chart.

5. Disagree; The F-16 has decreased slightly in number since 2000 but still makes up about one-half of the fighting force.

6. Answers will vary.　　　**7.** Company D

8. Company E

9. Company D; Company E

To determine the profit for each company, multiply revenue by profit percent (in decimal form). This shows that Company E makes the most profit.

Company A: $2.5 million
Company B: $18.75 million
Company C: $37.5 million
Company D: $35 million
Company E: $45 million

10. Answers will vary. *Sample answer:* Radar graphs are useful for showing that one item stands out as being significantly different than all the others.

11. The graph shows the price of a share of company C stock for each week of 2010. In general, the stock price started at about $24 for the first 6 weeks, then significantly decreased to about $15 from weeks 9 through 16, then gradually increased to about $20 by week 31, then significantly increased to about $30 by week 37, and then gradually decreased to about $25 by the end of the year.

12. About $19　　　**13.** Earned a profit

14. 100%; The lowest price of the year was about $15 in week 9. The highest price was about $30 in week 37. So, investors who bought the stock in week 9 and sold the stock in week 37 would have doubled their money, which is a return of 100%.

15. The graph shows the day of the week (*x*-axis), the type of change between the opening price and the closing price (green if increase, red if decrease), the amount of change from opening to closing (length of candlestick body), the opening price (bottom of candlestick body if green, top of candlestick body if red), the closing price (top of candlestick body if green, bottom of candlestick body if red), the highest price (top of shadow), the lowest price (bottom of shadow), and the range (length of shadow).

16. The closing price is higher than the opening price; The closing price is lower than the opening price.

17. $22.50; $22.75　　　**18.** $23.75; $23.50

19. Wednesday; Thursday

20. The opening price was the low price on Wednesday.

21. 12.5%; If you bought the stock at its lowest price ($22 on Monday) and sold it at its highest price ($24.75 on Friday), you would have earned $2.75 per share. This is a return of $\frac{2.75}{22} = 12.5\%$.

22. Answers will vary.　　　**23.** Answers will vary.

24. Answers will vary. *Sample answer:* You are likely to have more of a variety of activities over a year than you will in a particular week. Also, the activities and percent of time spent on each may change throughout the year due to factors like school, changing seasons, amount of daylight, and holidays.

25. The chart in Example 2 shows the changing parts of a whole, but the chart in Example 1 shows data for a total that changes over time.

26. Answers will vary. *Sample answer:* Yes; The graph would show if you are spending too much time on certain activities and not enough time on others.

27. Answers will vary. *Sample answer:* Income, expenses, debt, retirement savings, body weight, blood pressure, cholesterol level, food consumption, exercise routine, study routine, social habits, personal goal accomplishment, etc.

28. Answers will vary.

Section 9.2 *(page 418)*

1. Women's team: About 72.5 in.
Men's team: About 79.1 in.

The average player on the men's team is more than 6 inches taller than the average player on the women's team.

2. Women's team: 74 and 75 in.
Men's team: 74, 77, 79, and 84 in.

3. Women's team: 74 in.
Men's team: 79 in.

The median height of the men's team is 5 inches greater than the median height of the women's team.

4. 18.75%　　　**5.** Median

6. Mean and median (They are essentially both 79 inches.)

7. The mean and the median would each be 2 inches greater.

8. Answers will vary. The sum of the five heights must equal 401 inches. *Sample answer:* 76, 77, 79, 84, and 85 in.

9. About 10 or 11 colleges

10. Below; The median marks the middle of the data, and the mean is about $2500 greater than the median.

11. Uppermost (4th) quartile; Lower middle (2nd) quartile; The uppermost quartile has the greatest range of values ($41,350 − 24,900 = $16,450$), and the lower middle quartile of the data has the least range of values ($16,200 − 12,500 = 3700).

12. Lowest (1st) quartile

13. No; The histogram shows the $5000 interval in which the annual cost for each college occurs, rather than the actual cost. This information cannot be used to determine the sum, middle value, or most common value of the actual annual costs.

14. $10,000 to $15,000   **15.** 13

16. Private 4-year colleges; Most of the blocks on the right of the histogram are blue, which corresponds to private 4-year colleges.

17. 2004, 2005, 2008, and 2010

18. 2004

19. a. Mean: About 36,739   **b.** Mean: About 16,898
Median: 5530   Median: 4000

c. Mean; Because more than half of the data are grouped so closely together, removing the two outliers changes the middle value of the data to a number that is close to the original median. But because their values are so great, removing the outliers has a substantial effect on the mean.

20. The only time when outliers affect the mode of a data set is when the outliers are the mode.

21. Median; The median is close to the majority of the data, but the mean is greater than most of the data.

22. a. Not valid; Based on the graph, all of the earthquakes have a magnitude above 6.0, and the two most fatal earthquakes had magnitudes of about 7.0 and 9.0.

b. Not valid; There is no correlation between magnitude and number of fatalities in the graph.

23. a. Mode; Printer A has the greatest mode (32 ppm) of the 3 printers.

b. Mean; Printer B has the greatest mean (30.4 ppm) of the 3 printers.

c. Median; Printer C has the greatest median (31 ppm) of the 3 printers.

24. a. Printer B

b. The midrange is very sensitive to outliers and ignores all other data values except for the minimum and the maximum.

25.

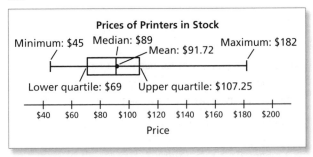

26. Answers will vary. *Sample answer:* The first 3 quartiles are evenly distributed. The 4th quartile has the largest range.

27.

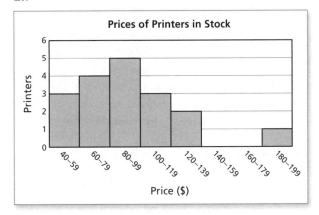

28. Answers will vary. *Sample answer:* Most of the data are distributed symmetrically, with the only exception being the outlier at $182.

9.1–9.2 Quiz   *(page 422)*

1. The chart shows the ranks and scores for the top 34 countries in reading, math, and science. The scores for each subject are given according to their rank from highest to lowest. The scores for each country are indicated by color coding and lines connecting the scores.

2. No; The countries are listed in order of greatest reading score.

3. No; The overall score for the United States is $500 + 487 + 502 = 1489$, but the overall score for Germany is $497 + 513 + 520 = 1530$.

4. Austria; Austria had a math score of 496, and Poland had a math score of 495.

5. **a.** Reading: The median is 496, and the mode is 500.
Math: The median is 496.5, and the mode is 487.
Science: The median is 501, and the modes are 500 and 508.

b. Reading: 493
Math: 496
Science: 501

6. Mean or median; The mean and median are so close that both describe the data equally well.

7. Answers will vary. *Sample answer:* The lowest and uppermost quartiles are more spread out than the middle quartiles. The lowest quartile is the most spread out, and the lower middle quartile is the least spread out.

8. Answers will vary. *Sample answer:* A politician or policymaker might use the chart to compare their country to other countries and to advocate changes in funding, policy, standards, and procedures to increase scores in all subjects.

Section 9.3 *(page 430)*

1. About 78 of the egg diameters lie within 1 standard deviation of the mean.

2. About 93%   **3.** 100%

4. Answers will vary. *Sample answer:* About 95 of the temperatures lie within one-half of a standard deviation of the mean.

5. About 51%   **6.** About 99%

7. Yes; The distribution of the data is approximately bell-shaped.

8. About 70%   **9.** About 97%

10. The percents are about the same.

11. The distribution of data values for machine 2 has less dispersion than the distribution of the data values for machine 1.

12. Machine 1: 86%
Machine 2: 98%

13. Males tend to have higher mathematics SAT scores than females; females tend to have higher writing SAT scores than males.

14. Males tend to have higher mathematics SAT scores than writing SAT scores; females tend to have the same mathematics SAT scores and writing SAT scores.

15. May and October; The school may have an SAT test in May or June and another SAT test in October or November, so this would account for the higher number of study hours in the months before the tests.

16. About 13.4%   **17.** Answers will vary.

18.

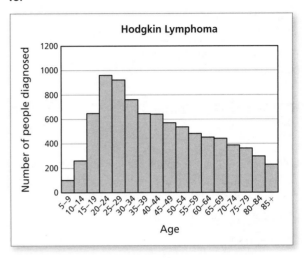

No; The histogram is similar to a right-skewed distribution because the number of people diagnosed peaks in the 20–24 age group and then decreases for each succeeding age group.

19.

x	x^2
16	256
12	144
23	529
20	400
18	324
15	225
18	324
19	361
$\sum x = 141$	$\sum x^2 = 2563$

$s \approx 3.3$

20.

x	x^2
33	1089
24	576
27	729
26	676
30	900
29	841
26	676
31	961
34	1156
20	400
$\sum x = 280$	$\sum x^2 = 8004$

$s \approx 4.3$

Section 9.4 *(page 440)*

1. 99 ± 4.99

2. 99 ± 3.53; When the sample size increases, the width of the confidence interval is narrower. This is because the larger the sample size, the closer you are getting to the actual population mean.

3. 23.3 ± 0.83

4. 23.3 ± 1.30; When the confidence level increases, the width of the confidence interval is wider. This is because the wider the interval, the more confidence you have that the population mean is in the interval.

5. People may lie to their dentists about flossing their teeth; Someone other than a dentist should conduct the survey.

6. Seniors are more likely to drive to school because they may have driver's licenses; You should randomly survey all students in the high school, not just seniors.

7. The one machine you choose could be producing hardly any defective items or could be producing more defective items than the other machines; You should choose items from all of the machines.

8. Students in the science club are more likely to want the science lab renovated; You should survey a random sample of students at the college.

9. People who have a very strong opinion will call in; The radio station should randomly survey people in the listening area.

10. People entering a sporting goods store are more likely to watch sports and will want a new baseball stadium; The city should survey a random sample of people in the city.

11. People living in the nursing homes are more likely to support the bill; You should survey a random sample of people in the city.

12. People from California, Florida, and North Carolina are closer to beaches than most other people from the United States, so they are more likely to have spent at least 1 week at the beach each year; The company should survey people in every state

13. 1068 people

14. 1842 people; When the confidence level increases, the sample size also increases. This is because the larger the sample size, the closer you are getting to the actual population mean and the more confidence you have in the results.

15. 385 people; When the margin of error increases, the sample size decreases. This is because the fewer people you survey, the more likely you are to have an error.

16. b; The question could produce biased results because it states that most of your neighbors think the solar panels are a waste of money.

17. a; The question could produce biased results because it states the policy is unfair and the project is time-consuming.

18. b; The question could produce biased results because it states the phone books are old and out-of-date.

19. Sample mean: $195.31
Margin of error: $16.56

20. Sample mean: $46,861
Margin of error: $1029

21. Sample mean: 5.5 days
Margin of error: 0.4 day

22. Sample mean: 160 oz
Margin of error: 0.03 oz

23. 104 newborns

24. 139 18-to-24-year olds

25. 865 people

26. 753 people

9.3–9.4 Quiz *(page 444)*

1. Yes; The distribution of the data is approximately bell-shaped.

2. About 73%

3. 100%

4. The percents are about the same.

5. 9.3 ± 0.36

6. 9.3 ± 0.47

7. People in the neighborhood around the fire station are more likely to want the fire station renovated; You should take a random sample of people in the city.

8. 664 people

Chapter 9 Review *(page 446)*

1. The graph shows the GDP per capita in thousands (*x*-axis), the percent who say that religion is an important part of their daily lives (*y*-axis), the country name (label), the population (size of sphere), and the dominant religion (color of sphere).

2. The chart uses a Gallup survey to compare the religiosity of various countries with its GDP per capita. It also shows the relative population size and dominant religion of each country.

3. United States   **4.** Catholic

5. Yes; The majority of the countries with a low GDP per capita have a high percent of the population who say that religion is an important part of their daily lives. The majority of the countries with a high GDP per capita have a low percent of the population who say that religion is an important part of their daily lives.

6. Russia; Because Russia's population is over 3 times as great as Argentina's population, Russia has more religious people even though Argentina has a higher percent of religious people.

7. The United States is one of the few countries with a high GDP per capita and a high percent of people who say that religion is an important part of their daily lives. The majority of the countries with high GDP per capita have a low percent of people who are religious.

8. No; A stacked area graph shows how one measurement changes for various categories over time. This graph shows four pieces of information for each country, and it represents a snapshot in time.

9. Mean: 5.85%; Median: 5.55%; Mode: 4.6% and 5.8%

10. Median; The mean is greater than most of the data due to the two outliers.

11. 9.3% and 9.6%

12. Mean; Without the outliers, the mean is 5.44% and the median is 5.45%.

13. About 25% of the data is between 4.0% and 4.7%. About 25% of the data is between 4.7% and 5.6%. About 25% of the data is between 5.6% and 6.3%. About 25% of the data is between 6.3% and 9.6%. The uppermost quartile has the greatest range. The other 3 quartiles have similar ranges.

14. Yes; The unemployment rate is between 4.0% and 7.0% in 17 of the 20 years.

15. Yes; The distribution of the data is approximately bell-shaped.

16. About 69%   **17.** About 92%

18. The percents are about the same.

19. The distribution of data values for women has less dispersion than the distribution of the data values for men.

20. Men: 16%; Women: 2%

21. $65,467 ± $1710.99   **22.** $65,467 ± $2247.86

23. Conservative people are more likely to have a positive opinion of a conservative president and a negative opinion of a liberal president; The magazine should send the survey to a random sample of people.

24. People who live in a primarily Republican neighborhood are more likely to vote for the Republican candidate; The pollster should conduct the exit poll in a neighborhood that consists of approximately an equal number of Republicans and Democrats.

25. 1691 people

26. a; The question could produce biased results because it states that most of the students think that the senator should resign.

Section 10.1 *(page 458)*

1. 115.5 lb   **2.** 127 lb

3. 163 lb   **4.** 68 lb

5. For a woman, subtract 3.75 pounds for every inch under 5 feet, and for a man, subtract 4 pounds for every inch under 5 feet; The Robinson formula gives a linear relationship between ideal weight and height; 93 lb.

6.

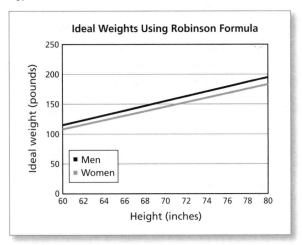

The ideal weight for a 5-foot tall man is 7 pounds greater than the ideal weight for a 5-foot tall woman. The difference increases by 0.25 pound for every inch over 5 feet.

7. a. About 21.0%   **b.** About 26.94

8. a. About 25.0%   **b.** About 21.83

9. The upper and lower limits for the target heart rate zone decrease over time. The difference between the upper and lower limits for the target heart rate zone decrease over time. These two trends are also true for the fat burning zone, which is part of the target heart rate zone.

10. Yes   **11.** No   **12.** Yes

13. Losing weight; incoming calories − outgoing calories = 1500 − 1992 = −492

14. Gaining weight; incoming calories − outgoing calories = 3000 − 2276 = 724

15.

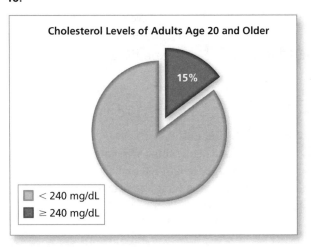

16. Answers will vary. *Sample answer:*

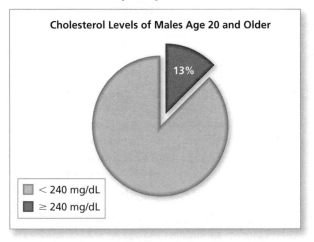

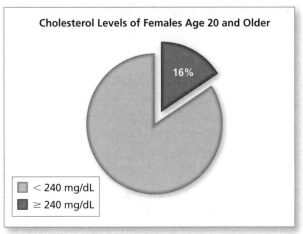

17.

Average Total Cholesterol of Adults Age 20 and Older

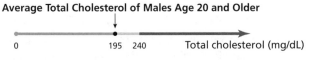

18. Answers will vary. *Sample answer:*

Average Total Cholesterol of Males Age 20 and Older

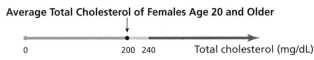

Average Total Cholesterol of Females Age 20 and Older

19. As total cholesterol rises, mortality from coronary heart disease rises.

20. The mortality rate shows a pronounced increase around the cholesterol levels indicated as high by the chart.

21. About 4 men per 1000

22. About 4 times greater

23.

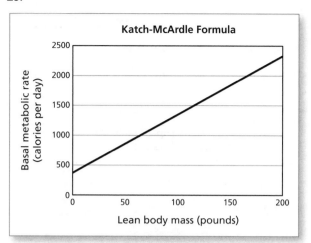

As lean body mass increases, basal metabolic rate increases.

24. 9.8 calories per day

25. 1350 calories per day

26. 1644 calories per day

27. 1546 calories per day

28. 1742 calories per day

29. About 2088 calories per day

30. About 2505 calories per day

Section 10.2 *(page 468)*

1. The winning distances increased over time and appear to have leveled off around 70 meters.

2. The concrete throwing circle helped the winning distances steadily increase until leveling off in the 1970s.

3. Between 50 and 55 m; The winning distance was increasing each year, and the winning distance in 1936 was about 50 meters.

4. About 70 m; In 5 of the last 6 Olympics, the winning distance has been about 70 meters.

5.

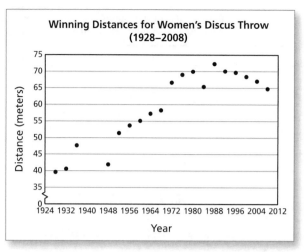

The winning distance increased in every Olympics from 1952 through 1980. The current Olympic record was set in 1988. From 1992 through 2008, the winning distance has decreased in every Olympics.

6.

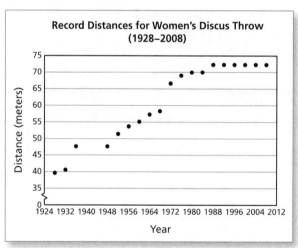

7. The winning time decreased every Olympics from 1960 through 1988. It increased in 1992, and then decreased through 2002. It increased in 2006 and 2010.

8. About 74 sec

9. About 71.4%

10.

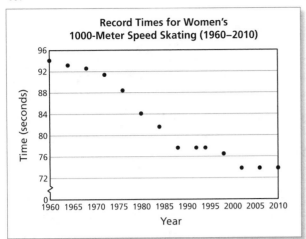

11.

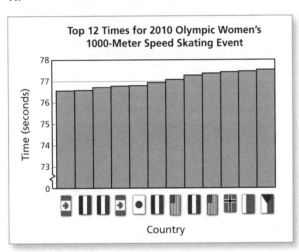

12.

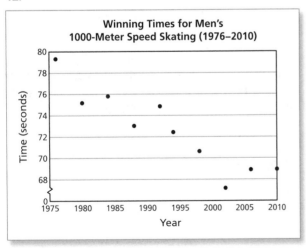

The winning times have decreased over time.

13. 44.2

14. 79.2

15. 55.2

16. 71.5

17. 120.7 points

18. 136 points

19. 94.5 points

20. 109.5 points

21.

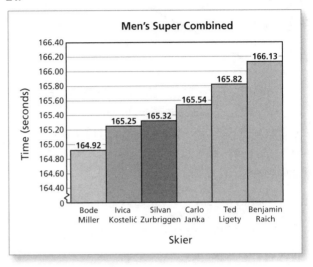

Gold medal: Bode Miller; Silver medal: Ivica Kostelić
Bronze medal: Silvan Zurbriggen

22.

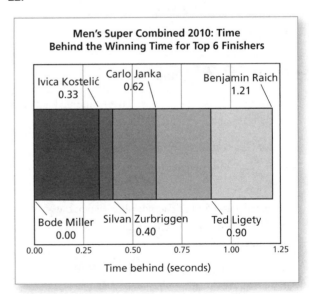

23. 51.76 sec; This would be the 6th best time when compared to the slalom times of the top 6 overall finishers.

24.

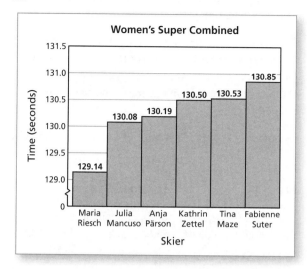

Gold Medal: Maria Riesch
Silver Medal: Julia Mancuso
Bronze Medal: Anja Pärson

25.

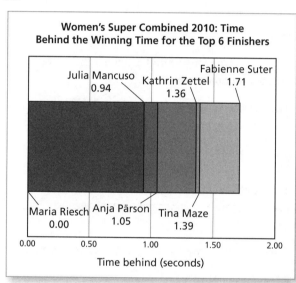

26. 44.97 sec; This would be the 5th best time when compared to the slalom times of the top 6 overall finishers.

10.1–10.2 Quiz (page 472)

1. About 26.1%

2. About 21.98

3. 198 beats per minute

4. 1359 calories per day

5. Losing weight; incoming calories − outgoing calories = 2400 − 2582 = −182

6. The winning distances have increased over time and appear to have leveled off at around 70 meters.

7. About 66.7%

8. About 75 m

Section 10.3 (page 480)

1. Josh Hamilton

2. Cabrera 0.622, Choo 0.484, Fielder 0.471, Hamilton 0.633, Mauer 0.469, Morneau 0.618, Pujols 0.596, Thome 0.627, Votto 0.600, Youkilis 0.564

3. Cabrera 0.420, Choo 0.401, Fielder 0.401, Hamilton 0.411, Mauer 0.402, Morneau 0.437, Pujols 0.414, Thome 0.412, Votto 0.424, Youkilis 0.411

4. Answers will vary.

5. Yes; This can happen when a player has a low number of bases on balls (BB) and hit by pitches (HBP), and a high number of sacrifice flies (SF).

6. $SB\% = \dfrac{SB}{SB + CS}$

7. Pass plays; The only time that coaches call more run plays is on 3rd down and 1 yard to go.

8. The conversion rate decreases as the yards to go increases for both pass plays and run plays.

9. 5, 6, 7, 8, and 10 yards

10. Pass play; According to the chart, coaches call a pass play about 65% of the time when it is 3rd down and 2 yards to go.

11. Run play; The conversion rate is greater for run plays when it is 3rd down and 2 yards to go. Also, the defense is probably expecting a pass play.

12. On 3rd down with 4 yards to go, coaches call a pass play about 85% of the time, but run plays have a greater conversion rate than pass plays. So a coach is more likely to call a pass play when the quarterback has a high passing efficiency. A coach is more likely to call a run play when the quarterback has a low passing efficiency.

13. No; The conversion rate for run plays is about 10% greater than the conversion rate for pass plays on 3rd down and 1 yard to go.

14. Answers will vary. *Sample answer:* Pass play; Statistically, pass plays are called about 90% of the time and run plays about 10%. This ratio of 9 passes to 1 run is the optimum mix because running and passing are equally effective from this distance, according to the "3rd Down Success" graph. Many variables are considered during play selection, such as offensive strengths, opponent's defensive strengths, clock management, score, and field position.

15. Durant; Durant attempted 18 field goals and Nowitzki attempted 15 field goals.

16. Nowitzki; Nowitzki had a field goal percentage of 80% (12-for-15) and Durant had a field goal percentage of about 56% (10-for-18).

17. 48 points

18. Dallas; The Mavericks scored 121 points $\left(\dfrac{48}{121} < 39.7\%\right)$.

19. 40%   20. 18 free throws

21. The majority of Nowitzki's shots are from mid-range with a preference for the right side of the court. Durant's shots are more scattered with some close, some mid-range, and some long-range (3-pointers).

22. Answers will vary. *Sample answer:* 40% from 3-point range; The expected value from the 3-point range is greater (40% × 3 = 1.2, 50% × 2 = 1). For instance, if you attempt ten 3-pointers during a game and make 4 (40%), you score 4 × 3 = 12 points. If you attempt 10 field goals from inside the 3-point line and make 5 (50%), you only score 5 × 2 = 10 points.

23. The size of the bubble represents the relative number of fans of a particular sport. The color of the bubble represents the political party that the fans of the sport are more likely to support.

24. PGA Tour; WWE

25. Republican; More of the bubbles are red, and most of the larger bubbles are red.

26. Good; According to the graph, the majority of sports fans are more likely to vote than the average American.

27. PGA Tour, College football, NASCAR; Men's and women's tennis, WNBA, NBA

28. Answers will vary. *Sample answer:* NBA game; More people watch the NBA, and NBA fans are more likely to vote Democrat.

Section 10.4 *(page 490)*

1. Older than 44 years old; 29.2% of campers are 45+, and 25.7% of campers are under 18.

2. About 19.4%

3. More; 65.1% of campers earn $50,000+.

4. 996

5. No; The graph does not tell you what percent of the general population participates in camping.

6. Each category on the education bar is progressive and includes categories below it. For instance, someone with a college degree is also a high school graduate. On the other four bars in the graph, the categories are mutually exclusive.

7. 23 mph   8. 18.4 mi   9. 14 ft to 20 ft

10. 14 ft   11. About 86,526 ft^2

12. 1171.5 lb   13. About 5.8 hr

14. Yes; The boat used one-fourth of a tank to get there. So it should use one-fourth of a tank to get back. The emergency backup is one-half of a tank, which is greater than one-third.

15. Yes; A line that decreases from left to right indicates a downhill section. Trail 5 appears to have the biggest downhill section between the 3-mile and 3.5-mile markers.

16. 50%

17. Trail 2; It is the longest trail and it has the steepest incline (after the 8-mile marker).

18. The purpose is to have a straight line reference against which to compare the steepness of each trail.

19. Mean: 2437.5 ft
    Median: 1800
    Yes; Trail 1 and trail 2 are outliers because the vertical rise of both trails is much greater than the rest of the data.

20. Answers will vary.   21. 162 fatalities per year

22. 62 fatalities per year

23. Yes; This corresponds to a heat index of 121°F. Any heat index value that exceeds 105°F warrants an excessive heat warning from the National Weather Service.

24. Yes; This corresponds to a heat index of 95°F, which warrants extreme caution. However, because you are on the west side of the mountain on a sunny afternoon, you will be in direct sunlight, which can increase the heat index up to 15°F. This would put the actual heat index at 110°F, which is in the danger zone.

25. No; The heat index increases at an increasing rate as the temperature increases.

26. Answers will vary. *Sample answer:* The heat index will affect such things as the type of clothes you wear, the time of day you go, the amount of water you bring, and the type of trail you hike. You may also decide to reschedule the hiking trip for another day if the heat index is going to be too high.

10.3–10.4 Quiz *(page 494)*

1. There is a data point missing for the NHL in 2004. The estimated value is 0.08.

2. NFL; The change in the average NFL team's win percentage each year is greater than all of the other leagues.

3. 42 to 58 games

4. Yes; The average MLB team's win percentage varies much less than the average NFL team's win percentage. This means that bad MLB teams have a good chance of remaining bad, while bad NFL teams have a good chance of improving.

5. Danger

6. Little danger (caution)

7. Extreme danger

8. Danger

Chapter 10 Review *(page 496)*

1. a. About 12.5%   **b.** About 19.70

2. a. About 25.5%   **b.** About 21.30

3. Gaining weight; incoming calories − outgoing calories = 3200 − 2819 = 381

4. Losing weight; incoming calories − outgoing calories = 1600 − 1958 = −358

5. Yes   **6.** No

7. The winning distances increased dramatically between 1948 and 1980. After a slight drop in 1984, the winning distances leveled off between 80 and 85 meters.

8. 56%   **9.** About 85 m

10. About 55 m; Around 1940, the winning distances were close to 55 meters.

11.

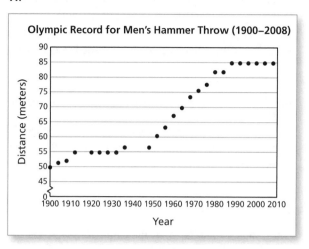

12.

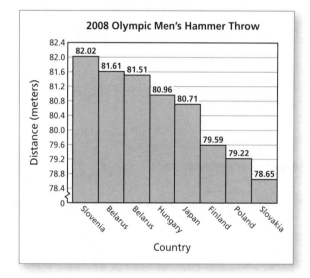

13. 53.9   **14.** 126.4

15. There is a positive correlation between win percentage on June 1 and final win percentage. In general, a team's final win percentage will be slightly less than the team's win percentage on June 1.

16. Answers will vary. *Sample answer:* (0.431, 0.543) and (0.549, 0.599)

17. Between 0.550 and 0.600

18. No; Teams that were bad in the first 2 months of the season finished with low winning percentages, and teams that were good in the first 2 months finished with high winning percentages. The statistics show that a team's fate was sealed by June 1.

19. No; All of the teams that had a win percentage below 0.500 on June 1 finished with a win percentage below 0.550. Because $0.550 \times 162 = 89.1$, which is less than 90, none of these teams could have made the playoffs.

20. No; A record of 90 wins means a final win percentage of $\dfrac{90 \text{ wins}}{162 \text{ games}} \approx 0.556$. In 2010, none of the teams with a losing record on June 1 had a final win percentage greater than 0.550. There are 30 teams in MLB, so you would expect 2 or 3 teams each year to accomplish the feat $(9\% \times 30 = 2.7)$.

21. River blind

22. The value of the blue bar is the value of the red bar divided by the value of the orange bar.

23. About 125 hr

24. Duration; It decreases from left to right and is the only statistic of the three that is ordered.

25. About 5%

26. About 1.9; Grasslands

27. Wetlands; It is based on more data. The hunting duration in the wetlands is 4 times the hunting duration on the lake shore.

28. Answers will vary.